G000300903

GCSE

Combined Science

Biology

The Complete Course for AQA

CGP

How to get your free Online Edition

Go to **cgpbooks.co.uk/extras** and enter this code...

4347 5947 7087 9852

This code will only work once. If someone has used this book before you,
they may have already claimed the Online Edition.

Contents

Introduction

How to use this book i

Working Scientifically

1. The Scientific Method 2
2. Scientific Applications and Issues 5
3. Limitations of Science 6
4. Risks and Hazards 7
5. Designing Investigations 9
6. Collecting Data 12
7. Processing Data 14
8. Graphs and Charts 16
9. Units 19
10. Conclusions and Evaluations 21

Topic 1 — Cell Biology

Topic 1a — Cell Structure and Cell Division

1. Cell Structure 23
2. Microscopy 25
3. Cell Differentiation and Specialisation 30
4. Chromosomes 33
5. Mitosis 35
6. Stem Cells 38
Exam-style Questions **43**

Topic 1b — Transport in Cells

1. Diffusion 45
2. Osmosis 48
3. Active Transport 52
4. Exchange Surfaces 54
5. Exchanging Substances 58
Exam-style Questions **64**

Topic 2 — Organisation

Topic 2a — Tissues, Organs and Organ Systems

1. Cell Organisation 66
2. The Lungs 70
3. Circulatory System — The Heart 73
4. Circulatory System — The Blood Vessels 77
5. Circulatory System — The Blood 80
6. Plant Cell Organisation 83
7. Transpiration and Translocation 85
8. Transpiration and Stomata 87
Exam-style Questions **93**

Topic 2b — Health and Disease

1. Introduction to Health and Disease 95
2. Cardiovascular Disease 97
3. Risk Factors for Non-Communicable Diseases 101
4. Cancer 103
Exam-style Questions **107**

Topic 2c — Enzymes and Digestion

1. Enzymes — 109
2. Investigating Enzymatic Reactions — 112
3. Enzymes and Digestion — 114
4. Food Tests — 118
Exam-style Questions — **122**

Topic 3 — Infection and Response

1. Communicable Disease — 124
2. Viral Diseases — 126
3. Fungal and Protist Diseases — 127
4. Bacterial Diseases and Preventing Disease — 128
5. Fighting Disease — 130
6. Fighting Disease — Vaccination — 132
7. Fighting Disease — Drugs — 134
8. Developing Drugs — 137
Exam-style Questions — **142**

Topic 4 — Bioenergetics

1. The Basics of Photosynthesis — 144
2. How Plants Use Glucose — 146
3. The Rate of Photosynthesis — 148
4. Investigating Photosynthesis Rate — 153
5. The Inverse Square Law — 155
6. Artificially Controlling Plant Growth — 156
7. Aerobic Respiration — 159
8. Anaerobic Respiration — 161
9. Exercise — 163
10. Metabolism — 165
Exam-style Questions — **168**

Topic 5 — Homeostasis and Response

Topic 5a — The Nervous System

1. Homeostasis — 170
2. The Nervous System — 172
3. Synapses and Reflexes — 174
4. Investigating Reaction Time — 177
Exam-style Questions — **180**

Topic 5b — The Endocrine System

1. Hormones — 181
2. Controlling Blood Glucose — 184
3. Puberty and the Menstrual Cycle — 189
4. Contraceptives — 193
5. Increasing Fertility — 195
6. Thyroxine and Adrenaline — 198
Exam-style Questions — **202**

Topic 6 — Inheritance, Variation and Evolution

Topic 6a — DNA and Reproduction

1. DNA — 204
2. Reproduction — 206
3. Meiosis — 208
Exam-style Questions — **211**

Topic 6b — Genetics

1. X and Y Chromosomes — 213
2. Alleles and Genetic Diagrams — 217
3. Inherited Disorders — 223
Exam-style Questions — **228**

Topic 6c — Evolution and Classification

1. Variation   230
2. Evolution and Extinction   234
3. Selective Breeding   238
4. Genetic Engineering   240
5. Fossils   243
6. Antibiotic-Resistant Bacteria   246
7. Classification   248
Exam-style Questions   **253**

Topic 7 — Ecology

Topic 7a — Organisms and Their Environment

1. Competition   255
2. Abiotic and Biotic Factors   258
3. Adaptations   261
4. Food Chains   263
5. Using Quadrats and Transects   265
6. The Cycling of Materials   269
Exam-style Questions   **273**

Topic 7b — Human Impacts on the Environment

1. Biodiversity and Waste   275
2. Global Warming   278
3. Deforestation and Land Use   281
4. Maintaining Ecosystems and Biodiversity 284
Exam-style Questions   **287**

Practical Skills

1. Measuring Substances   288
2. Heating Substances and Using Potometers 290
3. Stage Micrometers and Eyepiece Graticules 292
4. Sampling   293
5. Safety and Ethics   295

Maths Skills

1. Calculations   296
2. Algebra   301
3. Graphs   302

Exam Help

1. The Exams   305
2. Exam Technique   306
3. Question Types   308

Reference

Answers   312
Glossary   333
Acknowledgements   339
Index   341

Published by CGP

From original material by Richard Parsons.

Editors:
Charlotte Burrows, Katherine Faudemer, Emily Howe, Chris McGarry, Sarah Pattison, Sean Walsh.

Contributor:
Paddy Gannon.

ISBN: 978 1 78294 638 0

With thanks to Camilla Simson for the proofreading.
With thanks to Jan Greenway for the copyright research.

Printed by Elanders Ltd, Newcastle upon Tyne.
Clipart from Corel®

Text, design, layout and original illustrations © Coordination Group Publications Ltd. (CGP) 2016

All rights reserved.

Photocopying more than one chapter of this book is not permitted. Extra copies are available from CGP.
0800 1712 712 • www.cgpbooks.co.uk

How to use this book

4. Investigating Photosynthesis Rate

So you've seen a graph showing how light intensity affects the rate of photosynthesis back on page 149, but you also need to know how you'd actually get the data for that graph.

Investigating the rate of photosynthesis

To investigate the effect of different light intensities on the rate of photosynthesis, you need to be able to measure the rate. One way to do this involves an aquatic plant, such as Canadian pondweed. The rate at which the pondweed produces oxygen corresponds to the rate at which it's photosynthesising — the faster the rate of oxygen production, the faster the rate of photosynthesis.

Here's how the experiment works:

A source of white light is placed at a specific distance from the pondweed. You should then leave the pondweed for a couple of minutes to adjust to the new light intensity before starting the experiment. When you're ready to start, the pondweed is left to photosynthesise for a set amount of time. As it photosynthesises, the oxygen released will collect in the capillary tube.

At the end of the experiment, the syringe is used to draw the gas bubble in the tube up alongside a ruler and the length of the gas bubble is measured. This is proportional to the volume of O_2 produced.

Figure 1: Diagram showing the experimental set up used to measure the rate of photosynthesis in water plants.

The experiment is repeated twice with the light source at the same distance and the mean volume of O_2 produced is calculated. Then the whole experiment is repeated with the light source at different distances from the pondweed.

Learning Objectives:
- Be able to investigate how light intensity affects the rate of photosynthesis, using an aquatic plant (Required Practical 5).
- Be able to calculate the rate of photosynthesis.
Specification Reference 4.4.1.2

Tip: Make sure you do a risk assessment before you start this investigation, so that you carry it out safely. E.g. there's a slight risk of infection from the pond water, so make sure you wash your hands after handling the pondweed and cover up any cuts.

Figure 2: Pondweed giving off oxygen bubbles as a by-product of photosynthesis.

Tip: Taking repeat readings and calculating a mean reduces the effect of random errors, and will make your results more precise — see page 13.

Topic 4 Bioenergetics   153

Learning Objectives
- These tell you exactly what you need to learn, or be able to do, for the exam.
- There's a specification reference at the bottom that links to the AQA specification.

Tips and Exam Tips
- There are tips throughout this book to help you understand the theory.
- There are also exam tips to help you with answering exam questions.

Maths Skills
- There's a range of maths skills you could be expected to apply in your exams. The section on pages 296-304 is packed with plenty of maths that you'll need to be familiar with.
- Examples that show these maths skills in action are marked up with this symbol.

Working Scientifically
- Working Scientifically is a big part of GCSE Combined Science. There's a whole section on it at the front of the book.
- Working Scientifically is also covered throughout this book wherever you see this symbol.

Examples
These are here to help you understand the theory.

Required Practical Activities
There are some Required Practical Activities that you'll be expected to do throughout your course. You need to know all about them for the exams. They're all marked with stamps like this:

Tip: It's really important that the quadrats are placed randomly within the sample area. Taking random samples improves the validity of the study.

1. Place a 1 m² quadrat on the ground at a random point within the first sample area. E.g. divide the area into a grid and use a random number generator to pick coordinates (see page 293).
2. Count all the organisms within the quadrat.
3. Repeat steps 1 and 2 as many times as you can.
4. Work out the mean number of organisms per quadrat within the first sample area.

Tip: If you're counting flowering plants in your quadrat, make sure you count the number of actual plants, not the number of flowers. Some plants will have more than one flower, and some might not currently have any flowers on them.

Example

Anna counted the number of daisies in 7 quadrats within her first sample area and recorded the following results:

Quadrat	1	2	3	4	5	6	7
Number of Daisies	18	22	20	23	23	25	23

Here the mean is: $\dfrac{\text{total number of organisms}}{\text{number of quadrats}}$

$= \dfrac{154}{7} = $ **22 daisies per quadrat**

5. Repeat steps 1 to 4 in the second sample area.
6. Finally compare the two means. E.g. you might find 2 daisies per m² in the shade, and 22 daisies per m² (lots more) in the open field.

You might want to find and compare the mode and median of your data too.

Figure 2: A student using a quadrat to gather data on the distribution of organisms.

Example

1. The mode is the number that appears most often in the data. For Anna's data above, the mode is **23 daisies per quadrat**.
2. To find the median, you first need to put your data in numerical order. The median is the middle value in your data.

18, 20, 22, 23, 23, 23, 25

The median of Anna's data is **23 daisies per quadrat**.

Tip: There's more on means, modes and medians on page 14 of the Working Scientifically section.

Estimating population size
You can also use quadrats to work out the population size of an organism in one area.

Example

Students used 0.25 m² quadrats to randomly sample daisies on an open field. The students found a mean of 10.5 daisies per quadrat. The field had an area of 800 m². Estimate the population of daisies on the field.

266   Topic 7a Organisms and Their Environment

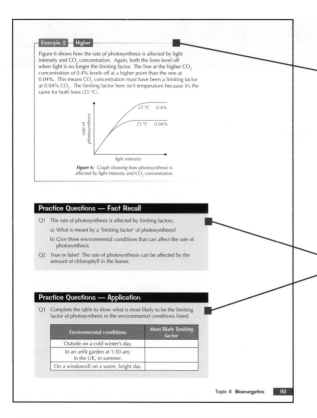

Higher Exam Material

- Some of the material in this book will only come up in the exam if you're sitting the higher exam papers.

- This material is clearly marked with boxes that look like this:

Practice Questions

- Fact recall questions test that you know the facts needed for your biology exams.

- Annoyingly, the examiners also expect you to be able to apply your knowledge to new situations — application questions give you plenty of practice at doing this.

- All the answers are in the back of the book.

Practical Skills

There's also a whole section on pages 288-295 with extra details on practical skills you'll be expected to use in the Required Practical Activities, and apply knowledge of in the exams.

Exam-style Questions

- Practising exam-style questions is really important — this book has some at the end of every topic to test you.

- They're the same style as the ones you'll get in the real exams.

- All the answers are in the back of the book, along with a mark scheme to show you how you get the marks.

- Higher-only questions are marked like this: **1.2**

Topic Checklist

Each topic has a checklist at the end with boxes that let you tick off what you've learnt.

Glossary

There's a glossary at the back of the book full of definitions you need to know for the exam, plus loads of other useful words.

Exam Help

There's a section at the back of the book stuffed full of things to help you with the exams.

1. The Scientific Method

Science is all about finding things out and learning things about the world we live in. This section is all about the scientific process — how a scientist's initial idea turns into a theory that is accepted by the wider scientific community.

Hypotheses

Scientists try to explain things. Everything. They start by observing something they don't understand — it could be anything, e.g. planets in the sky, a person suffering from an illness, what matter is made of... anything.

Then, they come up with a **hypothesis** — a possible explanation for what they've observed. (Scientists can also sometimes form a model — a description or a representation of what's physically going on — see page 3).

The next step is to test whether the hypothesis might be right or not. This involves making a **prediction** based on the hypothesis and testing it by gathering evidence (i.e. data) from investigations. If evidence from experiments backs up a prediction, you're a step closer to figuring out if the hypothesis is true.

Tip: Investigations include lab experiments and studies.

Testing a hypothesis

Normally, scientists share their findings in peer-reviewed journals, or at conferences. **Peer-review** is where other scientists check results and scientific explanations to make sure they're 'scientific' (e.g. that experiments have been done in a sensible way) before they're published. It helps to detect false claims, but it doesn't mean that findings are correct — just that they're not wrong in any obvious way.

Once other scientists have found out about a hypothesis, they'll start basing their own predictions on it and carry out their own experiments. They'll also try to reproduce the original experiments to check the results — and if all the experiments in the world back up the hypothesis, then scientists start to think the hypothesis is true.

However, if a scientist somewhere in the world does an experiment that doesn't fit with the hypothesis (and other scientists can reproduce these results), then the hypothesis is in trouble. When this happens, scientists have to come up with a new hypothesis (maybe a modification of the old hypothesis, or maybe a completely new one).

Tip: Sometimes it can take a really long time for a hypothesis to be accepted.

Accepting a hypothesis

If pretty much every scientist in the world believes a hypothesis to be true because experiments back it up, then it usually goes in the textbooks for students to learn. Accepted hypotheses are often referred to as **theories**.

Our currently accepted theories are the ones that have survived this 'trial by evidence' — they've been tested many, many times over the years and survived (while the less good ones have been ditched). However... they never, never become hard and fast, totally indisputable fact. You can never know... it'd only take one odd, totally inexplicable result, and the hypothesising and testing would start all over again.

Example

Over time scientists have come up with different hypotheses about how illnesses are caused:

- Hundreds of years ago, we thought demons caused illness.

- Then we thought it was caused by 'bad blood' (and treated it with leeches).

- Now we've collected more evidence, we know that illnesses that can be spread between people are due to microorganisms.

Figure 1: *Historical artwork of a woman using leeches to treat disease.*

Models

Models are used to describe or display how an object or system behaves in reality. They're often based on evidence collected from experiments, and should be able to accurately predict what will happen in other, similar experiments. There are different types of models that scientists can use to describe the world around them. Here are just a few:

- A **descriptive model** describes what's happening in a certain situation, without explaining why. It won't necessarily include details that could be used to predict the outcome of a different scenario. For example, a graph showing the measured rate of an enzyme-catalysed reaction at different temperatures would be a descriptive model.

- A **representational model** is a simplified description or picture of what's going on in real life. It can be used to explain observations and make predictions. E.g. the lock and key model of enzyme action is a simplified way of showing how enzymes work (see page 109). It can be used to explain why enzymes only catalyse particular reactions.

- **Spatial models** are used to analyse the way that data is arranged within a physical space. For example, a spatial model could be used to look for relationships between the distribution of a species and physical aspects of its environment.

- **Computational models** use computers to make simulations of complex real-life processes, such as climate change. They're used when there are a lot of different variables (factors that change) to consider, and because you can easily change their design to take into account new data.

- **Mathematical models** can be used to describe the relationship between variables in numerical form (e.g. as an equation), and therefore predict outcomes of a scenario. For example, an equation can be written to predict how quickly molecules will diffuse into cells based on factors such as how large they are. On a larger scale, a mathematical model can be used to predict the way that a disease might spread through a population, e.g. by estimating the number of people that will become infected with the disease based on the number of people that are currently infected.

Tip: Like hypotheses, models have to be tested before they're accepted by other scientists. You can test models by using them to make a prediction, and then carrying out an investigation to see whether the evidence matches the prediction.

Tip: Mathematical models are made using patterns found in data and also using information about known relationships between variables.

All models have limitations on what they can explain or predict. Climate change models have several limitations — for example, it's hard to take into account all the biological and chemical processes that influence climate. It can also be difficult to include regional variations in climate.

Communicating results

Some scientific discoveries show that people should change their habits, or they might provide ideas that could be developed into new technology. So scientists need to tell the world about their discoveries.

Example

Gene technologies make use of discoveries that scientists have made about genes and DNA. Some of these technologies are used in genetic engineering, to produce genetically modified crops. Information about these crops needs to be communicated to farmers who might benefit from growing them, and to the general public so they can make informed decisions about the food they buy and eat.

Reports about scientific discoveries in the media (e.g. newspapers or television) aren't peer-reviewed. This means that, even though news stories are often based on data that has been peer-reviewed, the data might be presented in a way that is over-simplified or inaccurate, leaving it open to misinterpretation.

It's important that the evidence isn't presented in a **biased** way. This can sometimes happen when people want to make a point, e.g. they overemphasise a relationship in the data. (Sometimes without knowing they're doing it.) There are all sorts of reasons why people might want to do this.

Examples

- They want to keep the organisation or company that's funding the research happy. (If the results aren't what they'd like they might not give them any more money to fund further research.)

- Governments might want to persuade voters, other governments or journalists to agree with their policies about a certain issue.

- Companies might want to 'big up' their products, or make impressive safety claims.

- Environmental campaigners might want to persuade people to behave differently.

There's also a risk that if an investigation is done by a team of highly-regarded scientists it'll be taken more seriously than evidence from less well known scientists. But having experience, authority or a fancy qualification doesn't necessarily mean the evidence is good — the only way to tell is to look at the evidence scientifically (e.g. is it repeatable, valid, etc. — see page 9).

2. Scientific Applications and Issues

New scientific discoveries can lead to exciting new ways of using science in our everyday lives. Unfortunately, these developments may also come with social, economic, environmental or personal problems that need to be considered.

Using scientific developments

Lots of scientific developments go on to have useful applications.

Examples

- When it was discovered that penicillin acted as an antibiotic, drugs were developed that used penicillin to treat bacterial infections.

- As scientists have investigated the role of reproductive hormones in the body, treatments that use these hormones have been developed to allow women to become pregnant who wouldn't be able to otherwise.

Tip: There's lots more about antibiotics on page 134.

Issues created by science

Scientific developments (e.g. new technologies or new advice) can create issues. For example, they could create political issues, which could lead to developments being ignored, or governments being slow to act if they think responding to the developments could affect their popularity with voters.

Example

Some governments were pretty slow to accept the fact that human activities are causing global warming, despite all the evidence. This is because accepting it means they've got to do something about it, which costs money and could hurt their economy. This could lose them a lot of votes.

Tip: See page 278 for more on global warming.

Scientific developments can cause a whole host of other issues too.

Examples

- Economic issues: Society can't always afford to do things scientists recommend (e.g. investing heavily in alternative energy sources) without cutting back elsewhere.

- Social issues: Decisions based on scientific evidence affect people — e.g. should junk food be taxed more highly (to encourage people to be healthy)? Should alcohol be banned (to prevent health problems)? Would the effect on people's lifestyles be acceptable?

- Environmental issues: Human activity often affects the natural environment — e.g. genetically modified crops may help us produce more food, but some people think they could cause environmental problems.

- Personal issues: Some decisions will affect individuals. For example, someone might support alternative energy, but object if a wind farm is built next to their house.

Figure 1: *Solar farms can be used to generate 'clean' electricity, but some people think that the money needed to invest in them should be spent elsewhere.*

3. Limitations of Science

Science has taught us an awful lot about the world we live in and how things work — but science doesn't have the answer for everything.

Questions science hasn't answered yet

We don't understand everything. And we never will. We'll find out more, for sure — as more hypotheses are suggested, and more experiments are done. But there'll always be stuff we don't know.

> **Examples**
>
> ▪ Today we don't know as much as we'd like about the impacts of global warming. How much will sea levels rise? And to what extent will weather patterns change?
>
> ▪ We also don't know anywhere near as much as we'd like about the universe. Are there other life forms out there? And what is the universe made of?

Figure 1: *Global warming could cause weather patterns to change — which may result in longer, hotter droughts in some areas.*

In order to answer scientific questions, scientists need data to provide evidence for their hypotheses. Some questions can't be answered yet because the data can't currently be collected, or because there's not enough data to support a theory. But eventually, as we get more evidence, we probably will be able to answer these questions once and for all. By then there'll be loads of new questions to answer though.

Questions science can't answer

There are some questions that all the experiments in the world won't help us answer — for example, the "should we be doing this at all?" type questions.

> **Example**
>
> Think about embryo screening (which lets you choose an embryo with certain characteristics). It's possible to do it, but does that mean we should?
>
> ▪ Some people say it's good... couples whose existing child needs a bone marrow transplant, but who can't find a donor, will be able to have another child selected for its matching bone marrow. This would save the life of their first child — and if they want another child anyway... where's the harm?
>
> ▪ Other people say it's bad... they say it could have serious effects on the new child. For example, the new child might feel unwanted — thinking they were only brought into the world to help someone else. And would they have the right to refuse to donate their bone marrow (as anyone else would)?

Tip: Some experiments have to be approved by ethics committees before scientists are allowed to carry them out. This stops scientists from getting wrapped up in whether they <u>can</u> do something, before anyone stops to think about whether they <u>should</u> do it.

The question of whether something is morally or ethically right or wrong can't be answered by more experiments — there is no "right" or "wrong" answer. The best we can do is get a consensus from society — a judgement that most people are more or less happy to live by. Science can provide more information to help people make this judgement, and the judgement might change over time. But in the end it's up to people and their conscience.

4. Risks and Hazards

A lot of things we do could cause us harm. But some things are more hazardous than they at first seem, whereas other things are less hazardous. This may sound confusing, but it'll all become clear...

What are risks and hazards?

A **hazard** is something that could potentially cause harm. All hazards have a **risk** attached to them — this is the chance that the hazard will cause harm.

The risks of some things seem pretty obvious, or we've known about them for a while, like the risk of causing acid rain by polluting the atmosphere, or of having a car accident when you're travelling in a car.

New technology arising from scientific advances can bring new risks. These risks need to be thought about alongside the potential benefits of the technology, in order to make a decision about whether it should be made available to the general public.

Example

Radiotherapy is a cancer treatment that uses radiation to kill cancer cells. However, radiation itself carries a risk of causing cancer in the patient.

The risk of cancer caused by radiotherapy has to be weighed against the risk of the existing cancer that needs to be treated.

In some cases, the risk from the original cancer far outweighs the risk from radiotherapy, which is why it is available to be used as a treatment.

Tip: The application of a new technology can change over time if new risks are discovered. For example, radiation was widely used as a medical treatment before it was known that it can cause cancer. These days, its use as a treatment is a lot more limited and techniques have been improved to reduce the risk.

Estimating risk

You can estimate the risk based on how many times something happens in a big sample (e.g. 100 000 people) over a given period (e.g. a year). For example, you could assess the risk of a driver crashing by recording how many people in a group of 100 000 drivers crashed their cars over a year.

To make a decision about an activity that involves a hazardous event, we don't just need to take into account the chance of the event causing harm, but also how serious the consequences would be if it did.

The general rule is that, if an activity involves a hazard that's very likely to cause harm, with serious consequences if it does, that activity is considered high-risk.

Example 1

If you go for a walk, you may sprain an ankle. But most sprains recover within a few weeks if they're rested, so going for a walk would be considered a low-risk activity.

Figure 1: BASE jumping is considered a high-risk activity.

Tip: Risks people choose to take are called 'voluntary risks'. Risks that people are forced to take are called 'imposed risks'.

Tip: You can find out about potential hazards by looking in textbooks, doing some internet research, or asking your teacher.

Figure 2: Scientists wearing safety goggles to protect their eyes during an experiment.

Example 2

If you go BASE jumping, you could die or get a serious injury that could cause further complications later on in life, and the chance of this happening is high. So BASE jumping would be considered a high-risk activity.

Perceptions of risk

Not all risks have the same consequences, e.g. if you chop veg with a sharp knife you risk cutting your finger, but if you go scuba-diving you risk death. You're much more likely to cut your finger during half an hour of chopping than to die during half an hour of scuba-diving. But most people are happier to accept a higher probability of an accident if the consequences are short-lived and fairly minor.

People tend to be more willing to accept a risk if they choose to do something (e.g. go scuba diving), compared to having the risk imposed on them (e.g. having a nuclear power station built next door).

People's perception of risk (how risky they think something is) isn't always accurate. They tend to view familiar activities as low-risk and unfamiliar activities as high-risk — even if that's not the case. For example, cycling on roads is often high-risk, but many people are happy to do it because it's a familiar activity. Air travel is actually pretty safe, but a lot of people perceive it as high-risk. People may over-estimate the risk of things with long-term or invisible effects.

Reducing risk in investigations

Part of planning an investigation is making sure that it's safe. To make sure your experiment is safe you must identify all the **hazards**. Hazards include:

- Microorganisms: e.g. some bacteria can make you ill.

- Chemicals: e.g. sulfuric acid can burn your skin and alcohols catch fire easily.

- Fire: e.g. an unattended Bunsen burner is a fire hazard.

- Electricity: e.g. faulty electrical equipment could give you a shock.

Once you've identified the hazards you might encounter, you should think of ways of reducing the risks from the hazards.

Examples

- If you're working with sulfuric acid, always wear gloves and safety goggles. This will reduce the risk of the acid coming into contact with your skin and eyes.

- If you're using a Bunsen burner, stand it on a heat proof mat. This will reduce the risk of starting a fire.

5. Designing Investigations

To be a good scientist you need to know how to design a good experiment.

Making predictions from a hypothesis

Scientists observe things and come up with hypotheses to explain them. To decide whether a **hypothesis** might be correct, you need to do an investigation to gather evidence, which will help support or disprove the hypothesis. The first step is to use the hypothesis to come up with a **prediction** — a statement about what you think will happen that you can test.

> **Example**
>
> If your hypothesis is "eating a diet containing a large amount of saturated fat causes a high blood cholesterol level", then your prediction might be "people who eat large amounts of saturated fats will have a high level of cholesterol in their blood".

Once a scientist has come up with a prediction, they'll design an investigation to see if there are patterns or relationships between two variables. For example, to see if there's a pattern or relationship between the variables 'amount of saturated fats eaten' and 'blood cholesterol level'.

Tip: A variable is just something in the experiment that can change.

Repeatable and reproducible results

Results need to be **repeatable** and **reproducible**. Repeatable means that if the same person does an experiment again using the same methods and equipment, they'll get similar results. Reproducible means that if someone else does the experiment, or a different method or piece of equipment is used, the results will be similar. Data that's repeatable and reproducible is **reliable** and scientists are more likely to have confidence in it.

> **Example**
>
> In 1998, a scientist claimed to have found a link between the MMR vaccine (for measles, mumps and rubella) and autism. This meant many parents stopped their children from being vaccinated, leading to a rise in the number of children catching measles. However, the results have never been reproduced. Health authorities have now concluded that the vaccine is safe.

Figure 1: *The MMR vaccine.*

Ensuring the test is valid

Valid results are repeatable, reproducible and answer the original question.

> **Example**
>
> **Do power lines cause cancer?** — Some studies have found that children who live near overhead power lines are more likely to develop cancer. What they'd actually found was a **correlation** (relationship) between the variables "presence of power lines" and "incidence of cancer". They found that as one changed, so did the other.
>
> But this data isn't enough to say that the power lines cause cancer, as there might be other explanations. For example, power lines are often near busy roads, so the areas tested could contain different levels of pollution. As the studies don't show a definite link they don't answer the original question.

Tip: Peer review (see page 2) is used to make sure that results are valid before they're published.

Tip: See page 18 for more on correlation.

Ensuring it's a fair test

Tip: For the results of an investigation to be valid the investigation must be a fair test.

In a lab experiment you usually change one variable and measure how it affects another variable. To make it a fair test, everything else that could affect the results should stay the same (otherwise you can't tell if the thing you're changing is causing the results or not — the data won't be valid).

> **Example**
>
> You might change only the temperature of an enzyme-controlled reaction and measure how it affects the rate of reaction. You need to keep the pH the same, otherwise you won't know if any change in the rate of reaction is caused by the change in temperature, or the change in pH.

The variable you change is called the **independent variable**. The variable you measure when you change the independent variable is called the **dependent variable**. The variables that you keep the same are called **control variables**.

> **Example**
>
> In the enzyme-controlled reaction example above, temperature is the independent variable, the rate of the reaction is the dependent variable and the control variables are pH, volume and concentration of reactants, etc.

Control experiments and control groups

Tip: Control experiments let you see what happens when you don't change anything at all.

To make sure no other factors are affecting the results, you also have to include a **control experiment** — an experiment that's kept under the same conditions as the rest of the investigation, but doesn't have anything done to it.

> **Example**
>
> You can investigate antibiotic resistance in bacteria by growing cultures of bacteria on agar plates, then adding paper discs soaked in antibiotic.
>
> If the bacteria are resistant to the antibiotic they will continue to grow. If they aren't resistant a clear patch will appear around the disc where they have died or haven't grown.
>
> A disc that isn't soaked in antibiotic is included to act as a control. This makes sure any result is down to the antibiotic, not the presence of a paper disc.
>
>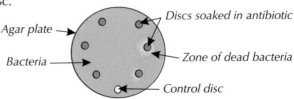
>
> **Figure 2:** *An investigation into antibiotic resistance.*

Tip: A study is an investigation that doesn't take place in a lab.

It's important that a study is a fair test, just like a lab experiment. It's a lot trickier to control the variables in a study than it is in a lab experiment though. Sometimes you can't control them all, but you can use a **control group** to help. This is a group of whatever you're studying (people, plants, lemmings, etc.) that's kept under the same conditions as the group in the experiment, but doesn't have anything done to it.

Example

If you're studying the effect of pesticides on crop growth, pesticide is applied to one field but not to another field (the control field). Both fields are planted with the same crop, and are in the same area (so they get the same weather conditions).

The control field is there to try and account for variables like the weather, which don't stay the same all the time, but could affect the results.

Tip: A pesticide is a chemical that can be used to kill insects.

Sample size

Data based on small samples isn't as good as data based on large samples. A sample should be representative of the whole population (i.e. it should share as many of the various characteristics in the population as possible) — a small sample can't do that as well.

The bigger the sample size the better, but scientists have to be realistic when choosing how big.

Tip: It's hard to spot anomalies if your sample size is too small.

Example

If you were studying how lifestyle affects people's weight it'd be great to study everyone in the UK (a huge sample), but it'd take ages and cost a bomb. Studying a thousand people with a mixture of ages, gender and race would be more realistic.

Tip: Samples should be selected randomly. There's an example of how to do this on page 293.

Trial runs

It's a good idea to do a **trial run** (a quick version of your experiment) before you do the proper experiment. Trial runs are used to figure out the range (the upper and lower limits) of independent variable values used in the proper experiment. If you don't get a change in the dependent variable at the upper values in the trial run, you might narrow the range in the proper experiment. But if you still get a big change at the upper values you might increase the range.

Tip: If you don't have time to do a trial run, you could always look at the data other people have got doing a similar experiment and use a range and interval values similar to theirs.

Example

For an experiment into the rate of an enzyme-controlled reaction, you might do a trial run with a temperature range of 10-50 °C. If there was no reaction at the upper end (e.g. 40-50 °C), you might narrow the range to 10-40 °C for the proper experiment.

Trial runs can be used to figure out the appropriate intervals (gaps) between the values too. The intervals can't be too small (otherwise the experiment would take ages), or too big (otherwise you might miss something).

Example

If using 1 °C intervals doesn't give much change in the rate of reaction each time, you might use 5 °C intervals instead, e.g. 10, 15, 20, 25, 30, 35, 40 °C.

Trial runs can also help you figure out whether or not your experiment is repeatable — e.g. if you repeat your experiment three times and the results are all similar, the experiment is repeatable.

Tip: Consistently repeating the results is crucial for checking that your results are repeatable.

6. Collecting Data

Once you've designed your experiment, you need to get on and do it. Here's a guide to making sure the results you collect are good.

Getting good quality results

When you do an experiment you want your results to be **repeatable**, **reproducible** and as **accurate** and **precise** as possible.

To check repeatability you need to repeat the readings and check that the results are similar — you should repeat each reading at least three times. To make sure your results are reproducible you can cross check them by taking a second set of readings with another instrument (or a different observer).

Your data also needs to be accurate. Really accurate results are those that are really close to the true answer. The accuracy of your results usually depends on your method — you need to make sure you're measuring the right thing and that you don't miss anything that should be included in the measurements. For example, estimating the amount of gas released from a reaction by counting the bubbles isn't very accurate because you might miss some of the bubbles and they might have different volumes. It's more accurate to measure the volume of gas released using a gas syringe.

Your data also needs to be precise. Precise results are ones where the data is all really close to the mean (average) of your repeated results (i.e. not spread out).

> **Tip:** Sometimes, you can work out what result you should get at the end of an experiment (the theoretical result) by doing a bit of maths. If your experiment is accurate there shouldn't be much difference between the theoretical result and the result you actually get.

> **Tip:** For more on means see page 14.

> **Example**
>
> Look at the data in this table. Data set 1 is more precise than data set 2 because all the data in set 1 is really close to the mean, whereas the data in set 2 is more spread out.
>
> | Repeat | Data set 1 | Data set 2 |
> |--------|-----------|-----------|
> | 1 | 12 | 11 |
> | 2 | 14 | 17 |
> | 3 | 13 | 14 |
> | Mean | 13 | 14 |

Choosing the right equipment

When doing an experiment, you need to make sure you're using the right equipment for the job. The measuring equipment you use has to be sensitive enough to measure the changes you're looking for.

> **Example**
>
> If you need to measure changes of 1 cm³ you need to use a measuring cylinder that can measure in 1 cm³ steps — it'd be no good trying with one that only measures 10 cm³ steps, it wouldn't be sensitive enough.

***Figure 1:** Different types of measuring cylinder and glassware — make sure you choose the right one before you start an experiment.*

The smallest change a measuring instrument can detect is called its **resolution**. For example, some mass balances have a resolution of 1 g, some have a resolution of 0.1 g, and some are even more sensitive.

Also, equipment needs to be **calibrated** by measuring a known value. If there's a difference between the measured and known value, you can use this to correct the inaccuracy of the equipment.

Tip: Calibration is a way of making sure that a measuring device is measuring things accurately — you get it to measure something you know has a certain value and set the device to say that amount.

> **Example**
>
> If a known mass is put on a mass balance, but the reading is a different value, you know that the mass balance has not been calibrated properly.

Errors

Random errors

The results of an experiment will always vary a bit due to **random errors** — unpredictable differences caused by things like human errors in measuring.

> **Example**
>
> Errors made when reading from a measuring cylinder are random. You have to estimate or round the level when it's between two marks — so sometimes your figure will be a bit above the real one, and sometimes a bit below.

You can reduce the effect of random errors by taking repeat readings and finding the mean. This will make your results more precise.

Systematic errors

If a measurement is wrong by the same amount every time, it's called a **systematic error**.

Tip: If there's no systematic error, then doing repeats and calculating a mean can make your results more accurate.

> **Example**
>
> If you measured from the very end of your ruler instead of from the 0 cm mark every time, all your measurements would be a bit small.

Just to make things more complicated, if a systematic error is caused by using equipment that isn't zeroed properly it's called a **zero error**. You can compensate for some of these errors if you know about them though.

Tip: A zero error is a specific type of systematic error.

> **Example**
>
> If a mass balance always reads 1 gram before you put anything on it, all your measurements will be 1 gram too heavy. This is a zero error. You can compensate for this by subtracting 1 gram from all your results.

Tip: Repeating the experiment in the exact same way and calculating a mean won't correct a systematic error.

Anomalous results

Sometimes you get a result that doesn't seem to fit in with the rest at all. These results are called **anomalous results** (or outliers).

> **Example**
>
> Look at the data in this table. The entry that has been circled is an anomalous result because it's much larger than any of the other data values.
>
> | Experiment | A | B | C | D | E | F |
> |---|---|---|---|---|---|---|
> | Rate of reaction (cm³/s) | 10.5 | 11.2 | 10.8 | (85.4) | 10.6 | 11.1 |

Tip: There are lots of reasons why you might get an anomalous result, but usually they're due to human error rather than anything crazy happening in the experiment.

You should investigate anomalous results and try to work out what happened. If you can work out what happened (e.g. you measured something totally wrong) you can ignore them when processing your results.

7. Processing Data

Once you've collected some data, you might need to process it.

Organising data

It's really important that your data is organised. Tables are dead useful for organising data. When you draw a table use a ruler, make sure each column has a heading (including the units) and keep it neat and tidy.

Person	Reaction time (s)
1	0.22
2	0.17

column   *heading*   *units*   *data*   *row*

Figure 1: *Table showing the time taken to react to a stimulus for two people.*

Tip: If you're recording your data as decimals, make sure you give each value to the same number of decimal places.

Tip: Annoyingly, it's difficult to see any patterns or relationships in detail just from a table. You need to use some kind of graph or chart for that (see pages 16-18).

Processing your data

When you've collected data from an experiment, it's useful to summarise it using a few handy-to-use figures.

Mean and range

When you've done repeats of an experiment you should always calculate the **mean** (a type of average). To do this add together all the data values and divide by the total number of values in the sample.

You might also need to calculate the **range** (how spread out the data is). To do this find the largest number and subtract the smallest number from it.

Example

Look at the data in the table below. The mean and range of the data for each test tube has been calculated.

Test tube	Repeat (g) 1	2	3	Mean (g)	Range (g)
A	28	36	32	(28 + 36 + 32) ÷ 3 = 32	36 − 28 = 8
B	47	52	60	(47 + 52 + 60) ÷ 3 = 53	60 − 47 = 13

Median and mode

There are two more types of average, other than the mean, that you might need to calculate. These are the **median** and the **mode**.

- To calculate the median, put all your data in numerical order — the median is the middle value.

- The number that appears most often in a data set is the mode.

Tip: You should ignore anomalous results when calculating the mean, range, median or mode — see page 13 for more on anomalous results.

Tip: If you have an even number of values, the median is halfway between the middle two values.

Example

The results of a study investigating how many minutes it took for people's heart rates to return to resting after sprinting 100 m are shown below:

3, 6, 5, 4, 6, 4, 6, 5, 7

First put the data in numerical order: 3, 4, 4, 5, 5, 6, 6, 6, 7

There are 9 values, so the median is the 5th number, which is **5**.

6 comes up 3 times. None of the other numbers come up more than twice. So the mode is **6**.

Uncertainty

When you repeat a measurement, you often get a slightly different figure each time you do it due to random error. This means that each result has some **uncertainty** to it. The measurements you make will also have some uncertainty in them due to limits in the resolution of the equipment you use. This all means that the mean of a set of results will also have some uncertainty to it. Here's how to calculate the uncertainty of a mean result:

Tip: There's more about errors on page 13.

$$\text{uncertainty} = \text{range} \div 2$$

The larger the range, the less precise your results are and the more uncertainty there will be in your results. Uncertainties are shown using the '±' symbol.

Example

The table below shows the results of a respiration experiment to determine the volume of carbon dioxide produced.

Repeat	1	2	3	mean
Volume of CO_2 produced (cm³)	20.2	19.8	20.0	20.0

1. The range is: $20.2 - 19.8 = 0.4 \text{ cm}^3$
2. So the uncertainty of the mean is: range $\div$ 2 = $0.4 \div 2 = 0.2 \text{ cm}^3$. You'd write this as **20.0 ± 0.2 cm³**

Measuring a greater amount of something helps to reduce uncertainty. For example, in a rate of reaction experiment, measuring the amount of product formed over a longer period compared to a shorter period will reduce the percentage uncertainty in your results.

Tip: Since uncertainty affects precision, you'll need to think about it when you come to evaluating your results (see page 22).

Rounding to significant figures

The first **significant figure** (s.f.) of a number is the first digit that isn't a zero. The second, third and fourth significant figures follow on immediately after the first (even if they're zeros). When you're processing your data you may well want to round any really long numbers to a certain number of significant figures.

Example

0.6874976 rounds to **0.69** to **2 s.f.** and to **0.687** to **3 s.f.**

When you're doing calculations using measurements given to a certain number of significant figures, you should try to give your answer to the lowest number of significant figures that was used in the calculation. If your calculation has multiple steps, only round the final answer, or it won't be as accurate.

Example

For the calculation: $1.2 \div 1.85 = 0.648648648...$

1.2 is given to 2 significant figures. 1.85 is given to 3 significant figures. So the answer should be given to 2 significant figures.

Round the final significant figure (0.6<u>4</u>8) up to 5: $1.2 \div 1.85 = $ **0.65 (2 s.f.)**

The lowest number of significant figures in the calculation is used because the fewer digits a measurement has, the less accurate it is. Your answer can only be as accurate as the least accurate measurement in the calculation.

Exam Tip
If a question asks you to give your answer to a certain number of significant figures, make sure you do this, or you might not get all the marks.

Tip: Remember to write down how many significant figures you've rounded to after your answer.

Tip: When rounding a number, if the next digit after the last significant figure you're using is less than 5 you should round it <u>down</u>, and if it's 5 or more you should round it <u>up</u>.

8. Graphs and Charts

It can often be easier to see trends in data by plotting a graph or chart of your results, rather than by looking at numbers in a table.

Plotting your data on a graph or chart

One of the best ways to present your data after you've processed it is to plot your results on a graph or chart. There are lots of different types you can use. The type you use depends on the type of data you've collected.

Bar charts

Tip: Categoric data is data that comes in distinct categories, for example, blood type, eye colour, sex (i.e. whether you're male or female).

If either the independent or dependent variable is **categoric** you should use a bar chart to display the data.

You also use a bar chart if one of the variables is **discrete** (the data can only take certain values, where there's no in-between value, e.g. number of people is discrete because you can't have half a person).

There are some golden rules you need to follow for drawing bar charts:

- Draw it nice and big (covering at least half of the graph paper).
- Leave a gap between different categories.
- Label both axes and remember to include the units.
- If you've got more than one set of data include a key.
- Give your graph a title explaining what it is showing.

Tip: These golden rules will make sure that your bar chart is clear, easy to read and easy to understand if someone else looks at it.

Have a look at Figure 1 for an example of a pretty decent bar chart.

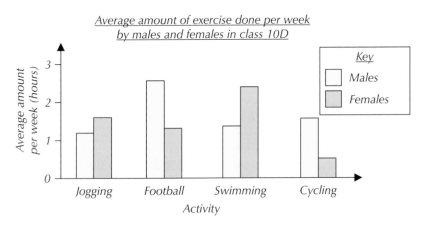

Figure 1: An example of a bar chart.

Histograms

Tip: Frequency is just the number of times that something occurs.

Histograms are a useful way of displaying frequency data when the independent variable is **continuous** (numerical data that can have any value within a range, e.g. length, volume, temperature). They may look like bar charts, but it's the area of the bars that represents the frequency (rather than the height). The height of each bar is called the **frequency density**.

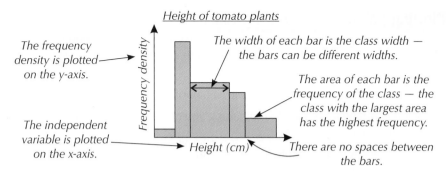

The frequency density is plotted on the y-axis.

The width of each bar is the class width — the bars can be different widths.

The area of each bar is the frequency of the class — the class with the largest area has the highest frequency.

The independent variable is plotted on the x-axis.

There are no spaces between the bars.

Figure 2: *An example of a histogram.*

You calculate the frequency density using this formula:

$$\text{frequency density} = \text{frequency} \div \text{class width}$$

Tip: Don't be fooled by the height of the bars in a histogram — the tallest bar doesn't always belong to the class with the greatest frequency.

Tip: If all the classes are the same width, you can just plot frequency on the y-axis, e.g.

This type of graph is called a frequency diagram.

Example

The table on the right shows the results of a study into variation in pea plant height. The heights of the plants were grouped into four classes.

Height of pea plant (cm)	Frequency
$0 \leq x < 5$	5
$5 \leq x < 10$	14
$10 \leq x < 15$	11
$15 \leq x < 30$	3

1. To draw a histogram of the data, you first need to work out the width of each class. Write the class width in a new column.

Class width
$5 - 0 = \mathbf{5}$
$10 - 5 = \mathbf{5}$
$15 - 10 = \mathbf{5}$
$30 - 15 = \mathbf{15}$

2. Use the formula above to calculate the frequency density for each class and write it in another new column.

3. Work out a suitable scale for each axis, then plot the histogram. It should look something like this:

Frequency density
$5 \div 5 = \mathbf{1}$
$14 \div 5 = \mathbf{2.8}$
$11 \div 5 = \mathbf{2.2}$
$3 \div 15 = \mathbf{0.2}$

Tip: The continuous data here has been split into classes. $0 \leq x < 5$ means the data in the class is more than or equal to 0 and less than 5.

Tip: The table in the example is a frequency table — it shows how many plants are in each height category.

Tip: You might have to round the frequency density — if so, choose a sensible number of decimal places that will be possible to plot using your graph's scale.

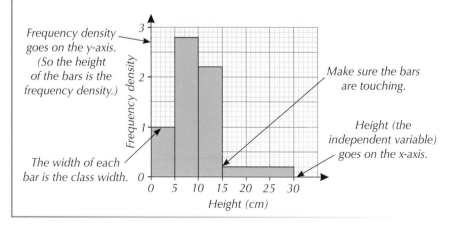

Frequency density goes on the y-axis. (So the height of the bars is the frequency density.)

Make sure the bars are touching.

Height (the independent variable) goes on the x-axis.

The width of each bar is the class width.

Tip: The width of the whole histogram shows the range of results (how spread out they are).

Tip: You can calculate the frequency of a class from a histogram by rearranging the formula: frequency = frequency density × class width.

Plotting points

If the independent and dependent variables are continuous you should plot points on a graph to display the data. Here are the golden rules for plotting points on graphs:

- Draw it nice and big (covering at least half of the graph paper).

- Put the independent variable (the thing you change) on the x-axis (the horizontal one).

- Put the dependent variable (the thing you measure) on the y-axis (the vertical one).

- Label both axes and remember to include the units.

- To plot the points, use a sharp pencil and make a neat little cross.

- In general, don't join the dots up. If you're asked to draw a line of best fit (or a curve of best fit if your points make a curve), try to draw the line through or as near to as many points as possible, ignoring anomalous results.

- If you've got more than one set of data include a key.

- Give your graph a title explaining what it is showing.

Exam Tip
You could be asked to plot points for a graph in your exam. If so, make sure you follow the golden rules or you could end up losing marks.

Tip: Use the biggest data values you've got to draw a sensible scale on your axes. Here, the highest rate of reaction is 22 cm³/s, so it makes sense to label the y-axis up to 25 cm³/s.

Tip: If you're not in an exam, you can use a computer to plot a graph and draw the line of best fit for you.

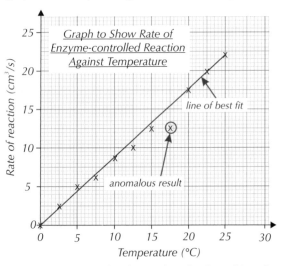

Figure 3: An example of a graph with a line of best fit.

Correlations

Graphs are used to show the relationship between two variables. Data can show three different types of **correlation** (relationship):

Tip: Just because two variables are correlated doesn't mean that the change in one is causing the change in the other. There might be other factors involved, or it may just be down to chance — see pages 21-22 for more.

Positive correlation
As one variable increases the other increases.

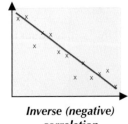

Inverse (negative) correlation
As one variable increases the other decreases.

No correlation
There's no relationship between the two variables.

9. Units

Using the correct units is important when you're drawing graphs or calculating values with an equation. Otherwise your numbers don't really mean anything.

SI units

Lots of different units can be used to describe the same quantity. For example, volume can be given in terms of cubic feet, cubic metres, litres or pints. It would be quite confusing if different scientists used different units to define quantities, as it would be hard to compare people's data. To stop this happening, scientists have come up with a set of standard units, called **SI units**, that all scientists use to measure their data. Figure 1 shows some SI units you'll see in biology:

Tip: SI stands for 'Système International', which is French for 'international system'.

Quantity	SI Base Unit
mass	kilogram, kg
length	metre, m
time	second, s

Figure 1: *Some common SI base units used in biology.*

Scaling prefixes

Quantities come in a huge range of sizes. For example, the volume of a swimming pool might be around 2 000 000 000 cm^3, while the volume of a cup is around 250 cm^3. To make the size of numbers more manageable, larger or smaller units are used. Figure 2 shows the prefixes which can be used in front of units (e.g. metres) to make them bigger or smaller:

prefix	tera (T)	giga (G)	mega (M)	kilo (k)	deci (d)	centi (c)	milli (m)	micro (µ)	nano (n)
multiple of unit	10^{12}	10^9	1 000 000 (10^6)	1000	0.1	0.01	0.001	0.000001 (10^{-6})	10^{-9}

Figure 2: *Scaling prefixes used with units.*

These prefixes are called **scaling prefixes** and they tell you how much bigger or smaller a unit is than the base unit. So one kilometre is one thousand metres.

Converting between units

To swap from one unit to another, all you need to know is what number you have to divide or multiply by to get from the original unit to the new unit — this is called the **conversion factor** and is equal to the number of times the smaller unit goes into the larger unit.

- To go from a bigger unit to a smaller unit, you multiply by the conversion factor.

- To go from a smaller unit to a bigger unit, you divide by the conversion factor.

Tip: If you're going from a smaller unit to a larger unit, your number should get smaller. If you're going from a larger unit to a smaller unit, your number should get larger. This is a handy way to check you've done the conversion correctly.

There are some conversions that'll be particularly useful for GCSE Combined Science. Here they are...

- Mass can have units of kg and g.

- Length can have lots of units, including mm, µm and nm.

Exam Tip
Being familiar with these common conversions could save you time when it comes to doing calculations in the exam.

- Time can have units of min and s.

- Volume can have units of m³, dm³ and cm³.

Tip: Volume is also often given in L (litres) or ml (millilitres). To convert, you'll need to remember that 1 ml = 1 cm³ and so 1 L =1000 cm³.

Examples

- To go from metres to centimetres, you'd multiply by the conversion factor (which is 100).

   2 m is equal to 2 × 100 = **200 cm**

- To go from grams to kilograms, you'd divide by the conversion factor (which is 1000).

   3400 g is equal to 3400 ÷ 1000 = **3.4 kg**

10. Conclusions and Evaluations

So... you've planned and carried out an amazing experiment, got your data and have processed and presented it in a sensible way. Now it's time to figure out what your data actually tells you, and how much you can trust what it says.

How to draw conclusions

Drawing conclusions might seem pretty straightforward — you just look at your data and say what pattern or relationship you see between the dependent and independent variables.

But you've got to be really careful that your conclusion matches the data you've got and doesn't go any further. You also need to be able to use your results to justify your conclusion (i.e. back up your conclusion with some specific data).

When writing a conclusion you need to refer back to the original hypothesis and say whether the data supports it or not.

Example

The table shows the heights of pea plant seedlings grown for three weeks with different fertilisers.

Fertiliser	Mean growth (mm)
A	13.5
B	19.5
No fertiliser	5.5

You could conclude that fertiliser B makes pea plant seedlings grow taller over a three week period than fertiliser A.

The justification for this conclusion is that over the three week period, fertiliser B made pea plants grow 6 mm more on average than fertiliser A.

You can't conclude that fertiliser B makes any other type of plant grow taller than fertiliser A — the results could be totally different.

The hypothesis for this experiment might have been that adding fertiliser would increase the growth of plants and that different types of fertiliser would affect growth by different amounts. The data supports this hypothesis.

Figure 1: *A pea plant seedling.*

Correlation and causation

If two things are correlated (i.e. there's a relationship between them) it doesn't necessarily mean that a change in one variable is causing the change in the other — this is really important, don't forget it. There are three possible reasons for a correlation:

1. Chance

Even though it might seem a bit weird, it's possible that two things show a correlation in a study purely because of chance.

Example

One study might find a correlation between the number of people with breathing problems and the distance they live from a cement factory. But other scientists don't get a correlation when they investigate it — the results of the first study are just a fluke.

Tip: Graphs can be useful for seeing whether two variables are correlated (see page 18).

Tip: Causation just means one thing is causing another.

Tip: Lots of things are correlated without being directly related. E.g. the level of carbon dioxide (CO_2) in the atmosphere and the amount of obesity have both increased over the last 100 years, but that doesn't mean increased atmospheric CO_2 is causing people to become obese.

2. They're linked by a third variable

A lot of the time it may look as if a change in one variable is causing a change in the other, but it isn't — a third variable links the two things.

> **Example**
>
> There's a correlation between water temperature and shark attacks. This isn't because warm water makes sharks crazy. Instead, they're linked by a third variable — the number of people swimming (more people swim when the water's hotter, and with more people in the water shark attacks increase).

3. Causation

Sometimes a change in one variable does cause a change in the other.

> **Example**
>
> There's a correlation between smoking and lung cancer.
> This is because chemicals in tobacco smoke cause lung cancer.

You can only conclude that a correlation is due to cause if you've controlled all the variables that could be affecting the result. (For the smoking example, this would include age and exposure to other things that cause cancer.)

Evaluation

An evaluation is a critical analysis of the whole investigation. Here you need to comment on the following points about your experiment and the data you gathered:

Tip: When you're commenting on the quality of your results, think about things like whether you took enough repeats and whether other people's results were similar to your own.

- **The method**: Was it valid? Did you control all the other variables to make it a fair test?

- **The quality of your results:** Was there enough evidence to reach a valid conclusion? Were the results repeatable, reproducible, accurate and precise?

- **Anomalous results**: Were any of the results anomalous? If there were none then say so. If there were any, try to explain them — were they caused by errors in measurement? Were there any other variables that could have affected the results? You should comment on the level of uncertainty in your results too.

Once you've thought about these points you can decide how much confidence you have in your conclusion. For example, if your results are repeatable, reproducible, accurate and precise and they back up your conclusion then you can have a high degree of confidence in your conclusion.

Tip: When suggesting improvements to the investigation, always make sure that you say why you think this would make the results better.

You can also suggest any changes to the method that would improve the quality of the results, so that you could have more confidence in your conclusion. For example, you might suggest changing the way you controlled a variable, or increasing the number of measurements you took. Taking more measurements at narrower intervals could give you a more accurate result.

You could also make more predictions based on your conclusion, then further experiments could be carried out to test them.

1. Cell Structure

All living things are made of cells — they're the building blocks of every organism on the planet. But different organisms have different cell structures...

Prokaryotes and eukaryotes

Cells can be either **prokaryotic** or **eukaryotic**. Eukaryotic cells are complex and include all animal and plant cells. Prokaryotic cells are smaller and simpler, e.g. bacteria (see next page).

Eukaryotes are organisms that are made up of eukaryotic cells. A **prokaryote** is a prokaryotic cell (it's a single-celled organism).

Both eukaryotic and prokaryotic cells contain various cell parts called **subcellular structures**.

Animal cells

Most animal cells have the following subcellular structures — make sure you know them all. The parts are labelled in Figure 1.

- **Nucleus** — contains genetic material that controls the activities of the cell.

- **Cytoplasm** — a gel-like substance where most of the chemical reactions happen. It contains enzymes (see p. 109) that control these chemical reactions.

- **Cell membrane** — holds the cell together and controls what goes in and out.

- **Mitochondria** — these are where most of the reactions for aerobic respiration take place (see p. 159). Respiration transfers energy that the cell needs to work.

- **Ribosomes** — these are where proteins are made in the cell.

Learning Objectives:
- Know that plant and animal cells are eukaryotic cells, and that bacterial cells are prokaryotic cells.
- Understand that prokaryotic cells are much smaller than eukaryotic cells.
- Know that most animal cells have a nucleus, cytoplasm, cell membrane, mitochondria and ribosomes, and know the function of each of these parts.
- Know that plant and algal cells have the same parts as animal cells, plus a cell wall.
- Know that plant cells also usually have a permanent vacuole and chloroplasts, and know the function of each of these parts.
- Know that bacterial cells have a cell wall, cell membrane, cytoplasm, a single loop of DNA and may have plasmids, and know the function of each of these parts.

Specification References 4.1.1.1, 4.1.1.2

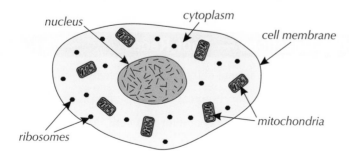

Figure 1: The structure of a typical animal cell.

Figure 2: A human cell seen under a microscope — the blue and yellow oval is the nucleus.

Plant cells

Tip: The diagrams on this page and the previous one all show 'typical' cells.
In reality the structure of a cell varies according to what job it does, so most cells won't look exactly like these.

Plant cells usually have all the bits that animal cells have, plus a few extra:

- **Cell wall** — a rigid structure made of cellulose. It supports and strengthens the cell. The cells of algae (e.g. seaweed) also have a rigid cell wall.

- **Permanent vacuole** — contains cell sap, a weak solution of sugar and salts.

- **Chloroplasts** — these are where photosynthesis occurs, which makes food for the plant (see page 144). They contain a green substance called **chlorophyll**, which absorbs the light needed for photosynthesis.

The subcellular structures of a typical plant cell are shown in Figure 4.

Figure 3: A cross-section of a plant cell seen under a microscope.

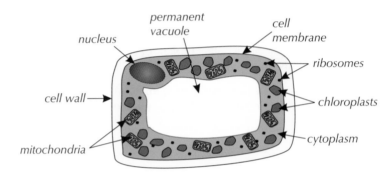

Figure 4: The structure of a typical plant cell.

Bacterial cells

Tip: Bacterial cells contain ribosomes, but they don't contain any chloroplasts or mitochondria.

Bacteria are prokaryotes. A bacterial cell has cytoplasm and a cell membrane surrounded by a cell wall. The cell doesn't have a 'true' nucleus — instead it has a single circular strand of DNA that floats freely in the cytoplasm (see Figure 5). Bacterial cells may also contain one or more small rings of DNA called **plasmids**.

Figure 5: The structure of a typical bacterial cell.

Practice Questions — Fact Recall

Exam Tip
You need to learn the functions of the subcellular structures, not just their names.

Q1 Which part of an animal cell controls its activity?

Q2 Where do most of the chemical reactions take place in a cell?

Q3 What are mitochondria needed for in a cell?

Q4 Name three things that a plant cell usually has, that an animal cell doesn't.

Q5 What is a plasmid?

2. Microscopy

Microscopy is the study of very small objects (such as cells) using an instrument called a microscope. It's an essential part of biology, really.

Microscopes

Microscopes let us see things that we can't see with the naked eye, such as individual cells and their subcellular structures. The microscopy techniques we can use have developed over the years as technology and knowledge have improved. Two common types of microscope are the light microscope and the electron microscope.

Light microscopes

Light microscopes use light and lenses to form an image of a specimen and magnify it (make it look bigger). They let us see individual cells and large subcellular structures, like nuclei. You can read all about how to use a light microscope on the next page.

Electron microscopes

Electron microscopes use electrons instead of light to form an image.

They have a much higher **magnification** than light microscopes. They also have a higher **resolution**. (Resolution is the ability to distinguish between two points, so a higher resolution gives a sharper image.)

Electron microscopes let us see much smaller things in more detail, like the internal structure of mitochondria and chloroplasts. They even let us see tinier things like ribosomes and plasmids.

Using a light microscope

REQUIRED PRACTICAL 1

You need to know the ins and outs of using a light microscope, including how to prepare your specimen, how to focus using the microscope and how to make accurate drawings of what you observe.

Preparing a slide

If you want to look at a specimen (e.g. plant or animal cells) under a light microscope, you need to put it on a microscope slide first. A slide is a strip of clear glass or plastic onto which the specimen is mounted.

For example, here's how to prepare a slide to view onion cells:

1. Add a drop of water to the middle of a clean slide.

2. Cut up an onion and separate it out into layers. Use tweezers to peel off some epidermal tissue from the bottom of one of the layers.

3. Using the tweezers, place the epidermal tissue into the water on the slide.

4. Add a drop of iodine solution. Iodine solution is a **stain**. Stains are used to highlight objects in a cell by adding colour to them.

> **Examples**
> - Iodine solution is used to stain starch in plant cells.
> - Eosin is used to make the cytoplasm show up.

Learning Objectives:

- Understand that, over the years, microscopy techniques have improved.

- Know the difference in magnification and resolving power between light microscopes and electron microscopes.

- Understand how the ability to see cells in more detail under an electron microscope has allowed biologists to have a better understanding of subcellular structures.

- Be able to use a light microscope to look at plant and animal cells, and to correctly draw and label observations (Required Practical 1).

- Be able to use the magnification formula and express answers in standard form.

- Be able to understand the size and scale of cells.

- Understand how to use estimations to work out the relative size or area of subcellular structures.

Specification References
4.1.1.1, 4.1.1.2, 4.1.1.5

Figure 1: *Blood cells seen under a light microscope (top) and an electron microscope (bottom).*

Tip: Make sure you carry out a risk assessment so that you're aware of any hazards, particularly for any stains you're using, before you start preparing your slide.

Tip: Sometimes you can place the specimen on the slide without it being suspended in liquid — it depends on what you're looking at.

Tip: In light microscopes, the beam of light passes through the object being viewed. An image is produced because some parts of the object absorb more light than others. Sometimes the object being viewed is completely transparent, so the whole thing looks white because the light rays just pass straight through. To get round this, stains are used to highlight parts of the object.

5. Place a cover slip (a square of thin, transparent plastic or glass) on top. To do this, stand the cover slip upright on the slide, next to the water droplet. Then carefully tilt and lower it so it covers the specimen. Try not to get any air bubbles under there — they'll obstruct your view of the specimen. Steps 1-5 are shown in Figure 2.

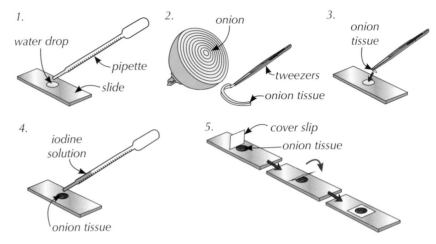

Figure 2: *Preparation of a microscope slide.*

Observing the specimen

You need to know how to set up and use a light microscope (see Figure 3) to observe your prepared slide:

Figure 3: *A light microscope.*

1. Start by clipping the slide you've prepared onto the stage.

2. Select the lowest-powered objective lens (i.e. the one that produces the lowest magnification).

3. Use the coarse adjustment knob to move the stage up to just below the objective lens.

4. Look down the eyepiece. Use the coarse adjustment knob to move the stage downwards until the image is roughly in focus.

5. Adjust the focus with the fine adjustment knob, until you get a clear image of what's on the slide.

6. If you need to see the slide with greater magnification, swap to a higher-powered objective lens and refocus.

Tip: <u>Don't</u> use the eyepiece while you're moving the stage up with the coarse adjustment knob, as you could cause the lens and stage to collide.

Drawing observations

When making a drawing of your specimen from under the microscope, make sure you use a pencil with a sharp point and that you draw with clear, unbroken lines. Your drawing should not include any colouring or shading. If you are drawing cells, the subcellular structures should be drawn in proportion (the correct sizes relative to each other). If you're asked to make your drawing in a certain amount of space (e.g. on a worksheet), it needs to take up at least half of the space available.

You also need to include a title of what you were observing and label the important features of your drawing (e.g. nucleus, chloroplasts) using straight, uncrossed lines. Finally, you need to work out and write down the magnification of your drawing.

Figure 4: Onion cells stained with iodine, viewed under × 400 magnification.

Onion cells

cytoplasm
nucleus
cell wall

real length = 0.3 mm

magnification of drawing = × 133

Figure 5: *A drawing of onion cells as viewed under a light microscope.*

Tip: You can work out the magnification of your drawing using this formula: magnification = length of drawing of cell ÷ real length of cell. For example, in Figure 6, 40 mm ÷ 0.3 mm = 133

Tip: Make sure you also know the magnification that your specimen was observed under.

Tip: You can measure the real size of the cells using a stage micrometer and an eyepiece graticule — see page 292.

Magnification

Magnification is how much bigger the image is than the real object that you're looking at. It's calculated using this formula:

$$\text{magnification} = \frac{\text{image size}}{\text{real size}}$$

Example

If you have a magnified image that's 2 mm wide and your specimen is 0.02 mm wide the magnification is:

$$\text{magnification} = \frac{\text{image size}}{\text{real size}}$$

$$= \frac{2}{0.02} = \mathbf{× 100}$$

2 mm

Tip: Both the image size and the real size should have the same units. If they don't, you'll need to convert them first (see page 19).

If you want to work out the image size or the real size of the object, you have to rearrange the equation.

Example

Calculating image size

If your specimen is 0.3 mm wide and the magnification of the microscope is × 50, then the size of the image is:

image size = magnification × real size
= 50 × 0.3 = **15 mm**

Exam Tip

If you find rearranging formulas hard you can use a formula triangle to help:

All you do is put your finger over the one you want and read off the formula. E.g. if you want the real size of the object, you put your finger over that and it leaves behind image size ÷ magnification.

Tip: All cells are really small, so you might see their sizes written in standard form. You can find out more about standard form on p. 296.

Calculating the real size of an object

If you have a magnified image that's 10 mm wide and the magnification is × 400, then the real size of the specimen you're looking at is:

$$\text{real size} = \frac{\text{image size}}{\text{magnification}} = \frac{10}{400} = \textbf{0.025 mm}$$

Also, you might need to write the real size of a specimen in **standard form**.

> **Example**
>
> To write 0.025 mm in standard form:
>
> 1. Move the decimal point to after the '2' so that the first number is between 1 and 10.
>
> 2. Write the number of places the decimal point has moved as the power of 10. Don't forget the minus sign because the decimal point has moved right.
>
> $$0.025 \longrightarrow \textbf{2.5} \times \textbf{10}^{-2}\textbf{ mm}$$

Converting between units

When you're calculating magnification you need to make sure that all measurements have the same units, e.g. all in millimetres. When dealing with microscopes these units can get pretty tiny. The table below shows common units and how to convert between them:

	Unit	How many millimetres it is	
To convert	Millimetre (mm)	1 mm	To convert
× 1000	Micrometre (μm)	0.001 mm	÷ 1000
× 1000	Nanometre (nm)	0.000001 mm	÷ 1000

> **Examples**
>
> - To convert from a smaller unit to a bigger unit you have to divide. So to convert 5 micrometres to millimetres you divide 5 by 1000. 5 ÷ 1000 = **0.005 mm**
>
> - To go from a bigger unit to a smaller unit you have to multiply. So to convert 0.025 micrometres to nanometres you multiply 0.025 by 1000. 0.025 × 1000 = **25 nm**
>
> - If you have a specimen that's 5 μm wide and an image that's 5 mm wide, you need to put both measurements in the same units before you can work out the magnification using the formula:
>
>   5 mm = 5 × 1000 = 5000 μm
>
> $$\text{magnification} = \frac{\text{image size}}{\text{real size}} = \frac{5000}{5} = \textbf{× 1000}$$

Tip: It doesn't matter which units you choose to convert to. In the calculation on the right, if you converted 5 μm to mm (5 ÷ 1000 = 0.005 μm) instead, you'd get the same answer of × 1000 magnification.

Estimating size and area of cell structures

You can estimate the size of a subcellular structure by comparing its size to that of the cell.

Tip: Estimates can come in handy if you don't have a small enough scale to measure something accurately.

Example

Figure 6 shows a cheek cell.

Estimate the width of the nucleus of the cell.

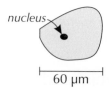

Figure 6: Cheek cell with scale.

1. Estimate the number of times that the nucleus could fit across the width of the cell.

The nucleus would fit across the cell about 8 times.

2. Divide the width of the cell by the number of times the nucleus would fit across it.

width of nucleus = 60 μm ÷ 8 = **7.5 μm**

Exam Tip
In the exam, you could be given a photomicrograph (a picture taken down a light microscope) of a cell and its subcellular structures rather than a diagram like this. You can estimate the size of the subcellular structures in a photomicrograph in the same way.

You can estimate the area of a subcellular structure by comparing it to a regular shape.

Example

Figure 7 shows a diagram of a mitochondrion measured under an electron microscope.

1.5 μm

4.6 μm

Figure 7: A mitochondrion.

The shape of the mitochondrion is close to that of a rectangle.

So to estimate its area, use the formula for the area of a rectangle:
area = length × width

Area = 4.6 μm × 1.5 μm = **6.9 μm²**

Tip: Don't forget to include the units of area in your answer.

Practice Questions — Application

Q1 A bacterial cell is 0.002 mm long. A magnified image of the cell is 18 mm long. What is the magnification?

Q2 A plant cell is 0.08 mm wide. It is examined under a × 400 microscope lens. Calculate the size of the magnified image.

Q3 A specimen is observed under × 1500 magnification. The magnified image is 10.5 mm wide. What is the real width of the specimen? Give your answer in μm.

Tip: If it helps you to work out what size you're looking for, you could draw a diagram of what the question is describing. So for Q2 it might be like this:

real size   image

- Understand that many cells are specialised — they perform a specific function.

- Understand that cells differentiate to become specialised as an organism develops, and that differentiation involves the cells developing different subcellular structures, which enable the cells to carry out their specific functions.

- Know that most animal cells lose the ability to differentiate at an early stage but lots of plant cells never lose the ability to differentiate.

- Know that mature animals mainly use cell division to replace and repair cells.

- Be able to relate the structure of different types of cell to their function, including sperm cells, nerve cells and muscle cells in animals and root hair cells, xylem and phloem cells in plants.

Specification References
4.1.1.3, 4.1.1.4

3. Cell Differentiation and Specialisation

Not all cells in an organism do the same job. A cell's structure is related to the job it does, so cell structure can vary. Different cell structures are the result of differentiation.

What is a specialised cell?

A specialised cell is one that performs a specific function. Most cells in an organism are specialised. A cell's structure (e.g. its shape and the parts it contains) helps it to carry out its function — so depending on what job it does, a specialised cell can look very different to the cells you saw on pages 23-24.

Cell differentiation

Differentiation is the process by which a cell changes to become specialised for its job. As cells change, they develop different subcellular structures and turn into different types of cells (see Figure 1).

undifferentiated cell   *Differentiation*   *differentiated white blood cell*

Figure 1: *Diagram showing cell differentiation.*

Most differentiation occurs as an organism develops. In most animal cells, the ability to differentiate is then lost after they become specialised. However, lots of plant cells don't ever lose this ability. The cells that differentiate in mature animals are mainly used for repairing and replacing cells, such as skin or blood cells.

Some cells are undifferentiated cells — they're called stem cells. There's more about them on pages 38-40.

Examples of specialised cells

In the exam, you could be asked to relate the structure of a cell to its function. The idea is that you apply your knowledge of cell structure (see pages 23-24) to the information you're given about the role of the cell in an organism. Don't panic — it's easier than it sounds. Here are a few examples to help you understand how cell structure and function are related:

1. Sperm cells (in animals)

Sperm cells are specialised for reproduction. The function of a sperm is to get the male DNA to the female DNA. It has a long tail and a streamlined head to help it swim to the egg. There are also lots of **mitochondria** (see p. 23) in the cell to provide the energy it needs to do this. It also carries enzymes in its head to digest through the egg cell membrane. The structure of a sperm cell is shown by Figures 2 and 3 on the next page.

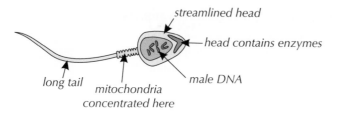

streamlined head

head contains enzymes

male DNA

mitochondria concentrated here

long tail

Figure 2: A sperm cell.

Figure 3: A microscope image of a sperm cell. It's easy to see the streamlined head and tail.

2. Nerve cells (in animals)

Nerve cells are specialised for rapid signalling. The function of nerve cells is to carry electrical signals from one part of the body to another. These cells are long (to cover more distance) and have branched connections at their ends to connect to other nerve cells and form a network throughout the body.

Tip: Nerve cells join together to form the nervous system (see page 172).

branched connections

long body

cell body

branched connections

Figure 4: An electron microscope image of the branched connections from the cell body of a nerve cell (left) and the whole structure of a nerve cell (right).

Tip: The electrical signals are slowed down when they pass between two nerve cells, so a few long cells are better for fast signal transmission than lots of short cells.

3. Muscle cells (in animals)

Muscle cells are specialised for contraction. The function of a muscle cell is to contract quickly. These cells are long (so that they have space to contract) and contain lots of mitochondria to transfer the energy needed for contraction.

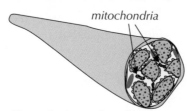

mitochondria

Figure 5: A muscle cell.

4. Root hair cells (in plants)

Root hair cells are cells on the surface of plant roots that are specialised for absorbing water and minerals. They grow into long "hairs" that stick out into the soil. This gives the plant a big surface area for absorbing water and mineral ions from the soil.

Figure 6: Root hair cells as seen under a microscope.

cell membrane

thin cell wall

vacuole

Figure 7: A root hair cell.

Tip: Root hair cells don't contain any chloroplasts — this is because they are underground and so they don't carry out photosynthesis.

5. Phloem and xylem cells (in plants)

Phloem and xylem cells are specialised for transporting substances. They form phloem and xylem tubes, which transport substances such as food and water around plants.

To form the tubes, the cells are long and joined end to end. Xylem cells are hollow in the centre and phloem cells have very few subcellular structures, so that substances can flow through them.

Tip: There's more about phloem and xylem on page 85.

Figure 8: *A phloem tube (left) and xylem tube (right).*

Practice Questions — Fact Recall

Q1 What is cell differentiation?

Q2 Describe the differences in the ability of plant and animal cells to differentiate.

Q3 a) What is the function of a nerve cell?

b) Describe two features of a nerve cell that make it specialised for its function.

Q4 Muscle cells need lots of energy for contraction. What feature of muscle cells make them specialised for this?

Practice Questions — Application

Tip: Think about the function of ribosomes — see page 23.

Q1 The function of gastric chief cells is to secrete enzymes (proteins) into the stomach during digestion. Comment on the amount of ribosomes you'd expect to find in a gastric chief cell.

Q2 A diagram of an epithelial cell from the small intestine is shown here:

Tip: You're not expected to actually <u>know</u> the answer to these questions — just make sensible suggestions using the information given and your knowledge about cell structure from pages 23-24.

lots of folds in the cell membrane

nucleus

cytoplasm

lots of mitochondria

These cells line the inner surface of the small intestine and their function is to absorb food molecules as they move through the intestine. Sometimes this process requires energy.

Tip: Look back at the examples on the last couple of pages if you're struggling with this one — the function of some of those cells involves absorption too.

Use this information and the diagram to suggest two ways in which the structure of these cells helps them to carry out their function.

4. Chromosomes

*Well, this is it. Probably the most important topic in the whole of biology —
DNA. It may not seem like a big deal right now, but this stuff is going to come
in really handy later on, I promise. So crack on and learn it.*

Learning Objectives:

- Know that
  chromosomes are
  found in the cell
  nucleus.
- Know that
  chromosomes are
  usually found in pairs
  in body cells.
- Know that
  chromosomes are
  made of DNA and
  carry genes.

**Specification Reference
4.1.2.1**

The cell nucleus

Most cells in your body have a structure called a **nucleus**. The nucleus
contains your genetic material (the instructions you need to grow and develop).
This material is stored in the form of **chromosomes** — see Figure 1.

Figure 1: *Diagram to show that a cell nucleus contains chromosomes.*

Body cells normally have two
copies of each chromosome
— one from the organism's
'mother', and one from its
'father'. So, humans have two
copies of chromosome 1, two
copies of chromosome 2, etc.

Figure 2 shows the 23 pairs of
chromosomes from a human cell.
(The 23rd pair are a bit different
— see page 213).

Figure 2: *The 23 pairs of chromosomes
from a female human body cell.*

Tip: You might
sometimes see
chromosomes drawn
like this:

That's because
chromosomes only
look like this:

just before a cell divides
for reproduction and
growth (see p. 35).

Chromosomes and DNA

Chromosomes are long lengths of a molecule called **DNA**.
The DNA is coiled up to form the arms of the chromosome (see Figure 3).

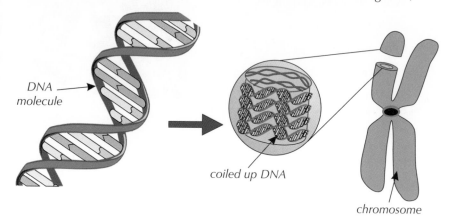

DNA
molecule

coiled up DNA

chromosome

Figure 3: *Diagram to show how DNA coils up to form a chromosome.*

Figure 4: *A pair of
human chromosomes
seen under a microscope.
(In fact, it's pair No. 3.)*

Chromosomes and genes

Each chromosome carries a large number of genes (see Figure 5). These are short sections of DNA. Genes control our characteristics. Different genes control the development of different characteristics, e.g. hair colour, eye colour. There's more about genes on page 204.

There's more about genes on page 204.

Tip: A chromosome contains thousands of genes, not just one. This diagram is just to help show you what's going on.

Figure 5: *Diagram showing relationship between chromosomes, genes and characteristics.*

Practice Questions — Fact Recall

Q1   Where in the cell are chromosomes found?

Q2   What molecule are chromosomes made up of?

Q3   a) What are genes?

b) What do we need different genes for?

Practice Questions — Application

The photograph on the right was taken under a microscope. It shows a cell, its nucleus and chromosomes.

Q1   Which arrow is pointing to:

a) the cell?

b) the nucleus?

c) a chromosome?

Q2   Suggest why it is not possible to see individual genes in this photograph.

Exam Tip
Make sure you don't get genes and chromosomes mixed up in the exam if you have to label them — chromosomes are long lengths of DNA and they carry genes.

5. Mitosis

Our body cells are able to make copies of themselves so that we can grow or repair any damaged tissue. It's pretty clever stuff...

Learning Objectives:

- Know that body cells divide by mitosis, which is a stage of the cell cycle.
- Know that mitosis allows organisms to grow and develop.
- Be able to describe how, during the cell cycle, body cells grow and increase their amount of subcellular structures, then copy their genetic material before undergoing a single division.
- Understand how a cell divides by mitosis to form two genetically identical cells.
- Be able to describe mitosis in a given context and recognise when mitosis is occurring.

Specification Reference 4.1.2.2

Mitosis and the cell cycle

Body cells in multicellular organisms divide to produce new cells as part of a series of stages called the cell cycle. The cell cycle starts when a cell has been produced by cell division and ends with the cell dividing to produce two identical cells. It can be summarised as a stage of cell growth and DNA replication, followed by a stage of cell division (see Figure 1).

The stage of the cell cycle when the cell divides is called **mitosis**:

> Mitosis is when a cell reproduces itself by splitting to form two identical offspring.

Multicellular organisms use mitosis to grow and develop or replace cells that have been damaged. The end of the cell cycle results in two new cells identical to the original cell, with the same number of chromosomes.

cell growth and DNA replication

Figure 1: *The cell cycle*

mitosis

As a cell goes through the cell cycle, it has to undergo some key changes.

What happens during the cell cycle?

Here are the steps involved in the cell cycle:

Growth and replication

1. In a cell that's not dividing, the DNA is all spread out in long strings.

2. Before it divides, the cell has to grow and increase the amount of subcellular structures such as mitochondria and ribosomes.

3. It then duplicates its DNA — so there's one copy of each chromosome for each new cell. The DNA is copied and forms X-shaped chromosomes. Each 'arm' of the chromosome is an exact duplicate of the other.

   Now the cell is ready for mitosis...

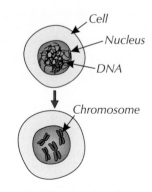

Cell
Nucleus
DNA
Chromosome

Figure 2: *Diagram showing the growth and replication stage of the cell cycle.*

Tip: When a cell has copied its DNA, the left arm of an X-shaped chromosome has the same DNA as the right arm.

right arm
left arm

Mitosis

Tip: Mitosis is really one continuous process, but it's often described as a series of stages.

4. The chromosomes line up at the centre of the cell and cell fibres pull them apart. The two arms of each chromosome go to opposite ends of the cell.

5. Membranes form around each of the sets of chromosomes. These become the nuclei of the two new cells — the nucleus has divided.

6. Lastly, the cytoplasm and cell membrane divide.

The cell has now produced two new daughter cells. The daughter cells contain exactly the same DNA — they're identical. Their DNA is also identical to the parent cell.

Tip: The key things to remember about mitosis are that the dividing cell already contains two copies of its DNA and it splits into two, to form two genetically identical daughter cells.

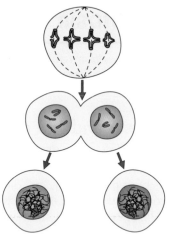

Figure 3: *Diagram showing the steps of mitosis in the cell cycle.*

Recognising mitosis

In your exam, you might have to identify or describe what's going on in photos of real cells undergoing mitosis.

> **Example**
>
> The photos below show onion cells in different stages of the cell cycle. Describe what is happening to each cell and identify which cells are going though mitosis.
>
> **A**   **B**   **C**
>
> In cell A, the chromosomes are visible in the nucleus. The DNA has formed X-shaped chromosomes because it's being duplicated. So this cell must be in the replication stage of the cell cycle — it is not yet going through mitosis.
>
> In cell B, the chromosomes are lined up across the centre of the cell. You can just about see the cell fibres, which will pull the two arms of each chromosome apart. So this cell is undergoing mitosis.
>
> In cell C, the chromosomes have been pulled apart to opposite ends of the cell. They have formed two separate nucleii. A cell membrane is visible between the two halves of the cell, dividing the cytoplasm, so the cell must be at the end stage of mitosis. It is about to form two identical daughter cells.

Tip: If the cell isn't going through the cell cycle (so it's not dividing or preparing to divide), you won't be able to see the chromosomes in the nucleus.

How long is each stage of the cell cycle?

The time taken for a stage of the cell cycle varies depending on the cell type and the environmental conditions. You can calculate how long a stage lasts if you're given the right information.

Example

A scientist observes a section of growing tissue under a microscope. He counts 120 cells in one field of view. Of those, 42 cells are in the replication stage of the cell cycle. One complete cell cycle of the cells in this tissue lasts 24 hours. How long do the cells spend in the replication stage of the cell cycle? Give your answer in minutes.

(MATHS SKILLS)

1. The scientist has observed that 42 out of 120 cells are in the replication stage of the cell cycle. This suggests that the proportion of time the cells spend in this stage must be 42/120th of the cell cycle.

2. You're told that the cell cycle in these cells lasts 24 hours. That's ($24 \times 60 =$) 1440 minutes.

3. So the cells spend 42/120th of 1440 minutes in the replication stage, which you can work out like this:

$$\frac{42}{120} \times 1440 = \textbf{504 minutes} \text{ in the replication stage of the cell cycle.}$$

Tip: The fraction of cells in any one stage of the cell cycle is proportional to the time taken for that stage. So if you know the number of cells in a particular stage, the total number of cells and the total time for the cell cycle, you can work out an estimate for how long that particular stage takes.

Practice Questions — Fact Recall

Q1 Give two uses of mitosis in multicellular animals.

Q2 How many times does a body cell divide during mitosis?

Practice Questions — Application

This photograph shows the last stage in mitosis — two new daughter cells are formed.

Q1 a) Will these new cells be genetically identical or genetically different to the parent cell?

b) How many sets of chromosomes will these cells have?

Exam Tip
You don't have to know anything to do with the specific cells to answer a mitosis question like this in the exam.

Q2 In a tissue sample of 198 cells, 6 cells are observed to be in the last stage in mitosis. One complete cell cycle in the tissue cells takes 1500 minutes. How long does the last stage in mitosis take for an average cell in this tissue? Give your answer in hours.

Learning Objectives:
- Know that stem cells are undifferentiated cells.
- Know that stem cells are able to produce more stem cells and differentiate into specialised cells.
- Know that stem cells from adult bone marrow and embryonic stem cells can be cloned and made to differentiate into different cell types, e.g. blood cells.
- Know that stem cells could be used to treat some medical conditions, e.g. diabetes, paralysis.
- Know that embryonic stem cells can be produced by therapeutic cloning for use in medical treatments, and know the advantages of this technique.
- Know that the use of stem cells in medical treatments carries risks, such as the potential transfer of viruses to patients.
- Know that some people object to using stem cells in medical treatments and research on ethical or religious grounds.
- Know that plant stem cells can be found in meristems and can differentiate into any plant cell at any point in the plant's life.
- Know that plant stem cells can be used to grow clones of a plant and understand the benefits of this.

Specification Reference
4.1.2.3

6. Stem Cells

All the cells in an organism originate from stem cells. Scientists are attempting to use these cells to do some pretty amazing things...

What are stem cells?

Some cells are undifferentiated (i.e. they have not yet changed to become specialised for a particular job — see page 30). These undifferentiated cells are called **stem cells**. They can divide to produce lots more undifferentiated cells. They can also develop into different types of cell, depending on what instructions they're given.

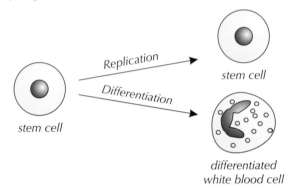

Figure 1: *Diagram showing stem cell replication and differentiation.*

Stem cells are found in early human embryos. They're exciting to doctors and medical researchers because they have the potential to turn into any kind of cell at all. This makes sense if you think about it — all the different types of cell found in a human being have to come from those few cells in the early embryo.

Adults also have stem cells, but they're only found in certain places, like bone marrow. These aren't as versatile as embryonic stem cells — they can't turn into any cell type at all, only certain ones, such as blood cells.

Stem cells from embryos and bone marrow can be grown in a lab to produce **clones** (genetically identical cells) and made to differentiate into specialised cells to use in medicine or research.

Adult stem cells in medicine

Adult stem cells are already used to cure disease.

> **Example**
>
> People with some blood diseases (e.g. sickle cell anaemia — a disease which affects the shape of the red blood cells) can be treated by bone marrow transplants. Bone marrow is the tissue found inside bone. It contains stem cells that can turn into new blood cells to replace the faulty old ones.

Embryonic stem cells in medicine

Embryonic stem cells could also be used to replace faulty cells in sick people in the future (see Figure 3).

Figure 2: *Microscope image of a human embryo that's about 4 days old. Stem cells can be taken from the embryo at this stage.*

Figure 3: *Diagram showing some potential uses of embryonic stem cells in medicine.*

In a type of cloning called **therapeutic cloning**, an embryo could be made to have the same genetic information as the patient. This means that the stem cells produced from it would also contain the same genes as the patient and so wouldn't be rejected by the patient's body if used to replace faulty cells.

However, there are risks involved in using stem cells in medicine. For example, stem cells grown in the lab may become contaminated with a virus which could be passed on to the patient and so make them sicker. There are also ethical issues related to the use of embryonic stem cells — see below.

Tip: The advantage of using embryonic stem cells for therapies over adult stem cells is that they have the potential to differentiate into many different types of cell (unlike adult stem cells, which are limited to differentiating into certain types of cell). They are also easier to grow in culture than adult stem cells.

Issues involved in stem cell research

Embryonic stem cell research has exciting possibilities, but it's also pretty controversial.

Some people are against it, because they feel that human embryos shouldn't be used for experiments since each one is a potential human life.

However, others think that curing patients who already exist and who are suffering is more important than the rights of embryos. One fairly convincing argument in favour of this point of view is that the embryos used in the research are usually unwanted ones from fertility clinics which, if they weren't used for research, would probably just be destroyed. But of course, campaigners for the rights of embryos usually want this banned too.

Campaigners for the rights of embryos feel that scientists should concentrate more on finding and developing other sources of stem cells, so people could be helped without having to use embryos. Research is being done into getting stem cells from alternative sources. For example, it may be possible to produce stem cells from differentiated adult cells by reprogramming the adult cells back to an undifferentiated stage. However, further research has to be done to make sure that this technique is safe for use in medical treatments.

In some countries stem cell research is banned, but it's allowed in the UK as long as it follows strict guidelines.

Tip: Obtaining stem cells from an embryo destroys the embryo.

Exam Tip
Questions on the issues associated with the use of embryonic stem cells might crop up in the exam, so make sure you know arguments for and against the use of embryonic stem cells.

Figure 4: *Plants grown from meristem tissue.*

Stem cells in plants

In plants, stem cells are found in the **meristems** (parts of the plant where growth occurs — see p. 83). Throughout the plant's entire life, cells in the meristem tissues can differentiate into any type of plant cell.

These stem cells can be used to produce clones (identical copies) of whole plants quickly and cheaply. This is useful for:

- growing crops of identical plants that have desired features for farmers.

- growing more plants of rare species (to prevent them being wiped out).

Example

Dutch elm disease is a fungal tree disease that has destroyed millions of elm trees worldwide. One way to protect elm trees from being wiped out by this disease could be to create and grow clones of naturally-resistant individuals.

Practice Questions — Fact Recall

Q1 What is a stem cell?

Q2 What type of cell can early embryonic stem cells turn into?

Q3 Give one place where stem cells can be found in an adult human.

Q4 Why could embryonic stem cells produced by therapeutic cloning be useful for replacing faulty cells in a sick person?

Q5 Name the tissue in plants where stem cells can be found.

Practice Questions — Application

Q1 Alzheimer's disease is a condition which damages the neurones (nerve cells) in the brain. These neurones die, but are not replaced, leading to a decrease in the amount of neurones in the brain. Symptoms of Alzheimer's disease include memory loss, confusion and changes in personality.

a) Suggest a way in which embryonic stem cells could potentially be used to treat people with Alzheimer's disease.

b) Give another possible use of embryonic stem cells in medicine.

Q2 Embryonic stem cells used for medical research are mostly taken from embryos left over from fertility clinics, which would otherwise be destroyed. Suggest a reason why some people are happier with using these embryos for stem cell research, rather than creating embryos purely with the purpose of being used for research.

Q3 Embryos begin to develop a nervous system 14 days after fertilisation. Some people think that it's morally acceptable to use an embryo for stem cell research before this point, as the embryo has no senses, so cannot be considered a life yet. Suggest a reason why some people may not agree with this view.

Exam Tip
It's important that you can look at something from the point of view of someone with different opinions to you.

Topic 1a Checklist — Make sure you know...

Cell Structure

☐ That plant and animal cells are eukaryotic cells, which make up eukaryotic organisms, and that bacterial cells are prokaryotic cells, which are much smaller than eukaryotic cells.

☐ That most animal cells have: a nucleus (which contains the genetic material that controls the activities of a cell), cytoplasm (where most of the chemical reactions happen), a cell membrane (which controls what goes in and out of the cell), mitochondria (where most of the reactions for aerobic respiration happen), and ribosomes (where proteins are made in the cell).

☐ That plant and algal cells have all the same parts as animal cells, plus a cell wall made of cellulose.

☐ That most plant cells also have a permanent vacuole containing cell sap and chloroplasts which absorb the light needed for photosynthesis.

☐ That a bacterial cell has cytoplasm, a cell membrane and a cell wall, and that its genetic material is a single DNA loop found in the cytoplasm (rather than in a nucleus) and potentially one or more plasmids (small rings of DNA).

Microscopy

☐ That microscopy techniques have developed over time due to improving technology, and that electron microscopes can produce images of higher magnification and higher resolution than light microscopes.

☐ That smaller subcellular structures, such as ribosomes, can be seen under an electron microscope (but not a light microscope), which has led to a greater understanding of subcellular structures.

☐ How to prepare a slide to observe plant or animal cells, use a light microscope and draw your observations (Required Practical 1).

☐ How to use the formula: magnification = image size ÷ real size, and how to write the answer to the calculation in standard form.

☐ About the size and scale of cells.

☐ How to use estimations to work out the relative size or area of subcellular structures.

Cell Differentiation and Specialisation

☐ That many cells are specialised to carry out a specific function.

☐ That cells in an organism become specialised as the organism develops, and that this involves developing specific subcellular structures, so that they can carry out their functions.

☐ That most animal cells lose the ability to differentiate (become specialised) early on, but lots of plant cells don't ever lose this ability. In mature animals, cell division is mainly used for growth and repair.

☐ How to relate a cell's structure (its shape and the subcellular structures it contains) to its function.

☐ How the structures of sperm cells, nerve cells, muscle cells, root hair cells, xylem cells and phloem cells relate to their functions.

cont...

Chromosomes

- [ ] That chromosomes are found in the cell nucleus.
- [ ] That body cells contain two sets of chromosomes and that these chromosomes are found in pairs.
- [ ] That chromosomes are made up of long molecules of DNA.
- [ ] That chromosomes carry genes, which are small sections of DNA.

Mitosis

- [ ] That body cells divide by mitosis, which is one stage of the cell cycle.
- [ ] That mitosis allows organisms to grow, develop and replace damaged cells.
- [ ] That during the cell cycle, the cell grows and increases its subcellular structures, copies its genetic material and then divides once (by mitosis), producing two cells which are genetically identical.
- [ ] How to recognise mitosis in cells and describe mitosis in a given context.

Stem Cells

- [ ] That stem cells are undifferentiated cells that can produce specialised cells and more stem cells.
- [ ] That adult stem cells can be taken from bone marrow and made to differentiate into certain types of cell, including blood cells. Adult stem cells already have some uses in medicine, e.g. in bone marrow transplants.
- [ ] That embryonic stem cells are found in early human embryos, and can be cloned and made to differentiate into any type of cell. This means they could be used to treat many medical conditions by replacing faulty cells, such as nerve cells in paralysis and insulin-producing cells in diabetes.
- [ ] That therapeutic cloning can be used to produce embryonic stem cells that are genetically identical to a patient, which means that the cells they produce will not be rejected by the patient's body.
- [ ] That the use of stem cells in medical treatments carries risks, e.g. viral infection, and that some people object to using stem cells for medical treatments and research on religious or ethical grounds.
- [ ] That plant stem cells are found in tissues called meristems, and they can differentiate into any type of plant cell throughout the life of the plant.
- [ ] That plant stem cells can be used to produce clones of plants quickly and cheaply.
- [ ] That cloning plants is useful for creating many identical crop plants with desired features and for protecting rare species from extinction.

Exam-style Questions

1   The genetic material of a multicellular organism
is found in cells in the form of chromosomes.

   1.1   Name the subcellular structure that contains chromosomes.

(1 mark)

   1.2   There are twenty three different chromosomes in a female human body cell.
How many copies of each chromosome does the cell have?

(1 mark)

   1.3   A body cell doubles its genetic material as it prepares to divide.
Name the process by which the body cell would divide
to produce identical daughter cells.

(1 mark)

2   **Figure 1** shows a palisade cell.

Figure 1

   2.1   Look at the structures labelled 1-4 in **Figure 1**.
Which of the following options gives the
correct labels for these structures?

     A   1 — permanent vacuole, 2 — cytoplasm, 3 — chloroplast, 4 — cell wall
     B   1 — cytoplasm, 2 — chloroplast, 3 — cell wall, 4 — permanent vacuole
     C   1 — cell wall, 2 — permanent vacuole, 3 — cytoplasm, 4 — chloroplast
     D   1 — cell wall, 2 — cytoplasm, 3 — chloroplast, 4 — permanent vacuole

(1 mark)

   2.2   Is a palisade cell an example of a eukaryotic cell or a prokaryotic cell?
Give a reason for your answer that refers to the cell's structure.

(1 mark)

   2.3   A palisade cell is a specialised cell. What is a specialised cell?

(1 mark)

   2.4   What name is given to the unspecialised cells in an organism?

(1 mark)

   2.5   Palisade cells are the main site of photosynthesis in a plant.
They are found grouped together near the top of a leaf.

Suggest one way that the structure of a palisade cell makes it
well adapted for its function.

(1 mark)

3   A scientist is studying sperm cells under a light microscope.

He places a drop of liquid containing the cells on the centre of a microscope slide and adds a drop of hematoxylin stain, which binds to DNA and stains it blue. The scientist then places a cover slip on the slide and clips the slide onto the microscope stage.

3.1   What is the purpose of a stain when viewing cells under a light microscope?

(1 mark)

3.2   Hematoxylin can cause irritation if it comes into contact with the skin or eyes. Suggest **one** precaution the scientist should take when using hematoxylin.

(1 mark)

3.3   Describe how the scientist would have placed the cover slip on the slide to avoid creating air bubbles underneath.

(2 marks)

Figure 2 shows sperm cells viewed under the microscope. The real length of sperm A is shown by the line.

Figure 2

The magnification equation is: magnification = $\dfrac{\text{image size}}{\text{real size}}$

3.4   Use the magnification equation to calculate the magnification of sperm A.

(3 marks)

3.5   The real size of the sperm head is 5 μm. Use the magnification equation to calculate the size of the image of the sperm head if it was viewed under × 500 magnification. Give your answer in millimetres.

(3 marks)

A sperm cell contains a nucleus, but does not contain ribosomes.

3.6   The scientist wants to study the internal structure of the nucleus in the sperm cell. What type of microscope should he use to do this? Explain your answer.

(2 marks)

3.7   Suggest a reason why sperm cells do not have ribosomes.

(1 mark)

Sperm cells are specialised for reproduction.

3.8   Explain how the structure of a sperm cell makes it specialised for its function.

(6 marks)

1. Diffusion

Particles tend to move about randomly and end up evenly spaced. This is important when it comes to getting substances in and out of cells.

What is diffusion?

"Diffusion" is simple. It's just the gradual movement of particles from places where there are lots of them to places where there are fewer of them. That's all it is — just the natural tendency for stuff to spread out.

Unfortunately you also have to learn the fancy way of saying the same thing, which is this:

> Diffusion is the spreading out of particles from an area of higher concentration to an area of lower concentration.

Diffusion happens in both solutions and gases — that's because the particles in these substances are free to move about randomly. The simplest type is when different gases diffuse through each other.

Example

When you spray perfume, the smell of perfume diffuses through the air in a room:

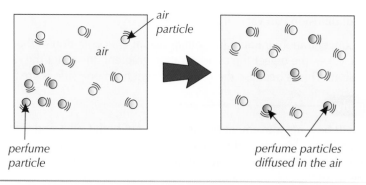

perfume
particle

air
particle

air

perfume particles
diffused in the air

Diffusion across cell membranes

Cell membranes are clever because they hold the cell together but they let stuff in and out as well. **Dissolved substances** can move in and out of cells by diffusion.

Only very small molecules can diffuse through cell membranes though — things like **oxygen** (needed for respiration — see page 159), glucose, amino acids and water. Big molecules like starch and proteins can't fit through the membrane (see Figure 2 on the next page).

Learning Objectives:
- Know the definition of 'diffusion'.
- Be able to describe how dissolved substances (such as oxygen) can move in and out of a cell, through the cell membrane, by diffusion.
- Understand that during diffusion, the net movement of substances will be from an area of higher concentration to an area of lower concentration.
- Be able to explain how the rate of diffusion is affected by the difference in the concentration of particles, the temperature and the surface area available for diffusion.

Specification Reference
4.1.3.1

Figure 1: The ink particles in this flask are diffusing into the water — they're moving from an area of high concentration (at the bottom of the flask) to an area of low concentration (higher up).

Exam Tip
If you're struggling to remember which way the particles move in diffusion, think of it like this: if you were in a really crowded place, you'd probably want to get out of there to somewhere with a bit more room. It's the same with particles — they always diffuse from an area of higher concentration to an area of lower concentration.

Figure 2: *Diagram to show diffusion across a cell membrane.*

Just like with diffusion in air, particles flow through the cell membrane from where there's a higher concentration (more of them) to where there's a lower concentration (fewer of them).

They're only moving about randomly of course, so they go both ways — but if there are a lot more particles on one side of the membrane, there's a **net** (overall) movement from that side.

Example

Particles are diffusing both in and out of this cell. However, the concentration of particles is higher inside the cell than outside, so the net movement of particles is out of the cell.

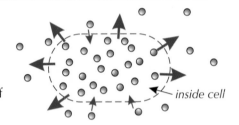

inside cell

The rate of diffusion

The **rate** of diffusion can vary. It's affected by:

- The concentration gradient (the difference in concentration of the particles) — the bigger the concentration gradient, the faster the rate of diffusion. This is because the net movement from one side is greater.

Example

There will be a net movement of particles out of both Cell 1 and Cell 2 (shown below). However, the rate of diffusion will be faster out of Cell 1, because there's a bigger difference in the concentration of particles on either side of the cell membrane.

Tip: As diffusion takes place, the difference in concentration between the two sides of the membrane decreases, until the concentration on both sides is equal. This means that diffusion slows down over time.

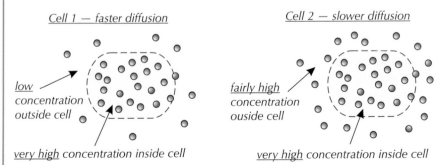

Cell 1 — faster diffusion

low concentration outside cell

very high concentration inside cell

Cell 2 — slower diffusion

fairly high concentration ouside cell

very high concentration inside cell

- The temperature — the higher the temperature, the faster the rate of diffusion. This is because the particles have more energy, so move around faster.

- The surface area — the larger the surface area (e.g. of the cell membrane), the faster the rate of diffusion. This is because more particles can pass through at once.

Tip: The thickness of the cell membrane also affects the rate of diffusion — see p. 56.

Example

Some specialised cells (e.g. epithelial cells in the small intestine) have lots of small projections on their surface, formed from folds in the cell membrane. These projections give the cell a larger surface area, which means that more particles can diffuse across the membrane in the same amount of time — increasing the rate of diffusion.

Practice Questions — Fact Recall

Q1 Give the definition of diffusion.

Q2 Name four molecules that can diffuse through a cell membrane.

Q3 Explain how increasing the temperature affects the rate of diffusion.

Practice Questions — Application

Q1 The diagrams below show three cells in different glucose solutions. The concentration of glucose inside and outside the cell is shown in each case. Which diagram shows a situation where the net movement of glucose will be out of the cell — A, B or C?

A 1.0 mol dm³ / 0.5 mol dm³   B 0.5 mol dm³ / 1.0 mol dm³   C 1.0 mol dm³ / 1.0 mol dm³

Q2 When cells respire they produce carbon dioxide as a waste product. The carbon dioxide diffuses from the cells into the bloodstream, so it can be removed from the body.
Is carbon dioxide concentration greater in the bloodstream or inside respiring cells? Explain your answer.

Q3 At a disco in a school hall, a DJ releases a short blast of smoke from a smoke machine at the front of the stage.

   a) Explain how the smoke reaches the people standing at the opposite end of the hall from the stage.

   b) Five minutes later the DJ sets the smoke machine off for a second time. Explain how the rate of diffusion of the smoke is now different from the first time the DJ set the smoke machine off.

Learning Objectives:

- Know the definition of osmosis.
- Be able to describe how water moves into or out of a cell by osmosis.
- Be able to investigate the effect of different concentrations of a sugar (or salt) solution on plant cells (Required Practical 2).
- Be able to work out the rate of osmosis.
- Be able to calculate percentage change in plant tissue mass.
- Be able to draw and interpret graphs showing the effect of concentration of a sugar or salt solution on the mass of plant tissue.

Specification Reference
4.1.3.2

2. Osmosis

Osmosis is an important process for life — it's how cells get the water they need to carry out chemical reactions.

What is osmosis?

> Osmosis is the movement of water molecules across a partially permeable membrane from a region of higher water concentration to a region of lower water concentration.

A **partially permeable membrane** is just one with very small holes in it. So small, in fact, only tiny molecules (like water) can pass through them, and bigger molecules (e.g. sucrose, a sugar) can't. This is shown in Figure 1.

The water molecules actually pass both ways through the membrane during osmosis. This happens because water molecules move about randomly all the time. But because there are more water molecules on one side than on the other, there's a steady net flow of water into the region with fewer water molecules, i.e. into the stronger sugar solution. This means the strong sugar solution gets more dilute. The water acts like it's trying to "even up" the concentration either side of the membrane.

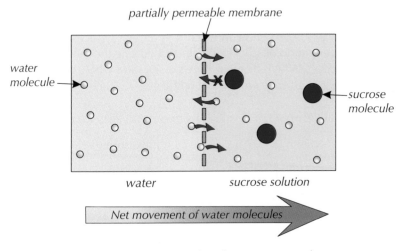

Figure 1: *Diagram to show how osmosis works.*

Osmosis is a type of **diffusion** — passive movement of water particles from an area of higher water concentration to an area of lower water concentration.

The movement of water in and out of cells

The solution surrounding a cell will usually have a different concentration to the fluid inside the cell. This means that water will either move into the cell from the surrounding solution, or out of the cell, by osmosis.

If a cell is short of water, the solution inside it will become quite concentrated (i.e. there'll be a low concentration of water molecules). This usually means the solution outside the cell is more dilute (there's a higher concentration of water molecules), and so water will move into the cell by osmosis.
If a cell has lots of water, the solution inside it will be more dilute, and water will be drawn out of the cell and into the fluid outside by osmosis.

This is summarised in Figure 2.

Figure 2: Diagram to show the movement of water molecules into and out of a cell.

Tip: When you exercise, you lose water and ions in your sweat. It's important to replace these because if the balance between ions and water in the body is wrong, too much or too little water is drawn into cells by osmosis, which can damage them. Sports drinks contain water and ions, so drinking them can replace those lost in sweat.

Tip: Cells that gain water by osmosis get a bit bigger (animal cells that gain too much water will eventually burst). Cells that lose water get a bit smaller.

Investigating the effect of sugar solutions on plant cells

REQUIRED PRACTICAL **2**

There's an experiment you can do to show osmosis at work:

1. Cut up a potato into identical cylinders and measure their masses.

2. Get some beakers with different sugar solutions in them. One should be pure water and another should be a very concentrated sugar solution (e.g. 1.0 mol/dm³). Then you can have a few others with concentrations in between (e.g. 0.2 mol/dm³, 0.4 mol/dm³, 0.6 mol/dm³, etc.)

3. Place one potato cylinder in each beaker, as shown in Figure 3. Leave them in the beakers for twenty four hours.

Tip: Remember to be aware of any risks in this experiment. E.g. if you're using a knife, make sure that you cut away from yourself and that the blade is clean and sharp.

Tip: Make sure there's no skin left on your potato cylinders, as this could affect your results.

Figure 3: A diagram to show the set-up of the experiment.

Tip: You could also carry out this experiment using different salt solutions and see what effect they have on potato cylinder mass.

4. Take the cylinders out, dry them with a paper towel and measure their masses again.

5. If the cylinders have drawn in water by osmosis, they'll have increased in mass. If water has been drawn out, they'll have decreased in mass. You can calculate the **percentage change** in mass (see p. 298), then plot a few graphs and things (see below).

Tip: By calculating the percentage change, you can compare the effect of sugar concentration on cylinders that didn't have the same initial mass. An increase in mass will give a positive percentage change and a decrease will give a negative percentage change.

Tip: You can read all about how to calculate a mean on page 14.

Tip: You could do a similar experiment to work out the rate of osmosis by leaving the potato cylinders for 30 minutes, then dividing the change in mass (in grams) by the time taken (in minutes). So the units for the rate would be g/min.

Tip: 'M' is a unit of concentration. The solution with a concentration of 0.00 M is pure water.

Tip: There's more about plotting graphs on page 18.

Variables and errors

The **dependent variable** in this experiment is the cylinder mass and the **independent variable** is the concentration of the sugar solution. All other variables (volume of solution, temperature, time, type of sugar used, etc.) must be kept the same in each case or the experiment won't be a fair test.

Like any experiment, you need to be aware of how **errors** (see p. 13) may arise. Sometimes they may occur when carrying out the method, e.g. if some potato cylinders were not fully dried, the excess water would give a higher mass, or if water evaporated from the beakers, the concentrations of the sugar solutions would change. You can reduce the effect of these errors by repeating the experiment and calculating a mean percentage change at each concentration.

Producing a graph of your results

You can create a graph of your results by plotting the percentage change in mass against the concentration of sugar solution. You can then draw a line of best fit, which you can use to determine the concentration of the solution in the potato cells:

Example

An experiment to investigate the effect of sugar concentration on potato cells gave the results in the table below.

Concentration of sugar solution (M)	0.1	0.25	0.5	1.0	2.0
Percentage change in mass (%)	16.5	2.5	−8.0	−15.5	−20.0

The results can be plotted as a graph with concentration of sugar solution on the x-axis and percentage change in mass on the y-axis, as shown in Figure 4.

The point at which the line of best fit crosses the x-axis (where the percentage change in mass is 0) is the point at which the concentration of the sugar solution is the same as the concentration of the solution in the potato cells (see Figure 4). You can estimate the concentration of the solution inside the potato cells by reading the value off the x-axis at this point.

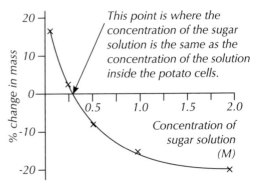

This point is where the concentration of the sugar solution is the same as the concentration of the solution inside the potato cells.

Figure 4: A graph to find the concentration of the solution inside the potato cells.

Practice Questions — Fact Recall

Q1 What is osmosis?

Q2 Explain how a cell that is short of water gains water from the surrounding solution.

Practice Question — Application

Q1 An experiment is carried out to investigate osmosis.

A potato is cut up into cylinders of the same known length and width.

Some of the potato cylinders are placed in a beaker of pure water. Others are placed in beakers with different concentrations of sugar solution.

The potato cylinders are left in the beakers for 24 hours. They are then removed and the length of each potato cylinder is recorded. The mean change in potato cylinder length for each beaker is then worked out.

The results of this experiment are shown in the table.

Concentration of solution (M)	Mean change in potato cylinder length (mm)
0.00	+ 3.1
0.25	+ 2.1
0.50	− 1.2
0.75	− 2.6
1.00	?

a) i) Describe what happened to the potato cylinders in the 0.00 M and 0.25 M solutions.

ii) Explain the changes you described in part a) i) in terms of osmosis.

b) Predict the mean change in length for the potato cylinders in the 1.00 M solution.

c) What was:

i) the dependent variable in this experiment?

ii) the independent variable in this experiment?

d) Give two variables that had to be controlled in this experiment to make it a fair test.

> **Exam Tip**
> You could get asked questions about any of the Required Practicals in the exam — so make sure you understand what's happening in each one.

> **Tip:** There's more on variables on page 10.

Learning Objectives:

- Know the definition of active transport.
- Be able to describe how substances move in and out of a cell by active transport.
- Know how plant roots are adapted to maximise the exchange of substances.
- Understand how the structure of a root hair cell is related to its function.
- Know that plant root hair cells can absorb mineral ions from very dilute solutions using active transport.
- Know that plants need these ions for healthy growth.
- Know that sugar can be absorbed from the gut into the blood (against the concentration gradient) using active transport.
- Know that sugar is used for respiration in cells.
- Know the differences between diffusion, osmosis and active transport.

Specification References
4.1.3.1, 4.1.3.3

3. Active Transport

Another way for molecules to move into and out of cells is via a process called active transport. But it needs energy...

What is active transport?

> Active transport is the movement of particles against a concentration gradient (i.e. from an area of lower concentration to an area of higher concentration) using energy transferred during respiration.

Active transport, like diffusion and osmosis, can be used to move substances in and out of cells. It allows cells to absorb ions from very dilute solutions.

Active transport in plant roots

The cells on the surface of plant roots grow into long "hairs" which stick out into the soil. Each branch of a root will be covered in millions of these microscopic hairs. This gives the plant a large surface area for absorbing water and mineral ions from the soil (see Figure 1).

water molecule   *mineral ions*   *root hair cell*

mineral ions and water move into plant

Figure 1: *Diagram to show the absorption of water and mineral ions by a root hair cell.*

Plants need these mineral ions for healthy growth. However, the concentration of minerals is usually higher in the root hair cells than in the soil around them, so the root hair cells can't use diffusion to take up minerals from the soil. Instead they use active transport.

Active transport allows the plant to absorb minerals from a very dilute solution, against a concentration gradient. This is essential for its growth. But active transport needs energy from respiration to make it work.

Active transport also happens in humans, for example in taking glucose from the gut (see next page), and from the kidney tubules.

Tip: Water is taken into root hair cells by osmosis. See page 48 for more on osmosis.

Tip: Minerals should move out of the root hairs if they followed the rules of diffusion.

Active transport in the gut

Active transport is used in the digestive system when there is a lower concentration of nutrients in the gut, but a higher concentration of nutrients in the blood. Here's how it works:

When there's a higher concentration of glucose and amino acids in the gut they diffuse naturally into the blood. BUT — sometimes there's a lower concentration of nutrients in the gut than there is in the blood (see Figure 2).

This means that the concentration gradient is the wrong way. The nutrients should go the other way if they followed the rules of diffusion. This is where active transport comes in.

Active transport allows nutrients to be taken into the blood, despite the fact that the concentration gradient is the wrong way. This is essential to stop us starving. It means that glucose can be taken into the bloodstream when its concentration in the blood is already higher than in the gut. The glucose can then be transported to cells, where it's used for respiration (see pages 159-161).

Inside the gut   *Inside the blood*

Figure 2: *Diagram to show active transport in the gut.*

Tip: Active transport comes in useful for loads of processes in the body. E.g. it's used in the kidneys to reabsorb useful substances, like glucose and ions, when making urine.

Summary of transport methods

This topic covers three different ways that substances can get in and out of cells. Here's a handy table to help you remember their similarities and differences:

Type of transport:	Description
Diffusion (see p. 45)	▪ Movement of particles from an area of higher concentration to an area of lower concentration. ▪ Doesn't require energy.
Osmosis (see p. 48)	▪ Movement of water molecules across a partially permeable membrane from a region of higher water concentration to a region of lower water concentration. ▪ Doesn't require energy.
Active transport	▪ Movement of particles against a concentration gradient. ▪ Requires energy.

Exam Tip
Make sure you know the definition of each type of transport off by heart.

Practice Questions — Fact Recall

Q1 What is active transport?

Q2 True or false? Cells cannot absorb ions from very dilute solutions.

Q3 Why do plants need to take up mineral ions?

Q4 Why do root hair cells need to use active transport to take mineral ions up from the soil?

Q5 Name one molecule that is taken up by active transport in the gut.

Learning Objectives:

- Be able to give examples of substances that move in and out of cells by diffusion.
- Be able to calculate surface area to volume ratios and know how to compare them.
- Understand that a single-celled organism has a larger surface area to volume ratio than a multicellular organism, which allows it to exchange enough substances across its membrane for its needs.
- Know that multicellular organisms have specialised exchange surfaces and transport systems for exchanging materials, and why they have these structures.
- Know how exchange surfaces in multicellular organisms are adapted for exchanging materials.

Specification Reference
4.1.3.1

Solutes are dissolved substances. Living organisms need to be able to exchange dissolved substances with their environment in order to survive. An organism's size and surface area affect how quickly this is done.

Movement of substances

Life processes need gases or other dissolved substances (solutes) before they can happen. Dissolved substances move to where they need to be by diffusion and active transport. Water moves by osmosis.

Cells can use diffusion to take in substances they need and get rid of waste products. For example:

- Oxygen and carbon dioxide are transferred between cells and the environment during gas exchange.
- In humans, urea (a waste product produced from the breakdown of proteins) diffuses from cells into the blood plasma for removal from the body by the kidneys.

How easy it is for an organism to exchange substances with its environment depends on the organism's surface area to volume ratio (SA : V).

Surface area to volume ratios

A **ratio** shows how big one value is compared to another. The larger an organism is, the smaller its surface area is compared to its volume. You can show this by calculating surface area to volume ratios. To do that, you first need to know an organism's **volume** and **surface area**. The easiest way to find them is to estimate the size of the organism in the form of a block.

Calculating volume and surface area

The volume of a block (e.g. a cube or cuboid) is found by the equation:

$$\text{volume} = \text{length} \times \text{width} \times \text{height}$$

Tip: The units of volume are given in units cubed (e.g. μm^3).

Example

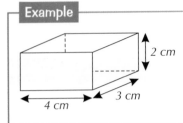

A block that measures 4 cm by 3 cm by 2 cm has the volume:

$$4 \text{ cm} \times 3 \text{ cm} \times 2 \text{ cm} = \textbf{24 cm}^3$$

The area of a square or rectangular surface is found by the equation:

$$\text{area} = \text{length} \times \text{width}$$

Tip: The area of a triangle is found by the equation:
½ × height × base.
E.g.

height = 4 cm
base = 6 cm

Area = ½ × 4 cm × 6 cm
= 12 cm²

To calculate the surface area of an object, just calculate the area of each side and add them all together.

Example

A block that measures 4 cm by 3 cm by 2 cm has six surfaces:

top and bottom: 4 cm × 3 cm = 12 cm²

two sides: 3 cm × 2 cm = 6 cm²

front and back: 4 cm × 2 cm = 8 cm²

So the total surface area of the block is:
12 + 12 + 6 + 6 + 8 + 8 = **52 cm²**

> **Tip:** The units of area are given in units squared (e.g. μm²).

Comparing surface area to volume ratios

Here's how to calculate surface area to volume ratios:

Example

A mouse can be represented by a cube measuring 1 cm × 1 cm × 1 cm.

"cube mouse"

Its volume is: 1 × 1 × 1 = 1 cm³

Its surface area is: 6 × (1 × 1) = 6 cm²

So the mouse has a surface area : volume ratio of **6 : 1**.

Compare this to a cube hippo measuring 2 cm × 4 cm × 4 cm.

Its volume is: 2 × 4 × 4 = 32 cm³

Its surface area is:

2 × (4 × 4) = 32 cm²
(top and bottom surfaces)

+ (4 × 2) × 4 = 32 cm² (four sides)

"cube hippo"

Total surface area = 64 cm²

The surface area to volume ratio of the hippo can be written as 64 : 32.

To simplify the ratio, divide both sides of the ratio by the volume.

So the hippo has a surface area : volume ratio of **2 : 1**.

Now you can compare the ratios:

The cube mouse's surface area is six times its volume, but the cube hippo's surface area is only twice its volume. So the mouse has a larger surface area compared to its volume.

> **Tip:** To write a ratio, you just need to write the number of one thing compared to the number of another thing, separated by a colon.

***Figure 1:** A hippo (top) has a small surface area : volume ratio. A mouse (bottom) has a large surface area : volume ratio.*

> **Tip:** To compare two ratios, it's easier if you write both of them in the form X : 1. There's more about writing and simplifying ratios on page 297.

Why are exchange surfaces needed?

In single-celled organisms, gases and dissolved substances can diffuse directly into (or out of) the cell across the cell membrane. It's because they have a large surface area compared to their volume, so enough substances can be exchanged across the membrane to supply the volume of the cell.

Multicellular organisms have a smaller surface area compared to their volume — not enough substances can diffuse from their outside surface to supply their entire volume. This means they need some sort of **exchange surface** for efficient diffusion.

Tip: There's more on diffusion on pages 45-47, osmosis on pages 48-49 and active transport on pages 52-53.

Example

Oxygen is able to diffuse from the air into a bacterial cell across the cell surface. A bacterium can get all the oxygen it needs for respiration this way.

But in the human body, there are trillions of cells and they all need to get enough oxygen to respire. Oxygen can't just diffuse in through your skin — it would never reach the cells deep inside you.

So humans need a specialised gas exchange surface (the alveoli, see page 58) for the oxygen to diffuse across and a specialised breathing system to get it there. They also need a circulatory system (see page 73) to transport the oxygen to every cell.

Tip: One trillion is 10^{12} or 1 000 000 000 000. I wonder who counted all those cells...

The exchange surface structures have to allow enough of the necessary substances to pass through.

Exchange surfaces are adapted to maximise effectiveness:

- They have a thin membrane, so substances only have a short distance to diffuse. The posh way of saying this is that the substances have a 'short diffusion pathway'.

- They have a large surface area so lots of a substance can diffuse at once.

- Exchange surfaces in animals have lots of blood vessels, to get stuff into and out of the blood quickly.

- Gas exchange surfaces in animals (e.g. alveoli, page 58) are often ventilated too — air moves in and out.

Tip: Gas exchange in animals means taking in oxygen from the environment and releasing carbon dioxide.

Practice Questions — Fact Recall

Q1 a) Give three ways that substances can move into and out of a cell.

   b) By which of these three ways can dissolved substances move into and out of a cell?

Q2 Give three ways in which exchange surfaces in animals may be adapted for effective exchange.

Practice Questions — Application

Q1 These photographs show an earthworm and an elephant. They are both animals.

An earthworm exchanges gases through its skin. An elephant has a specialised breathing system and exchanges gases in its lungs.

a) Suggest and explain two features that an earthworm's skin may have to make it effective as a gas exchange surface.

b) Explain why elephants need a specialised organ system for gas exchange while earthworms do not.

Q2 Three different cells can be represented by the shapes below:

A

B

C

Tip: These cells are not drawn to scale.

a) Calculate the surface area of each cell.

b) Calculate the volume of each cell.

c) Calculate the surface area to volume ratio for each cell. Write each ratio in the form n : 1.

d) Predict which cell is most efficient at absorbing substances by diffusion. Explain your answer.

Learning Objectives:
- Know how alveoli are adapted to maximise the exchange of gases in the lungs in mammals.
- Know how villi are adapted to aid the absorption of nutrients in the gut.
- Know how leaves are adapted to maximise the exchange of gases in plants.
- Know how gills are adapted to maximise the exchange of gases in fish.

Specification Reference
4.1.3.1

5. Exchanging Substances

There are a few examples of exchange surfaces that you need to know about. In humans (and other mammals), gases are exchanged in the lungs and nutrients are absorbed in the small intestine. In plants, gases are exchanged in the leaves. In fish, gases are exchanged in the gills.

Gas exchange in humans

The job of the **lungs** is to transfer oxygen to the blood and to remove waste carbon dioxide from it. To do this the lungs contain millions of little air sacs called **alveoli** (see Figure 1) where gas exchange takes place.

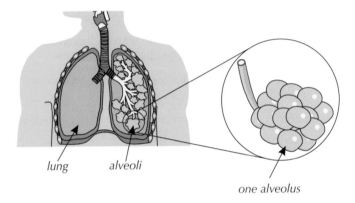

Figure 1: Diagram to show the location and structure of the alveoli.

lung   alveoli

one alveolus

Tip: It's one alveol<u>us</u> and two or more alveol<u>i</u>.

The alveoli are surrounded by a network of tiny blood vessels known as capillaries (see Figures 2 and 4). There is a higher concentration of oxygen in the air than in the blood, so oxygen diffuses out of the air in the alveoli and into the blood in the capillaries. Carbon dioxide (CO_2) diffuses in the opposite direction (see Figure 3). Air enters and leaves the alveoli via small tubes called bronchioles.

capillaries

Figure 2: The alveoli are surrounded by a network of capillaries.

Figure 4: Alveoli and surrounding capillaries as seen under a light microscope.

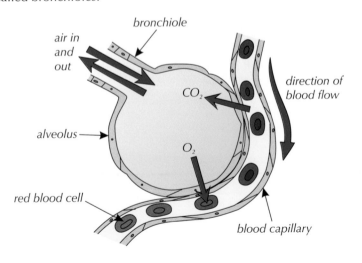

bronchiole

air in and out

direction of blood flow

CO_2

alveolus

O_2

red blood cell

blood capillary

Figure 3: Diagram to show gas exchange across an alveolus.

Adaptations of the alveoli

The alveoli are specialised to maximise the diffusion of oxygen and CO_2. They have:

- An enormous surface area (about 75 m² in humans).
- A moist lining for dissolving gases.
- Very thin walls.
- A good blood supply.

Tip: Remember, having a large surface area means that lots of a substance (e.g. CO_2) can diffuse across the exchange surface at once. See page 56 for more.

Absorbing the products of digestion

Nutrients, e.g. glucose and amino acids, are absorbed into the bloodstream from the **small intestine** — either by diffusion or active transport (see page 53). To aid this absorption, the inside of the small intestine is covered in millions and millions of tiny little projections called **villi** (see Figure 5).

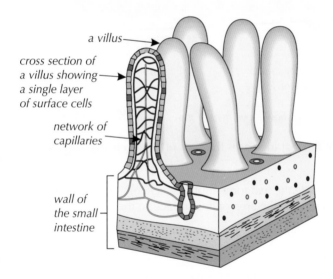

a villus

cross section of a villus showing a single layer of surface cells

network of capillaries

wall of the small intestine

Figure 5: *Diagram showing the structure of villi in the small intestine.*

Tip: It's one vill<u>us</u> and two or more vill<u>i</u>.

Figure 6: *A 3D view of villi in the small intestine, as seen under a microscope.*

Villi increase the surface area in a big way so that digested food is absorbed much more quickly into the blood. They also have:

- a single layer of surface cells.
- a very good blood supply to assist quick absorption.

Tip: Notice how many features the alveoli and the villi have in common — they both have a large surface area, very thin walls and a good blood supply. Lots of exchange surfaces have these features as they make diffusion more effective — see p. 56.

Practice Questions — Fact Recall

Q1 Give one feature of the alveoli that helps them to maximise gas exchange in the lungs.

Q2 Explain how villi aid the absorption of nutrients in the small intestine.

Gas exchange in leaves

Plants need **carbon dioxide** for photosynthesis. Carbon dioxide **diffuses** into the air spaces within the leaf, then it diffuses into the cells where photosynthesis happens. The leaf's structure is adapted so that this can happen easily.

The underneath of the leaf is an **exchange surface**. It's covered in little holes called **stomata** which the carbon dioxide diffuses in through. Oxygen (produced in photosynthesis) and water vapour also diffuse out through the stomata. This is shown in Figure 7.

Tip: 'Stomata' is the plural of 'stoma'. So you get one stoma, but two or more stomata.

O_2 H_2O O_2 stoma CO_2

Oxygen (O_2) and water vapour (H_2O) diffuse <u>out of</u> the leaf.

Carbon dioxide (CO_2) diffuses <u>into</u> the leaf.

Tip: Root hair cells are also adapted to maximise the surface area available for absorbing substances from the soil — see page 52.

Figure 7: *Diagram to show movement of gases into and out of a leaf.*

The flattened shape of the leaf increases the area of this exchange surface so that it's more effective.

The walls of the cells inside the leaf form another exchange surface. The air spaces inside the leaf increase the area of this surface so there's more chance for carbon dioxide to get into the cells.

Water loss in plants

Tip: The water vapour evaporates from the cells inside the leaf. Then it escapes by diffusion because there's a lot of it inside the leaf and less of it in the air outside.

Water vapour is lost from all over the leaf surface, but most of it is lost through the stomata. If the plant is losing water faster through its leaves than it can be replaced by the roots the stomata can be closed by **guard cells**. Without these guard cells, the plant would soon lose so much water that it would **wilt** (droop). There's more about the guard cells on page 88.

Gas exchange in fish

There's a lower concentration of oxygen in water than in air. So fish have special adaptations to get enough of it. In a fish, the gas exchange surface is the **gills**.

Structure of gills

Water (containing oxygen) enters the fish through its mouth and passes out through the gills — see Figure 8 on the next page. As this happens, oxygen diffuses from the water into the blood in the gills and carbon dioxide diffuses from the blood into the water.

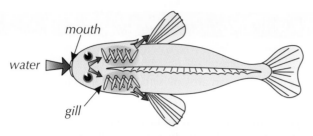

Figure 8: Water flowing through a fish's gills.

Tip: The gills are located inside a fish's head. Water flows in through the mouth, over the gills and out through openings behind the head.

Each gill is made of lots of thin plates called **gill filaments**, which give a large surface area for exchange of gases (and so increase the rate of diffusion). The gill filaments are covered in lots of tiny structures called **lamellae**, which increase the surface area even more — see Figure 10. The lamellae have lots of blood capillaries to speed up diffusion between the water and the blood. They also have a thin surface layer of cells to minimise the distance that the gases have to diffuse.

Figure 9: The gills inside a catfish.

Figure 10: A section of a fish's gill.

Blood flows through the lamellae in one direction and water flows over in the opposite direction. This maintains a large concentration gradient between the water and the blood (see Figure 11). The concentration of oxygen in the water is always higher than that in the blood, so as much oxygen as possible diffuses from the water into the blood.

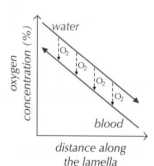

Figure 11: The concentration of oxygen in the water and blood along the lamella. The concentration in the water is always higher than in the blood.

Practice Questions — Fact Recall

Q1 How and where does carbon dioxide enter a leaf?

Q2 Name one other gas that is exchanged in a leaf.

Q3 How is the surface area of a leaf increased for gas exchange?

Q4 Explain how lamellae increase the efficiency of gas exchange across a gill.

Q5 How does the direction of the blood flow in the lamellae increase the efficiency of gas exchange in the gills?

Topic 1b Checklist — Make sure you know...

Diffusion

☐ That diffusion is the spreading out of particles from an area of higher concentration to an area of lower concentration.

☐ That dissolved substances such as oxygen (which is needed for respiration) move in and out of a cell by diffusion, and that the net (overall) movement will be to an area of lower concentration.

☐ That the bigger the difference in concentration, the faster the diffusion rate is, because the net movement from one side is greater.

☐ That the higher the temperature, the faster the diffusion rate is, because the particles have more energy so move faster.

☐ That the larger the surface area, the faster the diffusion rate is, because more particles can pass through at once.

Osmosis

☐ That osmosis is the movement of water molecules across a partially permeable membrane from a region of higher water concentration (a dilute solution) to a region of lower water concentration (a concentrated solution).

☐ How differences in the concentration of water molecules inside and outside of a cell will cause water molecules to move into or out of the cell by osmosis.

☐ How to investigate the effect of different concentrations of a sugar or salt solution on potato cells (Required Practical 2).

☐ How to work out the rate of osmosis and the units for it (g/min).

☐ How to calculate percentage change in mass for plant tissue (e.g. a piece of potato).

☐ How to draw and interpret graphs showing the effect of different concentrations of sugar or salt solution on potato cells.

Active Transport

☐ That active transport is the movement of particles against a concentration gradient (i.e. from an area of lower concentration to an area of higher concentration) using energy transferred by respiration.

☐ That the structure of a root hair cell gives it a large surface area to absorb mineral ions and water.

☐ That root hair cells use active transport to absorb mineral ions (which plants need for healthy growth) against a concentration gradient.

☐ That sugar is absorbed from the gut into the blood by active transport, for use in cellular respiration.

☐ How to describe the transport of substances in and out of cells by active transport, diffusion and osmosis.

☐ The differences between active transport, diffusion and osmosis.

cont...

Exchange Surfaces

☐ That oxygen and carbon dioxide move in and out of cells by diffusion in gas exchange, and urea diffuses out of cells into the blood plasma for excretion.

☐ How to calculate and compare surface area to volume ratios.

☐ That exchanging materials with the environment is more difficult in multicellular organisms than in single-celled organisms, due to their smaller surface area to volume ratios — so multicellular organisms need specialised organ systems for exchange, and transport systems to carry materials around the body.

☐ How exchange surfaces are adapted for exchanging materials — they're thin (so substances only have a short distance to diffuse), they have a large surface area (so lots of a substance can diffuse at once), they have lots of blood vessels (in animals, to get stuff in and out of the blood quickly), and they're often ventilated (for gas exchange in animals).

Exchanging Substances

☐ That alveoli (tiny air sacs) increase the surface area of the lungs in humans, maximising the diffusion of oxygen into the blood and carbon dioxide out of the blood.

☐ That alveoli also have a thin layer of cells, a moist lining and an efficient blood supply to aid the diffusion of gases.

☐ That villi increase the surface area of the small intestine in humans, contain a network of capillaries and have a single layer of surface cells, aiding the absorption of nutrients (by active transport and diffusion) into the blood.

☐ That carbon dioxide diffuses into a plant leaf from the air through the stomata (tiny holes on the underside of the leaf), and that oxygen and water vapour diffuse out of the leaf.

☐ That the flattened shape of the leaf and the internal air spaces between cells increase the surface area of the leaf for gas exchange.

☐ How the gills of a fish are adapted for efficient gas exchange — the gill filaments and lamellae increase the surface area, and the lamellae have a thin surface layer and an efficient blood supply to maximise the diffusion between water and the blood.

Exam-style Questions

1   Methods of exchanging substances with the environment vary between organisms.
Some organisms contain specialised exchange surfaces for this purpose.

Figure 1 shows a rod-shaped bacterium, with its approximate dimensions.

Figure 1

0.6 μm

3.0 μm   0.6 μm

1.1   Calculate the surface area to volume ratio of this bacterium.

(3 marks)

1.2   Explain why this bacterium doesn't need any specialised
surfaces for exchanging substances with the environment.

(3 marks)

Plants are organisms that have specialised exchange surfaces.
Most plants exchange gases through their stomata.

1.3   What are stomata?

(1 mark)

1.4   Carbon dioxide diffuses out through the stomata into the air outside the leaf.
What does this tell you about the concentration of carbon dioxide in the air?

(1 mark)

1.5   Other than stomata, describe **one** leaf adaptation for efficient gas exchange.

(1 mark)

Figure 2 shows a section of an organ with a specialised gas exchange surface.
This organ is found in fish.

Figure 2

1.6   Name the organ specialised for gas exchange in fish.

(1 mark)

1.7   If the water in a lake becomes polluted, the amount of oxygen dissolved in the
water is reduced. What effect would this have on the rate of diffusion of oxygen
into the gas exchange organs of fish that live in the lake? Explain your answer.

(2 marks)

2   In humans, glucose is absorbed into the bloodstream in the small intestine.
This is often done using active transport, which requires respiration.

2.1   Explain why glucose may be absorbed using active transport,
and why this requires respiration.

(2 marks)

2.2   *Giardia* is a parasite that attaches itself to the walls of the small intestine.
Infection with *giardia* can cause the villi in the small intestine to become damaged.

Suggest how this would affect the absorption of glucose and other nutrients in the
small intestine. Explain your answer.

(2 marks)

2.3   Water from food is absorbed into the bloodstream in the large intestine.

State by what process water is absorbed in the large intestine and explain
how it works.

(2 marks)

3   Eleanor is investigating osmosis using potatoes.

She cuts small wells into two pieces of potato, and sets up two experiments (A and B).
She then leaves the potatoes for five hours.

The diagrams show how the appearance of each experiment changes after five hours.

Experiment A

Experiment B

3.1   Explain the changes that Eleanor saw in experiment A.

(3 marks)

3.2   Suggest an explanation for why the water level in the dish in experiment B
didn't decrease as much as much as that in experiment A.

(3 marks)

Learning Objectives:

- Know that living things are made up of cells, which can be thought of as the basic building blocks of all organisms.
- Know that a tissue is a group of similar cells that work together to carry out a particular function.
- Know that organs are groups of different tissues that work together to perform a certain function.
- Know that organ systems are groups of organs that work together to perform a particular function.
- Know that the digestive system is an organ system and that its function is to digest and absorb food.
- Know that organ systems work together to form whole organisms.

Specification References 4.2.1, 4.2.2.1

1. Cell Organisation

Multicellular organisms (like humans) can have trillions of cells. To keep the organism going, those cells have to work together — which needs organisation.

How are cells organised?

Cells are the basic building blocks that make up all living organisms. As you know from page 30, **specialised cells** carry out a particular function. The process by which cells become specialised for a particular job is called **differentiation**. Differentiation occurs during the development of a multicellular organism.

Specialised cells are organised to form tissues, which form organs, which form organ systems — there's more about each of these over the next few pages.

Large **multicellular organisms** have different systems inside them for exchanging and transporting materials.

Example

Mammals have a breathing system — this includes the airways and lungs. The breathing system is needed to take air into and out of the lungs, so that oxygen and carbon dioxide can be exchanged between the body and the environment.

Tissues

You need to know what a tissue is:

> A tissue is a group of similar cells that work together to carry out a particular function.

A tissue can include more than one type of cell. Mammals (like humans), have several different types of tissue:

Examples

- Muscular tissue, which contracts (shortens) to move whatever it's attached to.

- Glandular tissue, which makes and secretes substances like enzymes (proteins that control chemical reactions, see p. 109) and hormones (chemical messengers, see p. 181).

- Epithelial tissue, which covers some parts of the body, e.g. the inside of the gut.

absorptive cells   *goblet cell*

Figure 1: *Epithelial tissue in the small intestine. It contains absorptive cells and goblet cells.*

Organs

Tissues are organised into organs:

> An organ is a group of different tissues that work together to perform a certain function.

Mammals have many different organs, which are made up of different tissues.

Example

The **stomach** is an organ made of these tissues:

- Muscular tissue, which moves the stomach wall to churn up the food.

- Glandular tissue, which makes digestive juices to digest food.

- Epithelial tissue, which covers the outside and inside of the stomach.

Figure 2: *A cross-section through part of the stomach. There's glandular tissue at the top (A) and muscular tissue at the bottom (B).*

Tip: Digestive juices are secretions from the digestive system that help to break down food. They contain enzymes (see pages 114-115).

Organ systems

Organs are organised into organ systems:

> An organ system is a group of organs working together to perform a particular function.

Example

The **digestive system** is the organ system that breaks down food in humans and other mammals. It's also an exchange system — it exchanges materials with the environment by taking in nutrients and releasing substances such as bile (see page 116).

The digestive system (see Figure 3) is made up of these organs:

- **Glands** (e.g. the **pancreas** and **salivary glands**), which produce digestive juices.

- The **stomach**, where food is digested.

- The **liver**, which produces bile.

- The **small intestine**, where food is digested and soluble food molecules are absorbed.

- The **large intestine**, where water is absorbed from undigested food, leaving faeces.

Tip: There's more on the digestive system on pages 114-116.

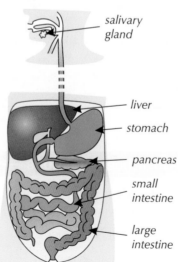

salivary gland

liver

stomach

pancreas

small intestine

large intestine

Figure 3: *A diagram of the human digestive system.*

Organ systems work together to make entire organisms.

Size and scale

It will help to have an understanding of the size and scale of all the structures that make up an organ system — from the tiny individual specialised cells to the organ system as a whole.

Exam Tip
You don't need to learn the lengths given in this example — they're just to give you an idea of size.

Tip: The digestive tract is the big long 'tube' which food passes through, including the small and large intestines. The intestines are all folded up, which is part of the reason why the digestive tract can be so long and yet still fit inside you.

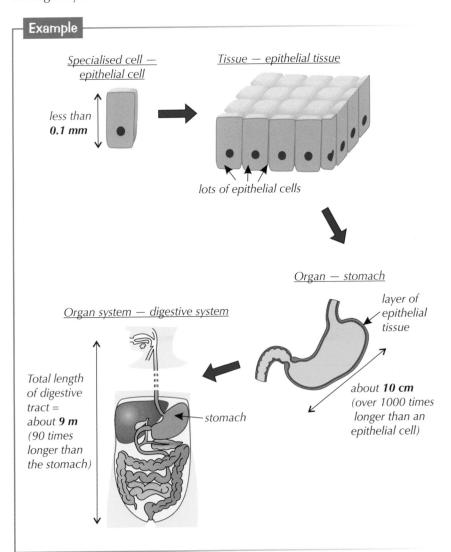

Example

Specialised cell — epithelial cell

less than **0.1 mm**

lots of epithelial cells

Tissue — epithelial tissue

Organ — stomach

layer of epithelial tissue

*about **10 cm** (over 1000 times longer than an epithelial cell)*

Organ system — digestive system

*Total length of digestive tract = about **9 m** (90 times longer than the stomach)*

stomach

Practice Questions — Fact Recall

Q1 What can be thought of as the basic building blocks that make up all living organisms?

Q2 What is a tissue?

Q3 What is an organ?

Q4 What term describes a group of organs which work together to perform a particular function?

Q5   Look at the diagram of the digestive system.

Write down the names of the organs labelled A-F and briefly say
what each one does.

Exam Tip
You need to know
where the organs of the
digestive system are on a
diagram for your exam,
so make sure you can
get them all right in Q5.

Practice Questions — Application

Q1   Blood is made up of specialised red blood cells and several
different types of white blood cells. Is blood an example of a
cell, tissue, organ or organ system? Explain your answer.

Q2   The fallopian tubes and uterus are part of the female reproductive
system. A fallopian tube contains muscular and epithelial tissue.
These work together to move a fertilised egg cell along the fallopian
tube to the uterus (an organ).

a) Suggest why a fallopian tube has muscular tissue.

b) Is a fallopian tube a cell, tissue, organ or organ system?
Explain your answer.

c) Rewrite the following list of structures in order of size.
Start with the smallest:

uterus   reproductive system   egg cell   muscular tissue

Tip: The definitions of
a tissue, an organ and
an organ system should
be really clear in your
head. Take a look back
at pages 66-67 if you're
not sure of them.

Learning Objectives:

- Know how the trachea, bronchi, alveoli and the capillary network surrounding the alveoli make up the structure of the human lungs.
- Understand the function of human lungs.
- Know how human lungs are adapted for exchanging gases.

Specification Reference 4.2.2.2

2. The Lungs

Exchanging substances is a complicated process for large, complex organisms. The lungs are essential for humans (and many other animals), because they play a vital role in the exchange of gases.

What is the purpose of the lungs?

You need to get oxygen from the air into your bloodstream so that it can get to your cells for respiration. You also need to get rid of the carbon dioxide in your blood. This exchange of gases all happens inside your **lungs**. Air is forced in and out of your lungs by the action of breathing.

The thorax

The lungs are in the **thorax** (see Figure 1). The thorax is the top part of your body. It's separated from the lower part of the body (the **abdomen**) by a muscle called the **diaphragm**. The lungs are like big pink sponges and are protected by the **ribcage**. They're surrounded by the **pleural membranes**.

Exam Tip
Make sure you know exactly where the trachea, bronchi and alveoli are in relation to each other in the lungs.

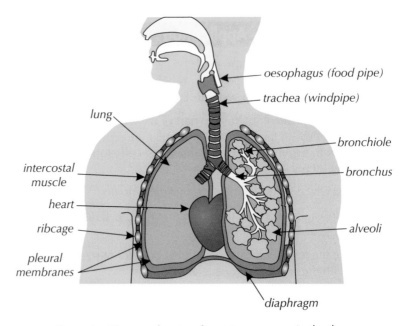

Figure 1: *Diagram showing the main structures in the thorax.*

Figure 2: *A 3D MRI scan of the thorax. The lungs appear black and the bronchioles orange.*

The air that you breathe in goes through the **trachea**. This splits into two tubes called '**bronchi**' (each one is 'a bronchus'), one going to each lung. The bronchi split into progressively smaller tubes called **bronchioles**.

The bronchioles finally end at small bags called **alveoli** where the gas exchange takes place by diffusion (see page 58).

Alveoli

The lungs contain millions and millions of little air sacs called alveoli, surrounded by a network of blood capillaries (see Figure 3). This is where **gas exchange** happens.

The blood passing next to the alveoli has just returned to the lungs from the rest of the body, so it contains lots of carbon dioxide and very little oxygen. Oxygen diffuses out of the alveolus (high concentration) into the blood (low concentration). Carbon dioxide diffuses out of the blood (high concentration) into the alveolus (low concentration) to be breathed out (see Figure 3).

> **Tip:** The alveoli have an enormous surface area, a moist lining, very thin walls and a good blood supply to maximise gas exchange. This has already been covered back on page 59, so head back there if you need a recap.

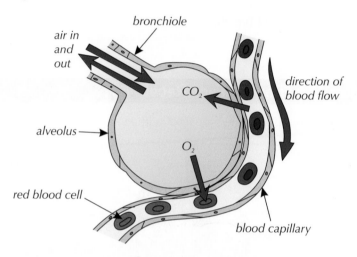

Figure 3: *Diagram showing gas exchange across an alveolus.*

When the blood reaches body cells, oxygen is released from the red blood cells (where there's a high concentration) and diffuses into the body cells (where the concentration is low). At the same time, carbon dioxide diffuses out of the body cells (where there's a high concentration) into the blood (where there's a low concentration). It's then carried back to the lungs (see Figure 4).

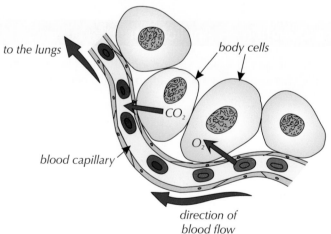

Figure 4: *Diagram showing gas exchange between a capillary and body cells.*

Calculating breathing rate

Rate calculations pop up all the time in biology, and you're expected to know how to do them — thankfully, they're pretty easy. Breathing rate is the sort of thing that you could get asked to work out in your exam. You can calculate someone's breathing rate in breaths per minute.

Example

Chris takes 112 breaths in 8 minutes.
Calculate his average breathing rate in breaths per minute.

breaths per minute = number of breaths ÷ number of minutes
$$= 112 \div 8$$
$$= 14 \text{ breaths per minute}$$

Tip: You can work out someone's heart rate in beats per minute in exactly the same way as this. Just replace number of breaths with number of beats.

Practice Question — Fact Recall

Q1   The diagram below shows a pair of human lungs.

a) Name the tube labelled A.

b) Name the tubes labelled B.

c) i) What is the name given to the part of the lungs labelled C?

   ii) Explain why part C is surrounded by a network of capillaries.

Practice Question — Application

Q1   While taking part in a race, Gibson took 366 breaths in 9 minutes. Calculate his average breathing rate in breaths per minute.

Exam Tip
Quick calculations like this can be a really easy way to pick up marks in the exam. It'd be a good idea to make sure that you're happy with how to do them.

3. Circulatory System — The Heart

Multicellular organisms need a way to transport materials between their cells. Humans (like many animals) have a transport system called the circulatory system to do just that, and the heart has a major role to play in it...

Function of the circulatory system

The circulatory system's main function is to get food and oxygen to every cell in the body. As well as being a delivery service, it's also a waste collection service — it carries waste products like carbon dioxide and urea to where they can be removed from the body. The circulatory system includes the heart, blood vessels and the blood.

A double circulatory system

Humans have a double circulatory system — two circuits joined together:

- In the first circuit, the right ventricle (see next page) pumps deoxygenated blood (blood without oxygen) to the lungs to take in oxygen. The blood then returns to the heart (see Figure 1a).

- In the second circuit, the left ventricle (see next page) pumps oxygenated blood around all the other organs of the body. The blood gives up its oxygen at the body cells and the deoxygenated blood returns to the heart to be pumped out to the lungs again (see Figure 1b).

deoxygenated blood

oxygenated blood

Figure 1a: *Blood circulation between the heart and the lungs.*

Figure 1b: *Blood circulation between the heart and the rest of the body.*

Structure of the heart

The heart is a pumping organ that keeps the blood flowing around the body. The walls of the heart are mostly made of **muscle tissue**, which contracts to pump the blood.

The heart has four chambers (the **right atrium**, **right ventricle**, **left atrium** and **left ventricle**) which it uses to pump blood around (see Figure 2). The main blood vessels leading into and out of these chambers are the **vena cava**, **pulmonary artery**, **aorta** and **pulmonary vein**.

Learning Objectives:
- Know that humans have a double circulatory system to transport blood around the body, in which the heart acts as a pump.
- Know that one of the 'circuits' in the human circulatory system is powered by the right ventricle and is responsible for pumping blood to the lungs, where gas exchange can take place.
- Know that the other 'circuit' in the human circulatory system is powered by the left ventricle and pumps blood around all the other parts of the body.
- Know the structure of the human heart, including its blood vessels: the aorta, vena cava, pulmonary artery, pulmonary vein and coronary arteries.
- Understand how the human heart functions.
- Know that the heart contains a group of cells located in the right atrium that act as a pacemaker to control the natural resting heart rate.
- Know that patients with an irregular heart beat can be fitted with an electrical artificial pacemaker to correct the issue.

Specification Reference
4.2.2.2

Exam Tip
You need to learn
the names of these
chambers and the main
blood vessels leading
into and out of the heart
for your exam.

Tip: Don't be confused
about the way the right
and left side of the
heart are labelled in this
diagram — this is the
right and left side of the
person whose heart it is.

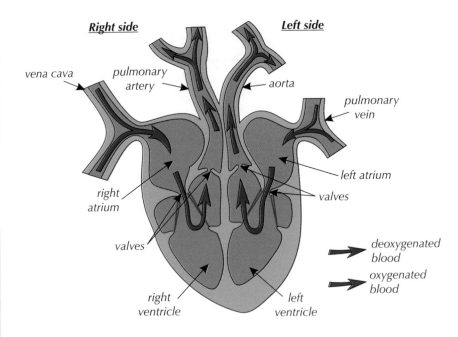

Figure 2: Diagram showing the structure of the heart and the direction of blood flow through the heart.

The heart has **valves** to make sure that blood goes in the right direction — they prevent it flowing backwards.

The heart also needs its own supply of oxygenated blood. Arteries called **coronary arteries** branch off the aorta and surround the heart, making sure that it gets all the oxygenated blood it needs.

Tip: The coronary
arteries are really
important. If they
become blocked, the
heart can become
starved of oxygen,
potentially leading to a
heart attack and heart
failure.

Blood flow through the heart

You need to know how the heart uses its four chambers to pump blood around the body. Here's what happens:

1. Blood flows into the two atria from the vena cava and the pulmonary vein (see Figure 3).

Tip: 'Atria' is the plural
of 'atrium'. So you get
one atrium, but two
atria.

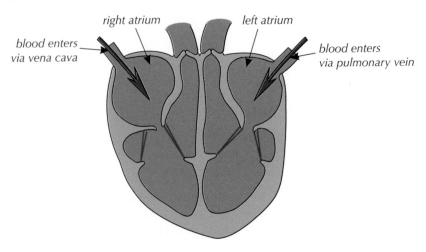

Figure 3: Diagram showing blood flowing into the heart.

2. The atria contract, pushing the blood into the ventricles (see Figure 4).

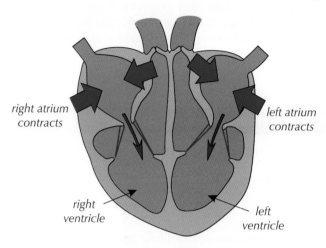

right atrium contracts

left atrium contracts

right ventricle

left ventricle

Figure 4: *Diagram showing blood being forced into the ventricles.*

3. The ventricles contract, forcing the blood into the pulmonary artery and the aorta, and out of the heart (see Figure 5).

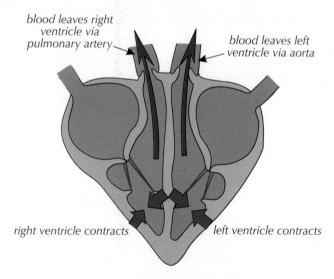

blood leaves right ventricle via pulmonary artery

blood leaves left ventricle via aorta

right ventricle contracts

left ventricle contracts

Figure 5: *Diagram showing blood being forced out of the heart.*

4. The blood then flows to the organs through arteries, and returns through veins.

5. The atria fill again and the whole cycle starts over.

> **Tip:** There's more about the different types of blood vessels, including arteries and veins, on pages 77-78.

The heart's pacemaker

Your resting heart rate is controlled by a group of cells in the right atrium wall that act as a pacemaker. These cells produce a small electric impulse which spreads to the surrounding muscle cells, causing them to contract.

Figure 6: *An X-ray of the chest of a patient fitted with an artificial pacemaker.*

An artificial pacemaker is often used to control heartbeat if the natural pacemaker cells don't work properly (e.g. if the patient has an irregular heartbeat). It's a little device that's implanted under the skin and has a wire going to the heart. It produces an electric current to keep the heart beating regularly.

Practice Questions — Fact Recall

Q1 What is the function of the circulatory system?

Q2 The human circulatory system is made up of two separate circuits. What is the function of each circuit?

Q3 Name the four chambers of the heart.

Q4 Name the two blood vessels which:

a) carry blood into the heart,   b) carry blood out of the heart.

Q5 Explain how blood flows through the heart.

Practice Questions — Application

Q1 Coronary heart disease is a condition where the coronary arteries become blocked. Suggest why coronary heart disease can cause heart attacks and heart failure.

Q2 Some heart conditions are caused by an irregular heart beat.

a) Describe how the resting heart rate is controlled in a healthy heart.

b) Pacemakers can be used to treat an irregular heartbeat. Describe a pacemaker and explain how it works.

Q3 In the circulatory system of a fish, blood is pumped from the heart, across the gills (to pick up oxygen), to the body tissues and then back to the heart in a single circuit.

Give one similarity and one difference between the circulatory system of a fish and that of a human.

4. Circulatory System — The Blood Vessels

Learning Objectives:
- Know that arteries, veins and capillaries are the three different types of blood vessel found in the body.
- Be able to explain how the structures of arteries, veins and capillaries are adapted to allow them to perform their functions.
- Be able to calculate the rate of blood flow.

Specification Reference 4.2.2.2

Our blood makes its way around our body in blood vessels. There are three different types of blood vessels you need to know about...

Arteries

Arteries are blood vessels which carry blood away from the heart, towards the organs. The heart pumps the blood out at high pressure, so the artery walls are strong and elastic. They contain thick layers of muscle to make them strong, and elastic fibres to allow them to stretch and spring back. The walls are thick compared to the size of the hole down the middle (the lumen) — see Figure 1.

elastic fibres and smooth muscle

lumen

Figure 1: *Diagram to show the structure of an artery.*

Capillaries

Arteries branch into **capillaries**. Capillaries are involved in the exchange of materials at the tissues — they carry the blood really close to every cell in the body to exchange substances with them. They supply food and oxygen to the cells, and take away waste products like carbon dioxide.

Capillaries are really tiny — too small to see. They have permeable walls, so the substances being exchanged with the cells can diffuse in and out. Their walls are usually only one cell thick (see Figure 2). This increases the rate of diffusion by decreasing the distance over which it occurs. Capillaries are also very narrow. This gives them a large surface area compared to their volume, which also increases the rate of diffusion.

Tip: Remember, diffusion is the process by which substances move from an area of higher concentration to an area of lower concentration.

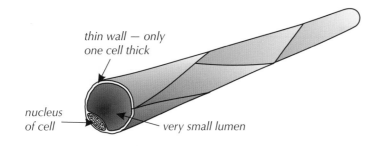

thin wall — only one cell thick

nucleus of cell

very small lumen

Figure 2: *Diagram to show the structure of a capillary.*

Figure 3: *A torn capillary with blood cells leaking out — you can see how thin the walls of the capillary are.*

Exam Tip
If you're struggling to remember which way arteries and veins carry blood in the exam, think: <u>arteries</u> are the '<u>way art</u>' (way out) of the heart, and <u>veins</u> are the '<u>vey in</u>' (way in).

Veins

Capillaries eventually join up to form **veins**. Veins carry blood to the heart.

The blood is at lower pressure in the veins, so the walls don't need to be as thick as artery walls. Veins have a bigger lumen than arteries to help the blood flow despite the lower pressure (see Figure 4).

large lumen

elastic fibres and smooth muscle

Figure 4: *Diagram to show the structure of a vein.*

Figure 5: *A cross-section through an artery and a vein — the walls of the blood vessels are pink. The walls of the artery (left) are much thicker than the walls of the vein (right).*

They also have valves to help keep the blood flowing in the right direction (see Figure 6).

valve

correct direction of blood flow

Figure 6: *Diagram to show how valves prevent the back flow of blood.*

Calculating the rate of blood flow

You might get asked to calculate the rate of blood flow in your exam. Thankfully, it's not too tricky. You just need to use this formula:

> rate of blood flow = volume of blood ÷ number of minutes

Take a look at this example:

Example

1464 ml of blood passed through an artery in 4.5 minutes. Calculate the rate of blood flow through the artery in ml/min.

rate of blood flow = volume of blood ÷ number of minutes
= 1464 ÷ 4.5
= **325 ml/min**

Practice Questions — Fact Recall

Q1   Describe the structure of an artery.

Q2   What type of blood vessel has walls that are only one cell thick?

Q3   Describe briefly how substances in the blood pass into body cells.

Q4   Give two differences between the structure of a vein and the
structure of an artery.

Practice Questions — Application

Q1   Alan has a condition known as SVCS. This condition is very serious
as it obstructs blood flow going into the heart. Which type of blood
vessel (artery, capillary or vein) do you think SVCS affects?
Give a reason for your answer.

Q2   The graph below shows the relative pressure inside two different
blood vessels — one is a vein and one is an artery.

Which blood vessel (A or B) would you expect to contain a higher
proportion of muscle tissue in its walls? Explain your answer.

Q3   In a particular artery in the body, the average rate of blood flow
should be between 270 and 315 ml/min. A doctor measured
the blood flow through this artery of one of his patients. In five
minutes, 1075 ml of blood flowed through the patient's artery. The
doctor thought that the patient may have a blockage in this artery.

Calculate the rate of blood flow through the patient's artery to
determine whether you agree with the doctor. Explain your answer.

Learning Objectives:

- Know that blood is a tissue that contains red blood cells, white blood cells and platelets, all suspended in a liquid called plasma.

- Know the functions of the components of blood.

- Understand how blood cells are adapted to their functions.

- Be able to identify the different blood cells in photographs and diagrams.

Specification Reference
4.2.2.3

5. Circulatory System — The Blood

Blood is a vital part of the circulatory system — it's constantly being pumped out by the heart, travelling through blood vessels to other organs of the body and then returning to the heart. Time to find out just what it's made of...

What is blood?

Blood is a tissue — it's a group of similar cells which work together to perform a specific function (see page 66). The function of the blood is to transport substances around the body. It's made up of **red blood cells**, **white blood cells** and **platelets**, which are all suspended in a liquid called **plasma**.

Red blood cells

The job of red blood cells is to transport oxygen around the body. They have a biconcave shape (see Figure 1) to give them a large surface area for absorbing oxygen and they contain a red pigment called **haemoglobin**, which carries the oxygen.

Red blood cells are different from most types of animal cell because they don't have a nucleus — this allows more room for haemoglobin, which means they can carry more oxygen.

Figure 1: A red blood cell has a biconcave shape — it looks like it's been squashed in the middle on both sides.

Tip: The more red blood cells you've got, the more oxygen can get to your cells. At high altitudes there's less oxygen in the air — so people who live there produce more red blood cells to compensate.

Transporting oxygen

All body cells need oxygen for respiration — a process which releases energy. Oxygen enters the lungs when you breathe in, then red blood cells transport the oxygen from the lungs to all the cells in the body:

- In the lungs, oxygen diffuses into the blood. The oxygen combines with haemoglobin in red blood cells to become oxyhaemoglobin (see Figure 2).

- In body tissues, the reverse happens — oxyhaemoglobin splits up into haemoglobin and oxygen, to release oxygen to the cells.

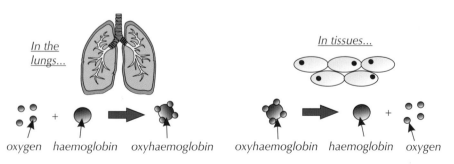

In the lungs...

oxygen   haemoglobin   oxyhaemoglobin

In tissues...

oxyhaemoglobin   haemoglobin   oxygen

Figure 2: Simplified diagram illustrating the formation and breakdown of oxyhaemoglobin.

White blood cells

There are different types of white blood cell but they all have the same function — they defend against microorganisms that cause disease. They can do this in different ways:

- They can engulf unwelcome microorganisms (in a process called phagocytosis) and digest them.

- They can produce antibodies to fight microorganisms.

- They can produce antitoxins to neutralise any toxins produced by the microorganisms.

Figure 3: A white blood cell.

Figure 4: A picture taken down a light microscope showing three different types of white blood cell (stained purple) surrounded by red blood cells (pale red).

Unlike red blood cells, white blood cells do have a nucleus.

Platelets

Platelets are small fragments (pieces) of cells. They have no nucleus. They help the blood to **clot** (clump together) at a wound — this seals the wound and stops you from losing too much blood (see Figure 5). It also stops microorganisms from getting in at the wound. A lack of platelets can cause excessive bleeding and bruising.

Figure 5: A blood clot formed by the action of platelets.

Tip: There's more on white blood cells on page 130.

Plasma

Plasma is a pale straw-coloured liquid which carries just about everything in blood. It carries:

- Red and white blood cells and platelets.

- Nutrients like glucose and amino acids. These are the soluble products of digestion, which are absorbed from the small intestine and taken to the cells of the body.

- Carbon dioxide from the organs to the lungs.

- Urea from the liver to the kidneys.

- Hormones.

- Proteins.

- Antibodies and antitoxins produced by the white blood cells.

Figure 6: A pouch of plasma, which has been extracted from donated blood.

Tip: Urea is a waste product produced from the breakdown of amino acids in the liver.

Practice Questions — Fact Recall

Q1 a) Name the red pigment found in red blood cells.

    b) Describe the role of this red pigment.

Q2 What is the function of white blood cells?

Q3 True or false? White blood cells don't have a nucleus.

Q4 What are platelets?

Q1 Sufferers of Bernard-Soulier syndrome often bleed for a long time after an injury, even when they only have a very small wound. Suggest what component of the blood is abnormal in someone with Bernard-Soulier syndrome. Explain your answer.

Q2 Thalassaemia is a blood disorder in which the body does not make enough haemoglobin. Explain how this disorder can lead to organs not functioning properly because of a lack of oxygen.

Q3 Dr McKenna is looking at blood test results for two of her patients, Fay and Imogen. Their results, along with the normal range for each of the blood components tested, are shown in the following table:

Tip: Don't worry about the unfamiliar units in this table. You don't need to know what they mean to answer the question.

	Red Blood Cells $(10^{12}/L)$	White Blood Cells $(10^9/L)$	Platelets $(10^9/L)$	Urea (mmol/L)	Blood Glucose (mmol/L)
Normal Range	3.9-5.6	4.0-11.0	150-400	3.0-7.0	3.3-5.6
Fay	4.2	3.2	250	3.2	3.6
Imogen	3.7	10.2	315	5.4	5.2

Which patient, Fay or Imogen, do you think is the most at risk of getting an infection? Explain your answer.

6. Plant Cell Organisation

Plant cells are organised in the same way as the cells of other multicellular organisms (see page 66). Cells are grouped into tissues, tissues are grouped into organs, and organs are grouped into organ systems.

How are plant cells organised?

Plants are made of **organs** like stems, roots and leaves. Plant organs work together to make **organ systems**. These can perform the various tasks that a plant needs to carry out to survive and grow — for example, transporting substances around the plant. Plant organs are made of **tissues** — see below for some examples:

Examples

- Epidermal tissue — this covers the whole plant.

- Palisade mesophyll tissue — this is the part of the leaf where most photosynthesis happens.

- Spongy mesophyll tissue — this is also in the leaf, and contains big air spaces to allow gases to diffuse in and out of cells.

- Xylem and phloem — they transport things like water, mineral ions and food around the plant (through the roots, stems and leaves — see page 85 for more).

- Meristem tissue — this is found at the growing tips of shoots and roots and is able to differentiate (change) into lots of different types of plant cell, allowing the plant to grow.

Learning Objectives:

- Know that the roots, stem and leaves work together in an organ system that transports substances around the plant.

- Know these examples of plant tissues and their functions:
  - epidermal tissue
  - palisade mesophyll tissue
  - spongy mesophyll tissue
  - xylem
  - phloem
  - meristem tissue

- Know that leaves are organs.

- Understand that the structures of the tissues in leaves are adapted to allow them to perform their functions.

Specification References
4.2.3.1, 4.2.3.2

Leaf structure

The leaf is an organ made up of several types of tissue. Leaves contain epidermal, mesophyll, xylem and phloem tissues (see Figures 1 and 2).

epidermal tissue
palisade mesophyll tissue
spongy mesophyll tissue
epidermal tissue
xylem
phloem
air space — *stomata* — *guard cell*

Figure 2: *Diagram showing a cross-section of a typical plant leaf.*

surface of the leaf

A
B
C
A
D

Figure 1: *A cross-section through a leaf, seen under a microscope. It shows the epidermal tissue (A), palisade mesophyll tissue (B), spongy mesophyll tissue (C) and xylem and phloem tissue (D).*

You need to know how the structures of the tissues that make up the leaf are related to their function:

- The epidermal tissues are covered with a waxy cuticle, which helps to reduce water loss by evaporation.

- The upper epidermis is transparent so that light can pass through it to the palisade layer.

- The palisade layer has lots of chloroplasts (the little structures where photosynthesis takes place). This means that they're near the top of the leaf where they can get the most light.

- The xylem and phloem form a network of vascular bundles, which deliver water and other nutrients to the entire leaf and take away the glucose produced by photosynthesis. They also help support the structure.

- The tissues of leaves are also adapted for efficient gas exchange (see page 60). E.g. the lower epidermis is full of little holes called stomata, which let CO_2 diffuse directly into the leaf. The opening and closing of stomata is controlled by guard cells in response to environmental conditions. The air spaces in the spongy mesophyll tissue increase the rate of diffusion of gases.

Exam Tip
If you're struggling to remember where the different tissues are in a leaf, think of it as epidermis is external and mesophyll is in the middle.

Tip: See page 88 for more on stomata and guard cells.

Practice Questions — Fact Recall

Q1 True or False? Leaves are organ systems.

Q2 Name the plant tissue where photosynthesis occurs.

Q3 What is the function of the air spaces in spongy mesophyll tissue?

Q4 Where in a plant is meristem tissue found?

Q5 Explain why the upper epidermis of a leaf is transparent.

7. Transpiration and Translocation

Just like animals, plants also have transport systems to move substances around...

Transport tissues in plants

Flowering plants have two separate types of tissue — phloem and xylem — for transporting substances around. Both types of tissue form 'tubes', which go to every part of the plant, but they are totally separate.

Phloem

Phloem tubes are made of columns of elongated living cells with small pores in the end walls to allow cell sap to flow through (see Figures 1 and 2). Cell sap is a liquid that's made up of the substances being transported and water.

Phloem tubes transport food substances (mainly dissolved sugars) made in the leaves to the rest of the plant for immediate use (e.g. in growing regions) or for storage. The transport goes in both directions — from the leaves down to the roots, and from the roots up to the leaves. This process is called **translocation**.

Figure 1: *Diagram showing the inside of a phloem tube.*

Figure 2: *Microscope image of the inside of a cut phloem tube — the small holes between the cells can be seen clearly.*

Xylem

Xylem tubes are made of dead cells joined end to end with no end walls between them and a hole down the middle (see Figures 3 and 4). They're strengthened with a material called lignin.

Xylem tubes carry water and mineral ions up the plant — from the roots to the stem and leaves. The movement of water from the roots, through the xylem and out of the leaves is called the **transpiration stream** (see next page).

Figure 3: *Diagram showing the inside of a xylem tube.*

Figure 4: *Microscope image showing a cut xylem tube (dark green).*

Learning Objectives:

- Know that phloem tubes are made up of columns of elongated cells with pores in the end walls through which cell sap can move, which makes them adapted for their function.
- Understand the role of phloem tissue in the transport of food (usually dissolved sugars) from the leaves to the rest of the plant and know that this process is called translocation.
- Know that xylem is made up of hollow tubes strengthened by lignin.
- Understand the role of xylem tissue in the transport of water and mineral ions to the stems and leaves from the roots.
- Understand that the structure of xylem is adapted for transporting water in the transpiration stream.
- Know how root hair cells are adapted for taking in water and mineral ions efficiently.

Specification Reference 4.2.3.2

Tip: The root hair cells take up water from the soil by osmosis, and take up mineral ions by active transport. There's more information about how they're adapted for this on page 52.

The transpiration stream

Transpiration is the loss of water from a plant. The transpiration stream is the movement of water through a plant from the roots to the leaves. It happens like this:

1. Water from inside a leaf evaporates and diffuses out of the leaf, mainly through the stomata (tiny holes found mainly on the lower surface of the leaf) — see Figure 5.

2. This creates a slight shortage of water in the leaf, and so more water is drawn up from the rest of the plant through the xylem vessels to replace it.

3. This in turn means more water is drawn up from the roots, and so there's a constant transpiration stream of water through the plant.

This is shown in Figure 6.

surface of leaf

water   stomata   water

Figure 5: *Cross-section of a leaf showing how water moves out during transpiration.*

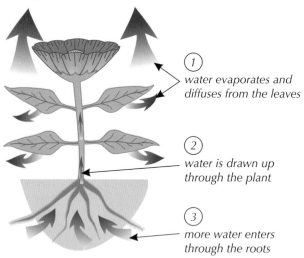

① *water evaporates and diffuses from the leaves*

② *water is drawn up through the plant*

③ *more water enters through the roots*

Figure 6: *Diagram showing how water moves through a plant in the transpiration stream.*

Tip: The rate of transpiration depends on the conditions in the plant's environment. Transpiration happens fastest in bright, hot and dry conditions where the air flow around the leaves is good, because this is when evaporation happens fastest — see next page for more.

Transpiration is just a side-effect of the way leaves are adapted for photosynthesis. They have to have stomata in them so that gases can be exchanged easily (see page 60). Because there's more water inside the plant than in the air outside, the water escapes from the leaves through the stomata by diffusion.

Practice Questions — Fact Recall

Q1 a) What is transported in phloem tubes?

   b) Which area of a plant do the phloem tubes transport substances from?

Q2 Give two substances that are transported in xylem tubes.

Q3 Explain how water is transported from the roots of a plant to its leaves.

8. Transpiration and Stomata

How quickly transpiration takes place is affected by several factors...

Factors affecting transpiration rate

Transpiration rate is affected by four main things:

Light intensity

The brighter the light, the greater the transpiration rate. Stomata begin to close as it gets darker. Photosynthesis can't happen in the dark, so they don't need to be open to let CO_2 in. When the stomata are closed, very little water can escape.

Temperature

The warmer it is, the faster transpiration happens. When it's warm, the water particles have more energy to evaporate and diffuse out of the stomata.

Air flow

The better the air flow around a leaf (e.g. stronger wind), the greater the transpiration rate. If air flow around a leaf is poor, the water vapour just surrounds the leaf and doesn't move away. This means there's a high concentration of water particles outside the leaf as well as inside it, so diffusion doesn't happen as quickly. If there's good air flow, the water vapour is swept away, maintaining a low concentration of water in the air outside the leaf. Diffusion then happens quickly, from an area of higher concentration to an area of lower concentration.

Humidity

The drier the air around a leaf, the faster transpiration happens. This is like what happens with air flow. If the air is humid there's a lot of water in it already, so there's not much of a difference between the inside and the outside of the leaf. Diffusion happens fastest if there's a really high concentration in one place, and a really low concentration in the other.

Investigating transpiration rate

You can estimate the rate of transpiration by measuring the uptake of water by a plant. This is because you can assume that water uptake by the plant is directly related to water loss by the leaves (transpiration). Figure 1 shows the apparatus you'll need.

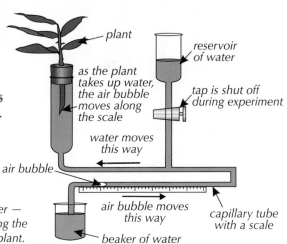

plant

as the plant takes up water, the air bubble moves along the scale

reservoir of water

tap is shut off during experiment

water moves this way

air bubble

air bubble moves this way

capillary tube with a scale

Figure 1: A potometer — apparatus for measuring the uptake of water by a plant.

beaker of water

- Understand how light intensity, temperature, air flow and humidity affect the rate of transpiration.

- Be able to read off a graph, draw graphs and interpret graphs, charts and tables relating to transpiration.

- Be able to calculate the rate of transpiration of a plant.

- Understand the role of stomata and guard cells in controlling gas exchange and water loss from leaves.

Specification Reference 4.2.3.2

Tip: Wet clothes dry as water evaporates from the fabric. You wouldn't expect clothes hung out in the garden to dry very quickly on a cold, wet day — so don't expect evaporation from a plant to be quick under those conditions either.

Exam Tip
In your exam you might need to read off data related to transpiration from a graph, chart or table and explain what the data is showing. You also need to be able to create your own graphs with suitable scales for the axes. See pages 16-18 and page 21 for more on these skills.

Tip: It's quite tough to set up a potometer. See page 291 for some tips.

To investigate the rate of transpiration, set up the apparatus as in the diagram, and then record the starting position of the air bubble. Start a stopwatch and record the distance moved by the bubble per unit of time, e.g. per hour. Keep the conditions constant throughout the experiment, e.g. the temperature and air humidity.

Calculating the rate of transpiration

You can use the data you collect in your experiment to calculate the rate of transpiration. Take a look at this example:

> ### Example
>
> A potometer was set up to measure the rate of transpiration of a plant. In 60 minutes, the bubble in the potometer moved 6.6 cm. Calculate the rate of transpiration. Give your answer in mm/min.
>
> 1. First, convert 6.6 cm into mm:
>
> $6.6 \times 10 = 66$ mm
>
> 2. Then divide the distance moved by the time taken:
>
> $66 \div 60 = \textbf{1.1 mm/min}$

Tip: Rates of transpiration can also be given in mm³/min, but this requires a bit more maths to find the actual volume of water that the plant has taken up.

Tip: Stoma is the singular word, stomata is the plural.

Guard cells

Two guard cells surround each stoma. They have a kidney shape which opens and closes the stomata in a leaf.

When the plant has lots of water, the guard cells fill with it and go plump and turgid. This makes the stomata open so gases can be exchanged for photosynthesis. When the plant is short of water, the guard cells lose water and become flaccid, making the stomata close (see Figure 3). This helps stop too much water vapour escaping.

guard cells turgid   *guard cells flaccid*

stoma open   *stoma closed*

Figure 3: *Diagram showing how guard cells open and close a stoma.*

Figure 2: *An open stoma (top) and a closed stoma (bottom).*

Thin outer walls and thickened inner walls make the opening and closing work. They're also sensitive to light and close at night to save water without losing out on photosynthesis. You usually find more stomata on the undersides of leaves than on the top. The lower surface is shaded and cooler — so less water is lost through the stomata than if they were on the upper surface. Guard cells are therefore adapted for gas exchange and controlling water loss within a leaf.

Investigating stomata and guard cells

Using a light microscope, you can investigate the distribution of stomata and guard cells on a leaf.

Tip: There is lots more about using microscopes, including how to make slides, on pages 25-27.

1. For some plants (e.g. *Kniphofia*), you can peel the epidermal tissue straight off the leaf and mount a piece on a microscope slide (see page 25). Using a pipette, put a large drop of water onto the slide, then place the tissue into the water using tweezers. Finally put a cover slip over the top.

2. For a leaf where peeling the top layer off isn't possible, you need to make an 'imprint' of its surface. You can do this using clear nail varnish. Apply a thin layer of varnish to the underside of the leaf and allow it to dry. Then use a piece of sticky tape to remove the varnish from the leaf by gently peeling it off and stick the sticky tape (with attached nail varnish imprint) to a microscope slide.

3. Now you're ready to view your slide. Put it on the microscope's stage and focus the microscope. Start with the least powerful objective lens and work your way up until you can see the stomata and guard cells clearly. You could draw a labelled diagram of what you can see down the microscope.

4. Now you can estimate the total number of stomata on the surface you're investigating. It would take ages to count every stoma on the surface, so it makes sense to just count a 'sample'.

5. Count the stomata that you can see in your 'field of vision' (the bit of the specimen that you can see when you look down the microscope). When you've finished, move the slide so you're looking at a new field of vision and count the stomata again. Do this at least three times and calculate the mean to determine the average number of stomata per field of vision.

6. To estimate the total number of stomata on the surface that you're investigating, you need to work out how many times the field of vision would fit into it. Find out the area of the field of vision and divide the total area of the surface by it. Finally, multiply your answer by the average number of stomata per field of vision. This gives you an estimate of the total number of stomata on the surface.

Figure 4: *A view of a lily leaf taken with a light microscope, showing many stomata and guard cells.*

You can easily compare the distribution of stomata in different areas of a leaf (e.g. the upper and lower surfaces) or between different leaves. To do this, carry out steps 1-5 for each of the leaf surfaces you're investigating and compare the mean number of stomata per field of vision on each of the surfaces.

Practice Questions — Fact Recall

Q1 What is the effect of increasing light intensity on the rate of transpiration?

Q2 Potometers can be used to estimate the rate of transpiration. What does a potometer actually measure?

Q3 a) Name the cells that control the size of the stomata.

b) Explain how these cells close the stomata.

Practice Questions — Application

Q1 Ben is investigating water loss in plants. He weighs two of the same type of plant, then leaves both plants in a room for 24 hours. One of the plants is placed next to a fan, the other one isn't. All other variables are controlled. After 24 hours, Ben weighs the plants again.

a) Both plants have lost mass. Explain why.

b) Which plant do you think will have lost the most mass? Explain your answer.

c) Ben wants to find out how temperature affects water loss in plants. Suggest how he could alter his experiment to investigate this.

Q2 A group of students set up a potometer as shown in the diagram.

The students wanted to find out how temperature affected transpiration rate, so they measured how far the bubble moved in the potometer when they did the experiment at three different temperatures. Their results are shown in the table:

Temperature (°C)	Distance moved by the bubble in 20 minutes (mm)
10	26
15	31
20	37

a) Explain the trend shown in the students' results.

b) Calculate the rate of transpiration of the plant at 10 °C. Give your answer in mm/min.

c) Suggest one way in which the students could have improved the validity of their investigation.

d) The students coated the underside of half of the plant's leaves with nail varnish, then did the experiment again at 10 °C. Would you expect the bubble to have moved more or less than 26 mm in this experiment? Explain your answer.

Tip: Head back to page 9 for information on what makes an experiment valid if you're struggling to answer Q2c).

Topic 2a Checklist — Make sure you know...

Cell Organisation

☐ That all living things are made up of basic building blocks called cells.

☐ That similar cells sometimes work together to form tissues, which have specific functions.

☐ That organs are made up of different types of tissue grouped together to perform a certain function.

☐ That organs work together in organ systems to perform a particular function in the body (e.g. the digestive system consists of glands, the stomach, the liver, the small intestine and the large intestine, which all work together to break down food and exchange materials with the environment).

☐ That organ systems work together to form whole organisms.

The Lungs

☐ That the human lungs consist of the trachea, the bronchi and lots of little air sacs called alveoli, which are surrounded by a network of capillaries.

☐ That when you breathe in, the air travels down the trachea, through the bronchi and into the alveoli, where gas exchange takes place. Oxygen diffuses from the alveoli into the blood in the capillaries and carbon dioxide diffuses the other way, into the alveoli, where it can be breathed out.

☐ That the alveoli and capillary network mean that the lungs are adapted for efficient gas exchange.

Circulatory System — The Heart

☐ That humans have a double circulatory system to get food and oxygen to every cell in the body via the blood, which is pumped around the body by the heart. One circuit, powered by the right ventricle, pumps deoxygenated blood to the lungs to take in oxygen, and the other circuit, powered by the left ventricle, pumps oxygenated blood to the rest of the body.

☐ That the four chambers of the human heart are the right atrium, right ventricle, left atrium and left ventricle, and that the chambers have valves to prevent backflow.

☐ That the vena cava, pulmonary artery, aorta and pulmonary vein are the four major blood vessels connected to the heart.

☐ That the coronary arteries branch off the aorta and supply the heart muscle with oxygenated blood.

☐ How the human heart functions to pump blood around the body.

☐ That a group of cells in the right atrium control the rate that the heart beats at, and that an artificial pacemaker (a small electrical device) can be fitted to treat patients with an irregular heartbeat.

Circulatory System — The Blood Vessels

☐ That there are three types of blood vessel found in the body — arteries, which carry blood away from the heart, capillaries, which carry blood close to the cells to allow substances to be exchanged, and veins, which carry blood back to the heart.

☐ How the structures of the different blood vessels are adapted to allow them to carry out their roles in the circulatory system.

☐ How to calculate the rate of blood flow in a blood vessel.

cont...

Circulatory System — The Blood

- [ ] That blood is a tissue and its main components are red and white blood cells, platelets and plasma.
- [ ] That red blood cells have no nucleus, have a biconcave shape and contain haemoglobin (a red pigment) that binds to oxygen, allowing them to carry oxygen from the lungs to the rest of the body.
- [ ] That white blood cells have a nucleus and help to defend against disease caused by microorganisms.
- [ ] That platelets are fragments of cells, don't have a nucleus and help blood to clot at a wound.
- [ ] That plasma carries just about everything in the blood including blood cells and platelets, nutrients released from digestion, carbon dioxide, urea, hormones, proteins, antibodies and antitoxins.
- [ ] How to recognise the different types of blood cell in diagrams and photographs.

Plant Cell Organisation

- [ ] That the roots, stem and leaves work together in an organ system that transports substances.
- [ ] That leaves are organs consisting of upper and lower epidermal tissue, palisade and spongy mesophyll tissue, xylem and phloem tissues, stomata and guard cells.
- [ ] That epidermal tissue covers the entire plant.
- [ ] That palisade mesophyll tissue is the location of photosynthesis and spongy mesophyll tissue contains air spaces for gas exchange.
- [ ] That xylem and phloem are the major transport tissues in plants.
- [ ] That meristem tissue is found at the tips of the growing regions of plants and can differentiate into different types of plant cell.
- [ ] How the tissues in leaves are adapted to carry out their roles in the organ.

Transpiration and Translocation

- [ ] That phloem is the plant tissue responsible for transporting food from the leaves to the rest of the plant in a process called translocation.
- [ ] That phloem is made up of columns of elongated living cells that have pores in the end walls to allow the cell sap containing the food (usually dissolved sugars) to pass through.
- [ ] That xylem transports water and mineral ions from the roots to the stems and leaves and is made up of hollow tubes of dead cells strengthened by lignin that have no end walls between them.
- [ ] That the structure of xylem is suited to carrying water in the transpiration stream, which is the movement of water through the plant from the roots to the leaves.

Transpiration and Stomata

- [ ] How high light intensity, high temperature, increased air flow and low humidity (drier air) increase the rate of transpiration and vice versa.
- [ ] How to read from and interpret graphs, charts and tables containing data on transpiration, and how to produce your own transpiration-related graphs.
- [ ] How to calculate the rate of transpiration.
- [ ] How stomata allow water to diffuse out of leaves and gas exchange to take place, and how guard cells control the opening of the stomata to regulate these processes.

Exam-style Questions

1   Humans have a specialised system for exchanging gases with their environment.

  1.1   Which of the following options gives the correct route taken by oxygen into the bloodstream?

        A   bronchi, trachea, capillaries, alveoli

        B   capillaries, alveoli, bronchi, trachea

        C   trachea, bronchi, alveoli, capillaries

        D   trachea, alveoli, capillaries, bronchi

(1 mark)

  1.2   Which of the following sentences best describes alveoli?

        A   Small blood vessels that carry deoxygenated blood to the lungs.

        B   Tubes that split from the trachea, one into each lung.

        C   Small air sacs found in the lungs that play a major role in gas exchange.

        D   Specialised cells found only in the lungs that regulate the breathing rate.

(1 mark)

2   **Figure 1** represents the heart.

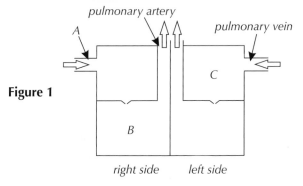

Figure 1

  2.1   Name each of the structures labelled A-C on the diagram.

(3 marks)

Figure 2 shows cross-sections through the pulmonary artery and the pulmonary vein.

Figure 2

  2.2   Which diagram (X or Y) shows the pulmonary vein? Explain your answer.

(1 mark)

3   **Figure 3** shows a group of blood cells.

Figure 3

Identify the blood cells shown in **Figure 3** and explain **three** ways in which they are adapted to their function.

(4 marks)

4   **Figure 4** shows a cross-section through a leaf.

Figure 4

4.1   What name is given to the tissue that covers the leaf?

(1 mark)

4.2   Some of the cells in the photograph contain lots of chloroplasts.
What plant tissue are these cells part of? Explain your answer.

(3 marks)

4.3   Throughout the day, the rate at which carbon dioxide diffuses into the leaf cells changes. Explain how a change in the concentration of carbon dioxide in the air spaces outside the cells could slow down the rate of diffusion.

(2 marks)

5   Desert plants are adapted for life in hot, dry conditions.
Like most plants, they exchange gases through their stomata.

Suggest and explain how the following adaptations help plants to survive in desert conditions:

5.1   Stomata are kept closed during the day, when it is hot and dry, and only opened at night, when it is cool.

(3 marks)

5.2   Stomata are located in sunken pits. The pits help to trap water vapour close to the surface of the leaf.

(2 marks)

1. Introduction to Health and Disease

Diseases are one cause of poor health. Sometimes, different diseases interact, leading to further health complications that don't appear related at first.

Diseases

Diseases are often responsible for causing ill health.

> Health is the state of physical and mental wellbeing.

Diseases can be communicable or non-communicable.

Communicable Diseases

Communicable diseases are those that can spread from person to person or between animals and people. They can be caused by things like bacteria, viruses, parasites and fungi. They're sometimes described as contagious or infectious diseases. Measles and malaria are examples of communicable diseases. There's more about them on pages 124-125.

Non-Communicable Diseases

Non-communicable diseases are those that cannot spread between people or between animals and people. They generally last for a long time and get worse slowly. Asthma, cancer and coronary heart disease (see page 97) are examples of non-communicable diseases.

Interaction of diseases

Sometimes diseases can interact and cause other physical and mental health issues that don't immediately seem related. Here are a few examples:

Examples

- People who have problems with their immune system (the system that your body uses to help fight off infection — see p. 130) have an increased chance of suffering from communicable diseases such as influenza (flu), because their body is less likely to be able to defend itself against the pathogen that causes the disease.

- Some types of cancer can be triggered by infection by certain viruses. For example, infection with some types of hepatitis virus can cause long-term infections in the liver where the virus lives in the cells. This can lead to an increased chance of developing liver cancer. Another example is infection with HPV (human papilloma virus), which can cause cervical cancer in women.

- Immune system reactions in the body caused by infection by a pathogen can sometimes trigger allergic reactions such as skin rashes or worsen the symptoms of asthma for asthma sufferers.

Learning Objectives:

- Know the definition of health, and know that diseases are often the cause of ill health.
- Know that a disease can be communicable (infectious) or non-communicable (not infectious).
- Understand that diseases can interact with each other.
- Know these examples of interacting diseases: immune system problems and communicable diseases; viruses and cancer; immune reactions and allergies; physical health problems and mental illness.
- Know that factors other than disease, such as diet, stress and life situations can also lead to ill health.
- Be able to read off a graph, and draw and interpret tables, charts and graphs relating to the incidence of disease.
- Be able to identify a correlation on a graph relating to the incidence of disease.
- Understand why sampling is used when collecting epidemiological data.

Specification Reference 4.2.2.5

- Mental health issues such as depression can be triggered when someone is suffering from severe physical health problems, particularly if they have an impact on the person's ability to carry out everyday activities or if they affect the person's life expectancy.

Tip: Stress can cause all sorts of physical health issues (e.g. high blood pressure, headaches and issues with the immune system) as well as mental health issues (e.g. depression).

Other factors affecting health

There are plenty of factors other than diseases that can also affect your health. Take a look at these examples:

Examples

- Whether or not you have a good, balanced diet that provides your body with everything it needs, and in the right amounts. A poor diet can affect your physical and mental health.

- The stress you are under — being constantly under lots of stress can lead to health issues.

- Your life situation — for example, whether you have easy access to medicines to treat illness, or whether you have access to things that can prevent you from getting ill in the first place, e.g. being able to buy healthy food or access condoms to prevent the transmission of some sexually transmitted diseases.

Exam Tip
In the exam, you may need to read off a graph, or draw or explain tables, graphs and charts showing data on the incidence of disease. The incidence of disease is the number of new cases of the disease within a given time. It may be given as, e.g. the number of new cases per 100 000 persons per year, so make sure you understand the units the data is shown in before answering the question.

Exam Tip
In the exam, you might need to identify a correlation between variables relating to disease incidence from a graph. To recap what correlation is, look at page 18.

Tip: Sampling is often used when collecting data related to health and patterns in diseases (epidemiological data). This is because it would take too long and cost too much to collect data from the entire population. See p. 293 for more on sampling.

Practice Questions — Fact Recall

Q1   What is meant by the term 'health'?

Q2   What is the main difference between communicable and non-communicable diseases?

Q3   Give three factors other than disease that could affect health.

Practice Question — Application

Q1   The graph below shows the results of a study into the average number of colds suffered by employees in high-stress jobs and low-stress jobs in the same company per year.

Describe and suggest an explanation for the results.

2. Cardiovascular Disease

Lots of things can go wrong with the heart and blood vessels. We have ways to effectively treat many of these issues. Read on for more...

What is cardiovascular disease?

Cardiovascular disease is a term used to describe diseases of the heart or blood vessels. A common example is **coronary heart disease**. Coronary heart disease is when the arteries that supply the blood to the heart muscle (the **coronary arteries**, see Figure 1) get blocked by layers of fatty material building up. This causes the arteries to become narrow, so blood flow is restricted and there's a lack of oxygen to the heart muscle — this can result in a heart attack.

outside of heart

coronary arteries

Figure 1: *The location of the coronary arteries.*

Cardiovascular disease can be treated in a few different ways:

Stents

Stents are wire mesh tubes that can be inserted inside arteries to widen them and keep them open (see Figure 1). They are particularly useful in people with coronary heart disease.

Stents keep the coronary arteries open, making sure blood can pass through to the heart muscles (see Figure 2). This keeps the person's heart beating (and the person alive).

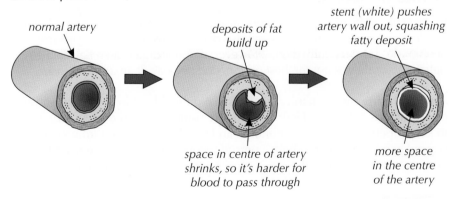

normal artery

deposits of fat build up

stent (white) pushes artery wall out, squashing fatty deposit

space in centre of artery shrinks, so it's harder for blood to pass through

more space in the centre of the artery

Figure 2: *A diagram showing how a stent can help to widen an artery.*

Advantages of stents

Stents are a way of lowering the risk of a heart attack in people with coronary heart disease. They are effective for a long time and the recovery time from the surgery is relatively quick.

Learning Objectives:

- Understand the causes of coronary heart disease and the complications it can lead to.
- Know that stents can be used to treat coronary heart disease by keeping the coronary arteries open.
- Know that statins can be used to reduce the amount of cholesterol in the blood and slow the formation of fatty deposits in arteries.
- Know that surgeons can transplant the heart, or heart and lungs, of an organ donor into a patient with heart failure.
- Know that in certain circumstances, artificial hearts can be fitted to a patient, usually on a temporary basis.
- Understand that heart valves can become damaged and faulty, leading to them being leaky or not opening fully when required.
- Know that replacement biological or mechanical heart valves are available.
- Be able to assess the pros and cons of different treatments for cardiovascular disease.

Specification Reference 4.2.2.4

Figure 3: *A stent that can be used to widen an artery.*

Disadvantages of stents

There is a risk of complications during the operation (e.g. heart attack) and a risk of infection from surgery. There's also the risk of patients developing a blood clot near the stent. This is called thrombosis.

Statins

Statins are drugs that can reduce the amount of 'bad' **cholesterol** present in the bloodstream. Cholesterol is an essential lipid that your body produces and needs to function properly. However, too much of a certain type of cholesterol (known as 'bad' or LDL cholesterol) can cause health problems. Having too much of this 'bad' cholesterol in the bloodstream can cause fatty deposits to form inside arteries, which can lead to coronary heart disease. Taking statins slows down the rate of fatty deposits forming.

Advantages of statins

By reducing the amount of 'bad' cholesterol in the blood, statins can reduce the risk of strokes, coronary heart disease and heart attacks. As well as reducing the amount of 'bad' cholesterol, statins can increase the amount of a beneficial type of cholesterol (known as 'good' or HDL cholesterol) in your bloodstream. This type can remove 'bad' cholesterol from the blood. Some studies suggest that statins may also help prevent some other diseases.

Disadvantages of statins

Statins are a long-term drug that must be taken regularly. There's the risk that someone could forget to take them. Also, statins can sometimes cause negative side effects, e.g. headaches. Some of these side effects can be serious, e.g. kidney failure, liver damage and memory loss. Another disadvantage is that the effect of statins isn't instant. It takes time for their effect to kick in.

Artificial hearts

If a patient has heart failure, doctors may perform a heart transplant (or heart and lungs transplant if the lungs are also diseased) using donor organs from people who have recently died. However, if donor organs aren't available right away or they're not the best option, doctors may fit an artificial heart.

Artificial hearts are mechanical devices that pump blood for a person whose own heart has failed (see Figure 4). They're usually used as a temporary fix, to keep a person alive until a donor heart (a replacement heart from another person) can be found or to help a person recover by allowing the heart to rest and heal. In some cases they're used as a permanent fix, which reduces the need for a donor heart.

> **Example**
>
> The SynCardia Total Artificial Heart is a modern artificial heart with a high success rate. The device kept one patient alive for 1374 days (which is nearly 4 years) before they were able to have a heart transplant.

Figure 4: *The first artificial heart to be inserted into a patient, in 1982.*

Advantages of artificial hearts

The main advantage of artificial hearts is that they're less likely to be rejected by the body's immune system than a donor heart. This is because they're made from metals or plastics, so the body doesn't recognise them as 'foreign' and attack in the same way as it does with living tissue.

Disadvantages of artificial hearts

Surgery to fit an artificial heart (as with transplant surgery) can lead to bleeding and infection. Also, artificial hearts don't work as well as healthy natural ones — parts of the heart could wear out or the electrical motor could fail.

Blood doesn't flow through artificial hearts as smoothly as through natural hearts either, which can cause blood clots and lead to strokes (a problem caused when the blood supply to part of the brain is cut off). A patient receiving an artificial heart has to take drugs to thin their blood and make sure clots don't occur. This can cause problems with bleeding if they're hurt in an accident because their blood can't clot normally to heal the wounds.

Also, having an artificial heart in the body (and any battery and controller that might be inserted as well) may be uncomfortable for the patient.

Replacement heart valves

The valves in the heart can be damaged or weakened by heart attacks, infection or old age. The damage may cause the valve tissue to stiffen, so it won't open properly. Or a valve may become leaky, allowing blood to flow in both directions rather than just forward. This means that blood doesn't circulate as effectively as normal.

Severe valve damage can be treated by replacing the valve. Replacement valves can be ones taken from humans or other mammals (e.g. cows or pigs) — these are **biological valves**. Or they can be man-made — these are **mechanical valves**.

Replacing a valve is a much less drastic procedure than a whole heart transplant. But fitting artificial valves is still major surgery and there can still be problems with blood clots.

artificial heart valve

Figure 5: *An artificial valve in a human heart (cut open).*

Artificial blood

When someone loses a lot of blood, e.g. in an accident, their heart can still pump the remaining red blood cells around (to get oxygen to their organs), as long as the volume of their blood can be topped up.

Artificial blood is a blood substitute, e.g. a salt solution ("saline"), which is used to replace the lost volume of blood. It's safe (if no air bubbles get into the blood) and can keep people alive even if they lose 2/3 of their red blood cells. This may give the patient enough time to produce new blood cells. If not, the patient will need a blood transfusion.

Ideally, an artificial blood product would replace the function of the lost red blood cells, so that there's no need for a blood transfusion. Scientists are currently working on products that can do this.

Practice Questions — Fact Recall

Q1 What is cardiovascular disease?

Q2 What causes coronary heart disease?

Q3 a) What is a stent?

b) Describe how stents can be used to treat people with coronary heart disease.

Practice Question — Application

Q1 A patient with heart failure requires a heart transplant. However, doctors cannot immediately find a suitable donor organ. They decide to fit an artificial heart instead.

a) Other than better availability, suggest another advantage of artificial hearts over donor hearts.

b) Suggest two disadvantages of artificial hearts.

c) The doctor who will carry out the surgery reads an article in a medical journal about artificial hearts. He makes notes about two of the artificial hearts he's read about:

Artificial heart one:

- Has been implanted in more than 1100 patients.
- Is connected to a battery pack outside the body with wires that pass through a small hole in the skin.

Artificial heart two:

- Has been implanted into 14 patients.
- Is powered by a battery which is inserted into the body and can be charged through the skin.

The doctor decides to recommend artificial heart two to the patient. Based on the information given, evaluate the decision to treat a patient with artificial heart two.

Exam Tip
For questions where you're asked to evaluate something, make sure you take into account and write about both the advantages and the disadvantages.

3. Risk Factors for Non-Communicable Diseases

Certain things can make developing a non-communicable disease more likely...

What are risk factors?

Risk factors are things that are linked to an increase in the likelihood that a person will develop a certain disease during their lifetime. They don't guarantee that someone will get the disease.

Risk factors are often aspects of a person's lifestyle (e.g. how much exercise they do). They can also be the presence of certain substances in the environment (e.g. air pollution) or substances in your body (e.g. asbestos fibres — asbestos was a material used in buildings until it was realised that the fibres could build up in your airways and cause diseases such as cancer later in life).

Many non-communicable diseases are caused by several different risk factors interacting with each other rather than one factor alone.

Lifestyle factors can have different impacts locally, nationally and globally. E.g. in developed countries, non-communicable diseases are more common as people generally have a higher income and can buy high-fat food. Nationally, people from deprived areas are more likely to smoke, have a poor diet and not exercise. This means the incidence of cardiovascular disease, obesity and Type 2 diabetes is higher in those areas. Your individual choices affect the local incidence of disease.

Risk factors that cause disease

Some risk factors are able to directly cause a disease.

> ### Examples
>
> ■ Smoking has been proven to directly cause cardiovascular disease, lung disease and lung cancer. It damages the walls of arteries and the cells in the lining of the lungs.
>
> ■ It's thought that obesity can directly cause Type 2 diabetes by making the body less sensitive or resistant to insulin, meaning that it struggles to control the concentration of glucose in the blood.
>
> ■ Drinking too much alcohol has been shown to cause liver disease. The liver breaks down alcohol, but the reaction can damage its cells. Liver cells may also be damaged when toxic chemicals leak from the gut due to damage to the intestines caused by alcohol. Too much alcohol can affect brain function too. It can damage the nerve cells in the brain, causing the brain to lose volume.
>
> ■ Smoking when pregnant reduces the amount of oxygen the baby receives in the womb and can cause lots of health problems for the unborn baby. Drinking alcohol has similar effects. Alcohol can damage the baby's cells, affecting its development and causing a wide range of health issues.

Learning Objectives:

■ Know that risk factors are things that are linked to an increase in the likelihood that a person will develop a certain disease.

■ Know that risk factors may be related to lifestyle, or the presence of substances in someone's body or in the environment.

■ Know that many non-communicable diseases are caused by multiple factors interacting.

■ Understand how lifestyle factors can affect how common a disease is at a local, national and global level.

■ Understand that some risk factors have been proven to cause a disease, but others have not, and be able to give examples of risk factors that have been proven to cause a disease.

■ Be able to identify a correlation on a graph relating to disease risk factors.

■ Be able to read from and interpret charts, graphs and tables containing data related to risk factors for diseases.

■ Know the human and financial costs of non-communicable diseases for individuals, local communities, nations and globally.

■ Know why sampling is used when collecting disease risk factor data.

Specification Reference
4.2.2.6

Tip: There's more about the risk factors of cancer on pages 103-104.

- Cancer can be directly caused by exposure to certain substances or radiation. Things that cause cancer are known as carcinogens. Carcinogens work in different ways. For example, some damage a cell's DNA in a way that makes the cell more likely to divide uncontrollably. Ionising radiation (e.g. from X-rays) is an example of a carcinogen.

Correlation and cause

Risk factors are identified by scientists looking for correlations in data, and correlation doesn't always equal cause. Some risk factors aren't capable of directly causing a disease, but are related to another risk factor that is.

Exam Tip
In the exam, you might need to identify a correlation between risk factors and diseases from a graph. To recap what correlation is, look at page 18.

Example

A lack of exercise and a high fat diet are heavily linked to an increased chance of cardiovascular disease, but they can't cause the disease directly. It's the resulting high blood pressure and high 'bad' cholesterol levels (see p. 98) that can actually cause it.

The cost of non-communicable diseases

Non-communicable diseases can be costly on different levels.

Human cost

The human cost of non-communicable diseases is obvious. Tens of millions of people around the world die from non-communicable diseases per year. People with these diseases may have a lower quality of life or a shorter lifespan. This not only affects the sufferers themselves, but their loved ones too.

Exam Tip
In the exam, you might need to read off data related to disease risk factors from a table, graph or chart, or explain what the data is showing. Remember to always check any units or graph scales carefully before answering any questions.

Financial cost

It's also important to think about the financial cost. The cost to the NHS of researching and treating these diseases is huge — and it's the same for other health services and organisations around the world. Families may have to move or adapt their home to help a family member with a disease, which can be costly. Also, if the family member with the disease has to give up work or dies, the family's income will be reduced. A reduction in the number of people able to work can also affect a country's economy.

Tip: To save time and money, scientists often use sampling when collecting data on risk factors for diseases rather than collecting data from the entire population. Turn to page 293 for more on sampling.

Practice Questions — Fact Recall

Q1 What is a risk factor?

Q2 Other than the presence of substances in the body, give two other things that risk factors can be.

Q3 Give an example of how lifestyle risk factors can affect the incidence of non-communicable diseases on a national level.

Q4 Give two diseases that smoking has been proven to cause.

Q5 Give a risk factor that is thought to cause Type 2 diabetes.

Q6 What is a carcinogen?

4. Cancer

There are risk factors that make it more likely that someone will develop cancer. Here's all you need to know about the disease and its risk factors.

Tumours

Cancer is caused by uncontrolled cell growth and division. This uncontrolled growth and division is a result of changes that occur to the cells and results in the formation of a tumour (a growth of abnormal cells). Not all tumours are cancerous. They can be benign or malignant.

Benign tumours

This is where the tumour grows until there's no more room. The tumour stays in one place (usually within a membrane) rather than invading other tissues in the body. This type isn't normally dangerous, and the tumour isn't cancerous.

Malignant tumours

This is where the tumour grows and spreads to neighbouring healthy tissues. Cells can break off and spread to other parts of the body by travelling in the bloodstream. The malignant cells then invade healthy tissues elsewhere in the body and form secondary tumours. Malignant tumours are dangerous and can be fatal — they are cancers.

Risk factors for cancer

Anyone can develop cancer. Cancer survival rates have increased due to medical advances such as improved treatment, being able to diagnose cancer earlier and increased screening for the disease. However, risk factors can increase the chance of developing some cancers. Having risk factors doesn't mean that you'll definitely get cancer. It just means that you're at an increased risk of developing the disease compared to people who have fewer risk factors, or don't have any risk factors at all. Some risk factors are associated with aspects of a person's lifestyle, and some are associated with genetics.

Lifestyle risk factors

Scientists have identified lots of lifestyle risk factors for various types of cancer. Here are a few examples:

> **Examples**
>
> - Smoking — It's a well known fact that smoking is linked to lung cancer, but research has also linked it to other types of cancer too, including mouth, bowel, stomach and cervical cancer.
>
> - Obesity — Obesity has been linked to many different cancers, including bowel, liver and kidney cancer. It's the second biggest preventable cause of cancer after smoking.
>
> - UV exposure — People who are often exposed to UV radiation from the Sun have an increased chance of developing skin cancer. People who live in sunny climates and people who spend a lot of time outside are at higher risk of the disease. People who frequently use sun beds are also putting themselves at higher risk of developing skin cancer.

Learning Objectives:

- Know that cancer is caused when changes occur in cells that cause them to grow and divide out of control.

- Know what benign tumours are and that they stay in one place in the body and don't spread to other body tissues.

- Know that malignant tumours are cancerous and that the cells are able to travel in the blood to spread to other parts of the body and form secondary tumours.

- Know that risk factors linked to lifestyle have been identified for cancer by scientists.

- Know that genetic risk factors have been identified for certain types of cancer.

Specification Reference 4.2.2.7

Figure 1: *The lung of a smoker, showing blackening by tar and a cancerous tumour near the top (white).*

Figure 2: *A cross section of a diseased liver with multiple cancerous tumours (white). These tumours may have been caused by infection with hepatitis B or C viruses.*

Tip: A mutation is a random change in an organism's DNA.

Tip: (height in metres)² just means that you multiply height in metres by itself.

- Viral infection — Infection with some viruses has been shown to increase the chances of developing certain types of cancer. For example, infection with hepatitis B and hepatitis C viruses can increase the risk of developing liver cancer. The likelihood of becoming infected with these viruses sometimes depends on lifestyle — e.g. they can be spread between people through unprotected sex or sharing needles.

Genetic risk factors

Genes control the activities of your cells and your characteristics — see page 217. The genes you have are inherited from your parents. Sometimes you can inherit faulty genes that make you more susceptible to cancer.

Example

Mutations in the BRCA genes have been linked to an increased likelihood of developing breast and ovarian cancer.

Practice Questions — Fact Recall

Q1 Are benign tumours cancerous?

Q2 Describe the characteristics of malignant tumours.

Practice Question — Application

Q1 The formula below shows how to calculate a person's BMI, which is one way to determine whether someone is a healthy weight.

$$BMI = \frac{weight~in~kg}{(height~in~metres)^2}$$

The table below shows how BMI relates to a person's weight.

BMI	Weight Classification
less than 18.5	underweight
18.5 – 24.9	ideal weight
25 – 29.9	overweight
30 – 39.9	obese
40 or higher	very obese

Robyn weighs 77 kg and is 178 cm tall.
Lauren weighs 75 kg and is 155 cm tall.

a) Calculate the BMI of each of the women.

b) Based on this information alone, who has the higher risk of developing cancer? Explain your answer.

Topic 2b Checklist — Make sure you know...

Introduction to Health and Disease

☐ That health is the state of physical and mental wellbeing, and that diseases are a large cause of ill health.

☐ That diseases can be communicable (can spread from person to person or between animals and people) or non-communicable (cannot be spread).

☐ That diseases can interact with each other to cause other physical and/or mental health issues. For example, people with immune system problems are more likely to develop communicable diseases, some cancers can be triggered by infection with certain viruses, certain immune reactions brought on by infection with a pathogen can lead to skin rashes and make asthma symptoms worse, and depression and other mental illness can develop in patients suffering from physical health problems.

☐ That as well as disease, a poor and unbalanced diet, high levels of stress, and disadvantaged life situations (e.g. no access to drugs) can contribute to ill health.

☐ How to draw, read from and interpret tables, charts and graphs (for example, frequency tables, frequency diagrams, bar charts and histograms) relating to the incidence of disease.

☐ How to identify a correlation between two variables in data relating to the incidence of disease by looking at data plotted on a graph.

☐ That sampling is often used when collecting epidemiological data (data relating to health and patterns in diseases) to save time and money.

Cardiovascular Disease

☐ That cardiovascular diseases are diseases of the heart or blood vessels.

☐ That coronary heart disease is a common example of a cardiovascular disease.

☐ That coronary heart disease occurs when the arteries that supply blood to the heart tissue (coronary arteries) are blocked by deposits of fatty material, starving the heart muscle of the oxygen it needs.

☐ That fitting stents to narrowed arteries to keep them open can help reduce the risk of a heart attack in patients with coronary heart disease.

☐ That statins are drugs used to reduce the amount of cholesterol in the bloodstream, which slows down the rate of fatty deposits forming inside arteries.

☐ That surgeons can treat a patient with heart failure by transplanting a healthy donor heart, or heart and lungs, into the patient.

☐ That as an alternative to a donor heart, a mechanical artificial heart can be fitted to a patient while they are waiting for a donor heart to become available, or to allow their own heart to rest and heal.

☐ That heart valves can become damaged or weakened, causing them to not open properly or to leak, meaning that the blood can't circulate as effectively as normal.

☐ That faulty heart valves can be replaced, and that the replacement valves can either be biological (from humans or other mammals) or mechanical (man-made devices).

☐ How to assess the pros and cons of using stents, statins, artificial hearts, transplants and heart valve replacements to treat cardiovascular disease.

cont...

Risk Factors for Non-Communicable Diseases

☐ That risk factors are things that increase the likelihood that someone will develop a certain disease, but having a risk factor doesn't mean that someone will definitely get the disease.

☐ That risk factors could be related to aspects of a person's lifestyle (e.g. how much alcohol they drink), the presence of certain substances in the environment (e.g. air pollution) or the presence of substances in someone's body (e.g. asbestos fibres).

☐ That many non-communicable diseases are caused by multiple risk factors interacting with each other — for example, Type 2 diabetes, cardiovascular disease, and some lung and liver diseases.

☐ How the incidence of non-communicable diseases can be affected by lifestyle-related risk factors (e.g. smoking and diet) at a global, national and local level.

☐ That some risk factors have been proven to directly cause a disease (e.g. smoking has been shown to directly cause lung disease and lung cancer), whereas some risk factors have not.

☐ That smoking can cause cardiovascular disease, that obesity can cause Type 2 diabetes, that alcohol can affect liver and brain function, that smoking can cause lung disease and lung cancer, that smoking and drinking alcohol while pregnant can cause issues for unborn babies, and that exposure to carcinogens (such as ionising radiation) can cause cancer.

☐ How to use graphs to identify correlation between risk factors and diseases.

☐ How to read off and interpret data on disease risk factors presented in charts, graphs and tables.

☐ The human and financial costs that non-communicable diseases can have on a local, national and global level.

☐ That scientists often use sampling to collect data about the risk factors for different diseases because collecting data from the entire population would take too long and cost too much.

Cancer

☐ That cancer is caused by uncontrolled cell growth and division triggered by certain changes in cells, which leads to the formation of growths of abnormal cells called tumours.

☐ That benign tumours are tumours that stay in one place in the body and aren't able to spread to and invade other tissues.

☐ That malignant tumours are cancerous and are able to grow and spread into neighbouring tissues.

☐ That cells can break off malignant tumours and travel in the bloodstream to cause secondary tumours in other parts of the body.

☐ That there are lots of different lifestyle-related risk factors for developing cancer that have been identified by scientists, such as smoking, obesity or exposure to too much UV radiation (e.g. from the Sun or sun beds).

☐ That there are also risk factors for cancer related to genetics — inheriting certain genes could increase a person's chances of developing certain cancers.

Exam-style Questions

1   A doctor was viewing the X-ray of a patient's chest shown in **Figure 1**.
She noticed that a large tumour had formed in the patient's left lung.

Figure 1

1.1   Which of these sentences best describes how tumours form?

A   Tumours are formed when body cells are unable to replicate.
B   Tumours are formed when body cells die.
C   Tumours are formed when body cells grow too slowly.
D   Tumours are formed when body cells grow and divide out of control.

(1 mark)

After further investigation, the doctor found another tumour in the patient's liver
made up of similar cells to the tumour in the lungs. This led her to suspect that the
tumours were cancerous.

1.2   What is the name for a cancerous tumour?

(1 mark)

1.3   Suggest why the doctor suspected the tumours to be cancerous.

(3 marks)

1.4   Which of these statements is true?

A   Neither genetic factors nor aspects of a person's lifestyle can be cancer risk factors.
B   Cancer risk factors are always related to genetics.
C   Both genetic factors and aspects of a person's lifestyle can be cancer risk factors.
D   All cancer risk factors are related to aspects of a person's lifestyle.

(1 mark)

1.5   The doctor asks if the patient takes any medication.
The patient takes statins. How do statins prevent coronary heart disease?

(2 marks)

2   A doctor is treating a patient who has damage to a heart valve. The doctor has decided that the best treatment for the patient would be to replace the damaged valve.

2.1   Describe the complications that can be caused by a damaged heart valve.

(3 marks)

2.2   The doctor decides to use a mechanical replacement valve.
Describe how mechanical replacement valves differ from biological replacement valves.

(2 marks)

2.3   Another patient requires a heart transplant. A donor has not yet been found.
Suggest what might be done to keep the patient alive until a donor has been found.

(1 mark)

3   After a heart attack, many patients have a stent fitted into the affected coronary artery. This could be a bare-metal stent or a drug-eluting stent, which gradually releases a drug to prevent new cells from growing over the stent.

In a trial, patients needing a stent were randomly given either a bare-metal stent or a drug-eluting stent. Following their surgery, the patients were monitored and any health problems recorded.

The results for 154 patients who received the drug-eluting stent and 153 patients who received the bare-metal stent are shown in **Table 1**:

Table 1

	Number of patients who died following treatment	Number of patients who had another heart attack	% of patients whose artery renarrowed
Drug-eluting stent	3	3	9
Bare-metal stent	7	3	21

3.1   Calculate the percentage of patients that died after receiving the drug-eluting stent.

(1 mark)

3.2   Explain why stents are often used in people who have had a heart attack.

(3 marks)

3.3   Based on the information given, some doctors may conclude that drug-eluting stents are more beneficial than bare-metal stents. Do you think this is a valid conclusion? Explain your answer.

(3 marks)

1. Enzymes

Enzymes are essential. There are loads of different types in the body.
They play an important role in speeding up chemical reactions in your insides.

Enzymes

Living things have thousands of different chemical reactions going on inside them all the time, including the reactions involved in metabolism (see page 165). These reactions need to be carefully controlled — to get the right amounts of substances.

You can usually make a reaction happen more quickly by raising the temperature. This would speed up the useful reactions but also the unwanted ones too... not good. There's also a limit to how far you can raise the temperature inside a living creature before its cells start getting damaged.

So... living things produce enzymes that act as **biological catalysts**. Enzymes reduce the need for high temperatures and we only have enzymes to speed up the useful chemical reactions in the body.

> A catalyst is a substance which increases the speed of a reaction, without being changed or used up in the reaction.

Enzymes are all large proteins and all proteins are made up of chains of amino acids. These chains are folded into unique shapes, which enzymes need to do their jobs (see below).

Active sites

Chemical reactions usually involve things either being split apart or joined together. Every enzyme has an **active site** with a unique shape that fits onto the substance involved in a reaction. Enzymes are really picky — they usually only catalyse one specific reaction. This is because, for the enzyme to work, the substrate has to fit into its active site. If the substrate doesn't match the enzyme's active site, then the reaction won't be catalysed.

active site
enzyme
substrate
enzyme unchanged after reaction
products

Figure 1: *Diagram to show how an enzyme works.*

Learning Objectives:
- Know that enzymes play a role in metabolism.
- Understand the function and characteristics of enzymes.
- Know that each enzyme has an active site with a unique shape that will only fit onto the substance involved in a specific reaction.
- Know that the 'lock and key' model of enzyme action is a simpler version of what actually takes place when an enzyme binds to its substrate.
- Understand how the activity of enzymes is affected by pH and temperature.

Specification Reference 4.2.2.1

Tip: The substance that an enzyme acts on is called the substrate.

Figure 2: Computer model of an enzyme bound to a substance (yellow).

Figure 1 (on the previous page) shows the 'lock and key' model of enzyme action.
This is simpler than how enzymes actually work. In reality, the active site changes shape a little as the substrate binds to it to get a tighter fit. This is called the 'induced fit' model of enzyme action.

Optimum conditions for enzymes

Enzymes need the right conditions, such as the right temperature and pH, for them to work best — these are called **optimum conditions**.

Temperature

Changing the temperature changes the rate of an enzyme-catalysed reaction. Like with any reaction, a higher temperature increases the rate at first. But if it gets too hot, some of the bonds holding the enzyme together break. This changes the shape of the enzyme's active site, so the substrate won't fit any more. The enzyme is said to be **denatured**.

Therefore enzymes have a temperature at which they are most active — this is called the optimum temperature (see Figure 3). Enzymes in the human body normally work best at around 37 °C.

Tip: Increasing the temperature increases the rate of a reaction because the reactants have more energy, so they move about more, and collide with each other more often.

Tip: If an enzyme is involved in speeding up a reaction, then the reaction is known as an 'enzyme-catalysed reaction', an 'enzymatic reaction' or an 'enzyme-controlled reaction'.

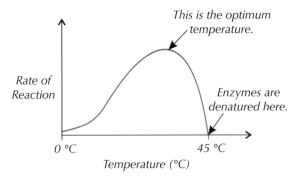

Figure 3: Graph to show how temperature affects enzyme action.

pH

The pH also affects enzymes. If it's too high or too low, the pH interferes with the bonds holding the enzyme together. This changes the shape of the active site and denatures the enzyme.

All enzymes have an optimum pH that they work best at — this is called the optimum pH (see Figure 4).

Tip: A low pH means that an environment is acidic. A high pH means that it is alkaline.

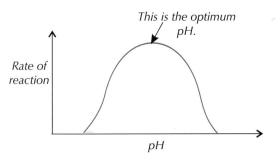

Figure 4: Graph to show how pH affects enzyme action.

The optimum pH is different for different enzymes depending on where they work. For many enzymes it's neutral pH 7, but not always.

Example

Pepsin is an enzyme used to break down proteins in the stomach. It works best at pH 2, which means it's well-suited to the acidic conditions in the stomach.

Practice Questions — Fact Recall

Q1 Why can enzymes be described as biological catalysts?

Q2 What is the name of the part of an enzyme that binds to the substrate?

Q3 True or false? All enzymes work best at pH 7.

Practice Question — Application

Q1 Hexokinase is an enzyme found in the human body that's involved in respiration. It catalyses this reaction:

$$\text{glucose} \xrightarrow{\text{hexokinase}} \text{substance A}$$

Enzymes in the human body work best at 37 °C.

A scientist heats up hexokinase to 50 °C and adds it to some glucose. Suggest the effect this will have on the rate of the reaction compared to if the reaction was at 37 °C. Explain your answer.

Tip: Respiration is the process of breaking down glucose, which transfers energy. There's loads more about it on pages 159-162.

Learning Objective:
- Be able to investigate the effect of pH on the rate of starch breakdown by the enzyme amylase (Required Practical 4).
- Be able to calculate the rate of chemical reactions.

Specification Reference
4.2.2.1

2. Investigating Enzymatic Reactions

You need to know how to investigate the effect of pH on the rate of the reaction catalysed by the enzyme amylase. Read on for more.

Investigating the effect of pH on amylase

The enzyme amylase catalyses the breakdown of starch to maltose. It's easy to detect starch using iodine solution — if starch is present, the iodine solution will change from browny-orange to blue-black. This is how you can investigate how pH affects amylase activity:

REQUIRED PRACTICAL **4**

1. Put a drop of iodine solution into every well of a spotting tile.

2. Place a Bunsen burner on a heat-proof mat, and a tripod and gauze over the Bunsen burner. Put a beaker of water on top of the tripod and heat the water until it is 35 °C (use a thermometer to measure the temperature). Try to keep the temperature of the water constant throughout the experiment.

3. Use a syringe to add 1 cm³ of amylase solution and 1 cm³ of a buffer solution with a pH of 5 to a boiling tube. Using test tube holders, put the boiling tube into the beaker of water and wait for five minutes.

4. Next, use a different syringe to add 5 cm³ of a starch solution to the boiling tube.

5. Immediately mix the contents of the boiling tube and start a stop clock.

6. Use continuous sampling to record how long it takes for the amylase to break down all of the starch. To do this, use a dropping pipette to take a fresh sample from the boiling tube every thirty seconds and put a drop into a well. When the iodine solution remains browny-orange, starch is no longer present.

7. Repeat the whole experiment with buffer solutions of different pH values to see how pH affects the time taken for the starch to be broken down.

8. Remember to control any variables each time (e.g. concentration and volume of amylase solution) to make it a fair test.

Tip: Don't forget to do a risk assessment before you do this experiment. You should always take basic safety precautions like wearing goggles and a lab coat.

Tip: Instead of using the Bunsen burner, tripod and gauze, you could set an electric water bath to 35 °C and place the boiling tube in that. See page 291 for more on water baths.

Tip: Remember to repeat the experiment at least three times at each pH and work out the mean time taken for the starch to break down.

Tip: See page 119 for more on testing for starch using iodine.

Tip: You could use a pH meter to accurately measure the pH of your solutions.

amylase, starch and buffer solution

mixture sampled every 30 seconds

dropping pipette

drop of iodine solution

spotting tile

Figure 1: *Apparatus for investigating the breakdown of starch.*

Calculating the rate of a reaction

It's often useful to calculate the rate of reaction after an experiment. Rate is a measure of how much something changes over time.

For the experiment on the previous page, you can calculate the rate of reaction using this formula:

$$\text{Rate} = \frac{1000}{\text{time}}$$

The units are s^{-1} since rate is given per unit of time.

Example

At pH 6, the time taken for amylase to break down all of the starch in a solution was 90 seconds. So the rate of the reaction = 1000 ÷ 90 = **11 s^{-1}**

If an experiment measures how much something changes over time, you calculate the rate of reaction by dividing the amount that it has changed by the time taken.

Example

The enzyme catalase catalyses the breakdown of hydrogen peroxide into water and oxygen. During an investigation into the activity of catalase, 24 cm^3 of oxygen was released in 50 seconds (s). Calculate the rate of the reaction. Write your answer in cm^3/s.

Amount of product formed = change = 24 cm^3

Rate of reaction = change ÷ time
= 24 cm^3 ÷ 50 s
= **0.48 cm^3/s**

Tip: Look back at page 88 for how to work out the rate of transpiration. Also look at page 154 for how to work out the rate of photosynthesis.

Practice Question — Application

Q1 A group of students were investigating the effect of pH on the rate of starch breakdown by the enzyme amylase. They mixed the enzyme and starch in a boiling tube, then every 10 seconds added a drop of the mixture to a well on a spotting tile containing iodine solution. They timed how long it took for all of the starch to be broken down.

a) Explain how the pH level of the enzyme and starch mixture could be controlled.

b) Explain how the students would know when all of the starch had been broken down.

c) It took 120 seconds for all of the starch to be broken down. Calculate the rate of the reaction. Give your answer in s^{-1}.

- Know that digestive
  enzymes break down
  big food molecules to
  smaller, soluble food
  molecules, which are
  able to be absorbed
  into the bloodstream.

- Know that the
  products of digestion
  are used to make new
  carbohydrates, lipids
  and proteins, and that
  some of the glucose
  produced is used for
  respiration.

- Know that
  carbohydrases convert
  carbohydrates to
  simple sugars.

- Know amylase (which
  breaks down starch) is
  a carbohydrase.

- Know that proteases
  convert proteins into
  amino acids.

- Know that lipases
  convert lipids into
  glycerol and fatty
  acids.

- Be able to understand
  word equations for
  digestion reactions.

- Know where in the
  digestive system
  amylase, proteases
  and lipases are made
  and where they act.

- Know that bile is an
  alkaline substance
  made by the liver
  and stored in the gall
  bladder.

- Know that bile
  neutralises the
  stomach acid and
  emulsifies fats into
  smaller droplets with
  increased surface area
  to speed up the action
  of lipase.

Specification Reference
4.2.2.1

3. Enzymes and Digestion

Digestion involves loads of reactions where large food molecules are broken down into smaller ones. Lots of enzymes are needed to catalyse all these reactions, so the body creates the ideal conditions for these enzymes to work in.

The digestive system

As you know from page 67, the digestive system is the organ system that breaks down food, so that nutrients can be absorbed into the body from the gut. (There's a reminder of what it looks like in Figure 1.)

Food is broken down in two ways:

- By mechanical digestion — this includes our teeth grinding down food and our stomach churning up food.

- By chemical digestion — where enzymes help to break down food.

You need to know all about how enzymes work in digestion.

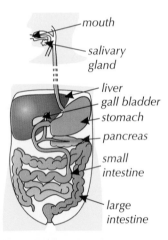

mouth
salivary gland
liver
gall bladder
stomach
pancreas
small intestine
large intestine

Figure 1: *The digestive system.*

Digestive enzymes

The enzymes involved in digestion work outside body cells. They're produced by specialised cells in glands and in the gut lining, and then released into the gut to mix with food molecules, such as carbohydrates, proteins and lipids (fats or oils).

Starch, proteins and lipids are big molecules. They're too big to pass through the walls of the digestive system, so digestive enzymes break these big molecules down into smaller ones like sugars (e.g. glucose and maltose), amino acids, glycerol and fatty acids. These smaller, soluble molecules can pass easily through the walls of the digestive system, allowing them to be absorbed into the bloodstream. The body makes good use of the products of digestion. They can be used to make new carbohydrates, proteins and lipids. Some of the glucose (a sugar) that's made is used in respiration (see p. 159).

Different digestive enzymes help to break down different types of food.

Carbohydrases

Carbohydrases convert carbohydrates into simple sugars. Amylase is an example of a carbohydrase. It breaks down starch — see Figure 2.

starch

AMYLASE ENZYME

maltose (and other sugars, e.g. dextrins)

Figure 2: *Diagram to show the breakdown of starch by amylase.*

Amylase is made in the salivary glands, the pancreas and the small intestine. It works in the mouth and the small intestine.

Tip: Most absorption of food molecules happens in the small intestine.

Proteases

Protease enzymes are digestive enzymes that catalyse the conversion of proteins into amino acids — see Figure 3.

proteins

PROTEASE ENZYMES

amino acids

Figure 3: *Diagram to show the breakdown of proteins by proteases.*

Proteases are made in the stomach, the pancreas and the small intestine. They work in the stomach and the small intestine.

Lipases

Lipase enzymes are digestive enzymes that catalyse the conversion of lipids into glycerol and fatty acids — see Figure 4.

Tip: Protease enzymes break down proteins. Lipase enzymes break down lipids.

lipid

LIPASE ENZYMES

glycerol & fatty acids

Figure 4: *Diagram to show the breakdown of lipids by lipases.*

Lipases are made in the pancreas and the small intestine. They work in the small intestine.

Enzymes in the digestive system

The table in Figure 5 summarises all the information you need to know about the digestive enzymes for your exam. Use Figure 5 to make sure you know exactly where each enzyme is made and where it works.

Enzyme(s) →	Amylase	Proteases	Lipases
Help(s) to break down...	Starch	Proteins	Lipids
...into...	Sugars	Amino acids	Glycerol and fatty acids
Made in the...	Salivary glands, pancreas and small intestine	Stomach, pancreas and small intestine	Pancreas and small intestine
Work(s) in the...	Mouth and small intestine	Stomach and small intestine	Small intestine

Figure 5: *Table summarising the key facts about amylase, proteases and lipases.*

Bile

Bile is produced in the liver. It's stored in the gall bladder before it's released into the small intestine (see Figure 6).

The hydrochloric acid in the stomach makes the pH too acidic for enzymes in the small intestine to work properly. Bile is alkaline — it neutralises the acid and makes conditions alkaline. The enzymes in the small intestine work best in these alkaline conditions.

Bile also emulsifies fats. In other words it breaks the fat into tiny droplets (see Figure 7). This gives a much bigger surface area of fat for the enzyme lipase to work on — which makes its digestion faster.

large fat droplet   tiny fat droplets

Figure 7: *Diagram to show the emulsification of fat by bile.*

liver

gall bladder

small intestine

Figure 6: *Bile is produced in the liver, stored in the gall bladder and released into the small intestine.*

Practice Questions — Fact Recall

Q1 True or false? Digestive enzymes build small molecules up into larger molecules.

Q2 Name the digestive enzyme produced in the salivary glands.

Q3 Where are protease enzymes involved in digestion produced?

Q4 Name the type of enzyme that catalyses the breakdown of lipids.

Q5 Describe how bile produces ideal conditions for enzymes in the small intestine to work in.

Q1　Here is a labelled diagram of the digestive system.

Complete this table using the appropriate letters from the diagram.
(If there's more than one answer to the question, make sure you write
down all the answers in the table.)

	Amylase	Proteases	Lipases	Bile
Made where?				
Work(s) where?				

- Know how to carry out qualitative tests to detect the presence of sugars (Benedict's test), starch (iodine test), proteins (biuret test) and lipids (Sudan III test) in foods (Required Practical 3).

Specification Reference 4.2.2.1

Tip: Make sure you're aware of the risks of the Benedict's test before you start. Wear eye protection and be very careful around the hot water in the water bath.

Figure 2: *A negative (left) and a positive (right) Benedict's test.*

Tip: A positive result is one where the test has identified the presence of what's being tested for (in this case a reducing sugar). A negative result is one where the test has not identified the presence of what's being tested for.

4. Food Tests

Your digestive system breaks down all sorts of substances from food, e.g. carbohydrates, proteins and lipids (see pages 114-116). You need to know how to test foods for the presence of sugars, starch, proteins and lipids.

Preparing a food sample

For each of the tests on the next few pages, you need to prepare a food sample. Luckily, you can prepare your sample for each test in the same way. The only thing that needs to change is the type of food you're using. Here's how a food sample can be prepared:

1. Get a piece of your food and break it up using a pestle and mortar.

2. Transfer the ground up food to a beaker and add some distilled water.

3. Give the mixture a good stir with a glass rod to dissolve some of the food.

4. Filter the solution using a funnel lined with filter paper. This will get rid of all the solid bits of food.

Testing for sugars

Sugars are found in all sorts of foods such as biscuits, cereal and bread. There are two types of sugars — non-reducing and reducing. You can test for reducing sugars in foods using the Benedict's test. Here's what you'd do:

1. Prepare a food sample using the method described above and transfer 5 cm³ to a test tube.

2. Prepare a water bath so that it's set to 75 °C.

3. Add some Benedict's solution to the test tube (about 10 drops) using a pipette.

4. Place the test tube in the water bath using a test tube holder and leave it in there for 5 minutes. Make sure the tube is pointing away from you.

5. During this time, if the food sample contains a reducing sugar, the solution in the test tube will change from the normal blue colour to green, yellow or brick-red (see Figure 1) — it all depends on how much sugar is in the food.

Figure 1: *Steps involved in the Benedict's test.*

Testing for starch

REQUIRED PRACTICAL **3**

You can check food samples for the presence of starch using the iodine test. Foods like pasta, rice and potatoes contain a lot of starch. Here's how to do the test:

1. Make a food sample using the method on the previous page and transfer 5 cm³ of your sample to a test tube.

2. Then add a few drops of iodine solution and gently shake the tube to mix the contents. If the sample contains starch, the colour of the solution will change from browny-orange to black or blue-black (see Figure 4).

> **Tip:** Make sure you assess and address the risks of the iodine starch test before you start. Wear eye protection, as iodine is an irritant to the eyes.

iodine

food sample

colour remains browny-orange if starch isn't present

colour changes to blue-black if starch is present

Figure 3: *The iodine test for starch.*

Figure 4: *A dark blue-black colour indicates the presence of starch in an iodine test.*

Testing for proteins

REQUIRED PRACTICAL **3**

You can use the biuret test to see if a type of food contains protein. Meat and cheese are protein rich and good foods to use in this test. Here's how it's done:

1. Use the method on the previous page to prepare a sample of your food and transfer 2 cm³ of your sample to a test tube.

2. Add 2 cm³ of biuret solution to the sample and mix the contents of the tube by gently shaking it.

3. If the food sample contains protein, the solution will change from blue to pink or purple. If no protein is present, the solution will stay blue (see Figure 6).

> **Tip:** Make sure you carry out a risk assessment before you perform the biuret test. The chemicals in the biuret solution are dangerous, so you'll need to wear safety goggles and make sure that you wash it off straight away if you get any on your skin.

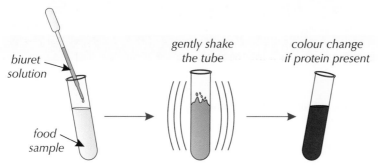

biuret solution

food sample

gently shake the tube

colour change if protein present

Figure 5: *Steps involved in the biuret test.*

Figure 6: *Diagram showing a negative (left) and positive (right) result for the biuret test for the presence of proteins.*

Testing for lipids

REQUIRED PRACTICAL **3**

Lipids are found in foods such as butter, chocolate and cheese. You can test for the presence of lipids in a food using the Sudan III test.

> **Tip:** Make sure you do a risk assessment before you start the test for lipids. Make sure you wear safety goggles. Also, Sudan III stain solution is flammable, so make sure you keep it away from any lit Bunsen burners.

1. Prepare a sample of the food you're testing using the method on page 118 and transfer about 5 cm^3 into a test tube.

2. Use a pipette to add 3 drops of Sudan III stain solution to the test tube and gently shake the tube.

3. Sudan III stain solution stains lipids. If the food sample contains lipids, the mixture will separate out into two layers. The top layer will be bright red (see Figure 7). If no lipids are present, no separate red layer will form at the top of the liquid.

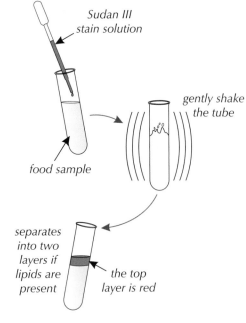

Sudan III stain solution

gently shake the tube

food sample

separates into two layers if lipids are present

the top layer is red

***Figure 7:** Steps involved in the Sudan III test.*

Practice Questions — Fact Recall

Q1 Name the reagent used to test for the presence of reducing sugars.

Q2 Describe the colour change that would occur in the iodine test if starch was present in the food sample.

Q3 What colour would biuret solution be if it was added to a food sample that didn't contain protein?

Practice Question — Application

Q1 A student has a piece of food and wants to know if it contains lipids. Outline a test he could carry out to find out.

Topic 2c Checklist — Make sure you know...

Enzymes

☐ That enzymes are large proteins that act as biological catalysts, speeding up the rate of chemical reactions involved in metabolism.

☐ That every enzyme has its own unique active site, and it's the shape of this active site that allows the enzyme to bind to its substrate.

cont...

☐ That enzymes will only bind to one specific substrate, so if the substrate doesn't fit the active site, the reaction won't be catalysed. This is the 'lock and key' model of enzyme action.

☐ That increasing the temperature increases the rate of an enzyme-controlled reaction until it gets so hot that some of the bonds holding the enzyme together break and the enzyme becomes denatured, so the active site no longer fits the substrate.

☐ That enzymes all have an optimum temperature at which they work best, and this is different for different enzymes.

☐ That extreme pH levels can denature enzymes.

☐ That enzymes all have an optimum pH level that they work best at, and this optimum level varies between different enzymes.

Investigating Enzymatic Reactions

☐ How to investigate the effects of pH on the rate of the breakdown of starch by the enzyme amylase (Required Practical 4).

☐ How to calculate the rate of a chemical reaction such as an enzyme controlled reaction.

Enzymes and Digestion

☐ That digestive enzymes break down large food molecules (which can't be absorbed into the bloodstream) into smaller, soluble food molecules that can be absorbed into the bloodstream.

☐ That the body makes new carbohydrates, proteins and lipids from the products of digestion and also uses some of the glucose produced in the process of respiration.

☐ That carbohydrases convert carbohydrates into simple sugars.

☐ That amylase is a carbohydrase, produced in the salivary glands, pancreas and small intestine, and that it works in the mouth and small intestine to break down starch.

☐ That protease enzymes catalyse the conversion of proteins into amino acids.

☐ That proteases are made in the stomach, pancreas and small intestine, and act in the stomach and small intestine.

☐ That lipases catalyse the conversion of lipids (fats and oils) into glycerol and fatty acids.

☐ That lipases are made in the pancreas and small intestine, and act in the small intestine.

☐ That bile is produced by the liver and stored in the gall bladder.

☐ That bile helps to speed up the action of lipases by neutralising the hydrochloric acid from the stomach (providing more suitable pH conditions for the lipases to work in) and emulsifying fats (breaking fats down into smaller droplets with increased surface area for the lipases to work on).

Food Tests

☐ How to test for the presence of sugars, starch, proteins and lipids in different foods using the Benedict's test, iodine test, biuret test and Sudan III test (Required Practical 3).

Exam-style Questions

1   Enzymes are needed for many processes in the body.

    1.1   What type of biological molecule is an enzyme?

        A   a lipid   **B**   a hormone   **C**   a protein   **D**   an amino acid

(1 mark)

    1.2   What is the function of an enzyme?

(1 mark)

    1.3*   One of the processes in the body that requires enzymes is digestion.
Describe the action, production and release of different types of enzymes in digestion.

(6 marks)

2   A student was measuring the rate that carbon dioxide (CO_2) was produced in a
reaction controlled by enzyme X. He performed the experiment at three different
temperatures — 10 °C, 25 °C and 50 °C. The experiment at 50 °C produced no
carbon dioxide at all.

His results are shown in **Figure 1**.

Figure 1

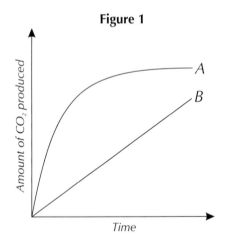

    2.1   Enzyme X is only able to catalyse this reaction.
Explain why most enzymes can only catalyse a single reaction.

(2 marks)

    2.2   Suggest which line on **Figure 1** represents the experiment carried out at 25 °C.
Explain your answer.

(1 mark)

    2.3   Suggest why the experiment at 50 °C failed to produce any CO_2.

(3 marks)

3 Scientists can use a range of simple tests to detect the presence of certain substances in different types of food. A scientist was testing a food sample for the presence of glucose, a reducing sugar.

3.1 Which of the following reagents should she use?

    A   Benedict's solution

    B   Biuret solution

    C   Iodine solution

    D   Sudan III stain solution

(1 mark)

3.2 The result of the test was no colour change.
What does this suggest about the presence of glucose in the sample?

(1 mark)

3.3 Describe how the scientist should have prepared the food sample before the reagent was added.

(4 marks)

3.4 Following the test for reducing sugars, she decided to test a fresh sample of the food for starch. Name the reagent that she would have used and describe what she would have seen if the result was positive.

(3 marks)

4 The conditions inside the stomach are acidic due to the presence of hydrochloric acid. An experiment was done to show how digestion in the stomach works. The enzyme pepsin is a protease found in the stomach. In the experiment, three equally sized pieces of meat were added to each of three test tubes. Then the test tubes were filled with equal volumes of the following substances:

Test tube 1 — hydrochloric acid (HCl acid)
Test tube 2 — pepsin
Test tube 3 — pepsin and hydrochloric acid (HCl acid)

The results are shown in **Figure 2**.

Figure 2

Describe the results and explain what they suggest about pepsin.

(3 marks)

Learning Objectives:
- Know that pathogens are microorganisms that cause infectious disease in plants and animals.
- Know that a pathogen can be a bacterium, virus, protist or fungus.
- Know that bacteria and viruses can reproduce quickly.
- Understand that bacteria can make people feel ill by producing poisons that damage body tissues.
- Know that viruses make people feel ill by causing cell damage when they reproduce.
- Know how pathogens can be spread (water, air and direct contact).

Specification Reference
4.3.1.1

1. Communicable Disease

Disease isn't a particularly pleasant thing, but you've still got to learn about it. First up in the section is meeting the microorganisms that cause disease.

Pathogens

Pathogens are microorganisms that enter the body and cause disease. They cause **communicable (infectious) diseases** — diseases that can spread (see p. 95). Both plants and animals can be infected by pathogens. There are several types of pathogen.

Bacteria

Bacteria are very small cells (about 1/100th the size of your body cells), which can reproduce rapidly inside your body. They can make you feel ill by producing **toxins** (poisons) that damage your cells and tissues.

> **Example**
>
> *Salmonella* bacteria — these bacteria cause food poisoning (see page 128).

Viruses

Viruses are not cells. They're tiny, about 1/100th the size of a bacterium. Like bacteria, they can reproduce rapidly inside your body. They live inside your cells and replicate themselves using the cells' machinery to produce many copies of themselves. The cell will usually then burst, releasing all the new viruses. This cell damage is what makes you feel ill.

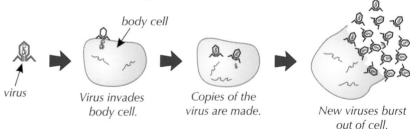

body cell

virus | Virus invades body cell. | Copies of the virus are made. | New viruses burst out of cell.

Figure 1: *A virus replicating in a human cell.*

> **Example**
>
> HIV (see page 126) — this virus infects and destroys cells that normally help to defend the body against disease (like white blood cells, see page 81). This makes HIV sufferers more likely to get ill from infection by other pathogens.

Protists

There are lots of different types of protists. But they're all eukaryotes (see page 23) and most of them are single-celled. Some protists are parasites. Parasites live on or inside other organisms and can cause them damage. They are often transferred to the organism by a **vector**, which doesn't get the disease itself — e.g. an insect that carries the protist.

Figure 2: *A Salmonella typhimurium bacterium (top). HIV particles (blue) infecting a white blood cell (bottom).*

Example

> **Example**
>
> Malaria is caused by a protist that lives inside a mosquito (see page 127).

Fungi

Some fungi are single-celled. Others have a body which is made up of hyphae (thread-like structures). These hyphae can grow and penetrate human skin and the surface of plants, causing diseases. The hyphae can produce spores, which can be spread to other plants and animals.

> **Example**
>
> The black spot fungus infects rose plants — see page 127 for more.

Figure 3: Black spot fungus spores.

The spread of pathogens

Pathogens can be spread in many ways. Here are a few that you need to know about.

Water

Some pathogens can be picked up by drinking or bathing in dirty water.

> **Example**
>
> Cholera is a bacterial infection that's spread by drinking water contaminated with the diarrhoea of other sufferers.

Air

Pathogens can be carried in the air and can then be breathed in.

> **Example**
>
> The influenza virus that causes flu is spread in the air in droplets produced when you cough or sneeze.

Direct contact

Some pathogens can be picked up by touching contaminated surfaces, including the skin.

> **Example**
>
> Athlete's foot is a fungus which makes skin itch and flake off. It's most commonly spread by touching the same things as an infected person, e.g. shower floors and towels.

Exam Tip
If you're asked in the exam to suggest how someone may have been infected with a disease, just use the information you've been given to work out whether it was likely to be via water, air or by direct contact.

Figure 4: Athlete's foot fungus on human skin (top). Toes infected with athlete's foot (bottom).

Practice Questions — Application

Q1 *Clostridium tetani* is the bacterium that causes tetanus.
It usually enters the body through deep cuts.
Suggest how *Clostridium tetani* bacteria may make you feel ill.

Q2 The chickenpox virus can be carried in droplets in the air.
Suggest how an infected student could infect someone else who is sitting in another part of the same classroom.

Learning Objectives:

- Know how the measles virus is spread.

- Know the symptoms of the measles virus and understand that it can lead to complications and even death in some circumstances.

- Know the symptoms of HIV and that they can be controlled with antiretroviral drugs.

- Understand how the virus attacks the body and how the disease progresses to late stage HIV infection, or AIDS.

- Know how HIV is spread.

- Know that the tobacco mosaic virus affects some plants.

- Know the symptoms of tobacco mosaic virus, and how the growth of the plant is affected.

Specification Reference 4.3.1.2

2. Viral Diseases

So, you know that diseases can be caused by viruses, fungi, protists and bacteria. It's time to look at some in a bit more detail. First up, viral diseases...

Examples of viral diseases

You need to know about these three viral diseases.

Measles

Measles is a viral disease. It is spread by through droplets from an infected person's sneeze or cough. People with measles develop a red skin rash, and they'll show signs of a fever (a high temperature).

Measles can be very serious or even fatal if there are complications. For example, measles can sometimes lead to pneumonia (a lung infection) or a brain infection called encephalitis. Most people are vaccinated against measles when they're young.

HIV

HIV is a virus spread by sexual contact, or by exchanging bodily fluids such as blood. This can happen when people share needles when taking drugs.

HIV initially causes flu-like symptoms for a few weeks. Usually, the person doesn't then experience any symptoms for several years. During this time, HIV can be controlled with antiretroviral drugs. These stop the virus replicating in the body. The virus attacks the immune cells (cells of the immune system — see page 130). If the body's immune system is badly damaged, it can't cope with other infections or cancers. At this stage, the virus is known as late stage HIV infection, or AIDS.

Tobacco mosaic virus

Tobacco mosaic virus (TMV) is a virus that affects many species of plants, e.g. tomatoes. It causes a mosaic pattern on the leaves of the plants — parts of the leaves become discoloured (see Figure 1). The discolouration means the plant can't carry out photosynthesis as well, so the virus affects growth.

Figure 1: A plant infected with tobacco mosaic virus.

Practice Questions — Fact Recall

Q1 How is the measles virus spread?

Q2 Give two symptoms of measles.

Q3 Outline how the HIV virus can be spread.

Q4 What type of drugs are used in the early stages of HIV?

Q5 Name one type of plant that can be infected by the tobacco mosaic virus.

Q6 Explain why growth is affected in a plant infected with the tobacco mosaic virus.

3. Fungal and Protist Diseases

Two types of pathogen to contend with on this page — fungi and protists.

Fungal diseases

Rose black spot

Rose black spot is a fungus that causes purple or black spots to develop on the leaves of rose plants (see Figure 1). The leaves can then turn yellow and drop off. This means that less photosynthesis can happen, so the plant doesn't grow very well. It spreads through the environment in water or by the wind.

Gardeners can treat the disease using fungicides and by stripping the plant of its affected leaves. These leaves then need to be destroyed so that the fungus can't spread to other rose plants.

Protist diseases

Malaria

Malaria is caused by a protist (see page 124). Part of the malarial protist's life cycle takes place inside the mosquito. The mosquitoes are vectors — they pick up the malarial protist when they feed on an infected animal. Every time the mosquito feeds on another animal, it infects it by inserting the protist into the animal's blood vessels.

Malaria causes repeating episodes of fever. It can be fatal. The spread of malaria can be reduced by stopping the mosquitoes from breeding.

> **Example**
>
> Mosquitoes can breed in standing water, so mosquitoes can be prevented from breeding by removing these water sources. For example, people who live in areas with a risk of malaria should make sure that they empty or get rid of any containers on their land that fill with rainwater.

People can also be protected from mosquito bites to stop the spread of the disease.

> **Examples**
>
> - Spraying any exposed skin with an insect repellant can prevent people from being bitten by mosquitoes.
> - Sleeping under a mosquito net can prevent people from being bitten when they're asleep.

Learning Objectives:

- Know that rose black spot is an example of a fungal disease in plants.
- Know the symptoms of rose black spot.
- Understand why being infected with rose black spot affects the growth of a plant.
- Know how rose black spot is spread, and how it can be treated.
- Know that malaria is caused by a protist.
- Know that part of the life cycle of the malarial protist takes place inside a mosquito.
- Be able to give the symptoms of malaria.
- Know how the spread of malaria can be controlled.

Specification References
4.3.1.4, 4.3.1.5

Figure 1: *A rose plant infected with rose black spot fungus.*

Practice Questions — Fact Recall

Q1 Describe the signs that suggest that a plant has been infected with black spot fungus.

Q2 Why are mosquito nets used in areas with a high risk of malaria?

Learning Objectives:
- Know that *Salmonella* is a type of bacteria that causes food poisoning.
- Know the symptoms of *Salmonella* food poisoning.
- Know how *Salmonella* food poisoning is spread and controlled.
- Know that gonorrhoea is a sexually transmitted disease caused by bacteria.
- Know how gonorrhoea is spread.
- Know the symptoms of gonorrhoea.
- Understand why gonorrhoea is not easily treated with penicillin anymore.
- Know how the spread of gonorrhoea is controlled.
- Understand ways that the spread of disease can be reduced or prevented.

Specification References
4.3.1.1, 4.3.1.3

4. Bacterial Diseases and Preventing Disease

Last but not least, you need to know about bacterial diseases. Then it's on to how we can reduce (or even prevent) the spread of diseases.

Bacterial diseases

Salmonella food poisoning

Salmonella is a type of bacteria that causes food poisoning. Infected people can suffer from fever, stomach cramps, vomiting and diarrhoea. These symptoms are caused by the toxins that the bacteria produce (see page 124).

You can get *Salmonella* food poisoning by eating food that's been contaminated with *Salmonella* bacteria.

> **Examples**
>
> - Eating chicken that caught the disease whilst it was alive.
> - Eating food that has been contaminated by being prepared in unhygienic conditions.

In the UK, most poultry (e.g. chickens and turkeys) is given a vaccination against *Salmonella*. This is to control the spread of the disease. The vaccination prevents the poultry from catching the disease, which stops it from being passed on to humans.

Gonorrhoea

Gonorrhoea is a sexually transmitted disease (STD). STDs are passed on by sexual contact, e.g. having unprotected sex. Gonorrhoea is caused by bacteria. A person with gonorrhoea will get pain when they urinate. Another symptom is a thick yellow or green discharge from the vagina or the penis.

Gonorrhoea was originally treated with an antibiotic called penicillin, but this has become trickier now because strains of the bacteria have become resistant to it (see page 134). To prevent the spread of gonorrhoea, people can be treated with other antibiotics and should use barrier methods of contraception (see page 194), such as condoms.

Reducing and preventing the spread of disease

There are things that we can do to reduce, and even prevent, the spread of disease. For example:

Being hygienic

Using simple hygiene measures can prevent the spread of disease.

> **Example**
>
> Doing things like washing your hands thoroughly before preparing food or after you've sneezed can stop you infecting another person.

Destroying vectors

Some protist diseases are carried by vectors (see page 124). These spread the disease to humans. By getting rid of these organisms that spread disease, you can prevent the disease from being passed on.

> **Example**
>
> Vectors that are insects can be killed using insecticides or by destroying their habitat so that they can no longer breed.

Isolating infected individuals

If you isolate someone who has a communicable disease, it prevents them from passing it on to anyone else.

> **Example**
>
> Ebola is a virus spread by direct contact with the bodily fluids of a person with the disease. In an Ebola outbreak, patients with the disease are isolated to prevent the spread of the disease, and medical staff wear protective clothing (see Figure 1).

Vaccination

Vaccinating people and animals against communicable diseases means that they can't develop the infection and then pass it on to someone else. There's more about how vaccination works on page 132.

> **Example**
>
> Children often get vaccinated against common diseases — for example, they are often given the meningitis C vaccine at around 3 months of age. The meningitis B vaccine is usually given at 2 months, 4 months, and 12 months of age.

Exam Tip
How to prevent the spread of a disease is linked to how it spreads. For example, if a disease is spread by direct contact, the way to prevent it will be to prevent infected people coming into contact with people who aren't infected.

Figure 1: *Medical staff dressed in protective clothing whilst treating Ebola patients.*

Tip: Remember, only communicable diseases can be spread from person-to-person — non-communicable diseases can't.

Practice Questions — Fact Recall

Q1 List three symptoms of *Salmonella* food poisoning.

Q2 Suggest one way that *Salmonella* food poisoning is spread.

Q3 How is gonorrhoea treated?

Q4 How does destroying vectors prevent the spread of disease?

Practice Questions — Application

Q1 A patient in a hospital has a communicable disease where they need to be put into isolation. Suggest why they have been put into isolation.

Q2 A nurse working in a GP surgery washes his hands carefully after seeing patients. Suggest how this will prevent the spread of disease.

- Be able to explain the ways that the body defends itself against the entry of pathogens using non-specific defence systems.

- Understand the role of the immune system and how the white blood cells help to defend the body against pathogens and destroy them.

Specification Reference 4.3.1.6

Figure 1: Bacteria (yellow) sticking to mucus (blue) on microscopic hairs in the nose.

Figure 2: A white blood cell (blue/pink) engulfing a pathogen (yellow/green). Seen under a microscope.

Exam Tip
Don't be tempted to write 'white blood cells engulf disease' in the exam — white blood cells engulf pathogens (which cause disease).

5. Fighting Disease

Part of being healthy means being free from disease. But that's easier said than done...

The body's defences

In order to cause disease, pathogens first need to enter the body. The human body has got features that stop a lot of nasties getting inside in the first place. These are the body's non-specific defence systems.

> **Examples**
>
> - The skin acts as a barrier to pathogens. It also secretes antimicrobial substances which kill pathogens.
>
> - Hairs and mucus in your nose trap particles that could contain pathogens.
>
> - The trachea and bronchi (breathing pipework — see page 70) secrete mucus to trap pathogens.
>
> - The trachea and bronchi are lined with cilia. These are hair-like structures, which waft the mucus up to the back of the throat where it can be swallowed.
>
> - The stomach produces hydrochloric acid. This kills pathogens that make it that far from the mouth.

The immune system

If pathogens do make it into your body, your immune system kicks in to destroy them. The most important part of your immune system is the **white blood cells**. They travel around in your blood and crawl into every part of you, constantly patrolling for microbes. When they come across an invading microbe they have three lines of attack.

1. Consuming them

White blood cells can engulf foreign cells and digest them. This is called phagocytosis.

Figure 3: A white blood cell engulfing a pathogen.

2. Producing antitoxins

These counteract toxins produced by the invading bacteria.

3. Producing antibodies

Every invading pathogen has unique molecules (called **antigens**) on its surface. When your white blood cells come across a foreign antigen (i.e. one they don't recognise), they will start to produce proteins called **antibodies** to lock onto the invading cells so that they can be found and destroyed by other white blood cells.

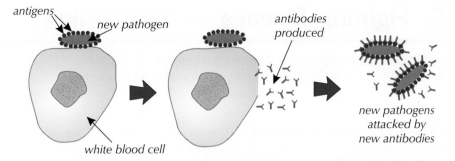

antigens

new pathogen

antibodies produced

white blood cell

new pathogens attacked by new antibodies

Figure 4: *Diagram showing the production of antibodies.*

Exam Tip
Don't get antigens and antibodies mixed up in the exam. Remember, the <u>body</u> makes anti<u>bodies</u> against the antigens on pathogens.

The antibodies produced are specific to that type of antigen — they won't lock on to any others. Antibodies are then produced rapidly and carried around the body to find all similar bacteria or viruses.

If the person is infected with the same pathogen again the white blood cells will rapidly produce the antibodies to kill it — the person is naturally immune to that pathogen and won't get ill.

Tip: The white blood cells that produce antibodies are also known as B-lymphocytes.

Practice Questions — Fact Recall

Q1 Give two ways in which the skin helps to defend the body against disease.

Q2 Give three ways in which white blood cells help to defend the body against disease.

Practice Questions — Application

Q1 The SARS coronavirus (SARS-CoV) causes SARS, a respiratory disease. It can enter the body by being inhaled in droplets. Describe one feature of the body that helps to prevent SARS-CoV from entering the body.

Q2 As a child, John suffered from measles. Measles are caused by a virus.

a) Explain why John is unlikely to get ill with measles again.

b) German measles are caused by a different virus, which John has never had before. Explain why John could still become ill from German measles.

Exam Tip
In the exam, you might get asked questions about pathogens or diseases you've never heard of before. Don't let that put you off though — you should be able to work out the answers by applying what you already know.

Learning Objectives:
- Understand how vaccinations work.
- Understand that if enough people are immune to a particular pathogen, the spread of the pathogen is reduced.

Specification Reference
4.3.1.7

6. Fighting Disease — Vaccination

Vaccinations have changed the way we fight disease.
We don't always have to deal with the problem once it's happened —
we can prevent it happening in the first place.

What are vaccinations?

When you're infected with a new pathogen, it takes your white blood cells a few days to learn how to deal with it. But by that time, you can be pretty ill. Vaccinations can stop you feeling ill in the first place.

Vaccinations involve injecting small amounts of dead or inactive pathogens. These carry antigens, which cause your white blood cells to produce antibodies to attack them — even though the pathogen is harmless (since it's dead or inactive).

> **Example**
>
> The MMR vaccine is given to children. It contains weakened versions of the viruses that cause measles, mumps and rubella (German measles) all in one vaccine.

Tip: The 'weakened' viruses in the MMR vaccine are still alive, but aren't able to cause disease.

If live pathogens of the same type then appear at a later date, the white blood cells can rapidly mass-produce antibodies to kill off the pathogen. The vaccinated person is now immune to that pathogen and won't get ill (see Figure 1).

Tip: Remember, antibodies are specific to a particular type of pathogen (see p. 131). So a vaccination against the typhoid virus will only protect you against typhoid — it won't make you immune to anything else.

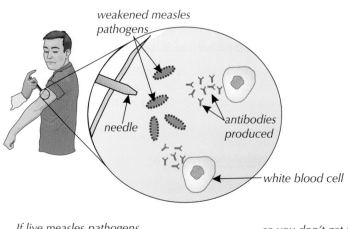

weakened measles pathogens

needle

antibodies produced

white blood cell

Tip: Some vaccinations "wear off" over time. So booster injections may need to be given to increase levels of antibodies again.

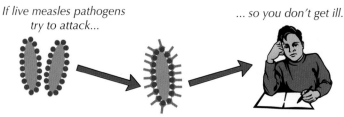

If live measles pathogens try to attack...

... so you don't get ill.

... they are quickly recognised and attacked by antibodies...

Figure 1: *A diagram to show how vaccination works.*

Vaccinations — pros and cons

There are both pros and cons of vaccinations.

Pros

- Vaccines have helped control lots of infectious diseases that were once common in the UK (e.g. polio, measles, whooping cough, rubella, mumps, tetanus...). Smallpox no longer occurs at all, and polio infections have fallen by 99%.

- Big outbreaks of disease — called **epidemics** — can be prevented if a large percentage of the population is vaccinated. That way, even the people who aren't vaccinated are unlikely to catch the disease because there are fewer people able to pass it on. But if a significant number of people aren't vaccinated, the disease can spread quickly through them and lots of people will be ill at the same time.

Cons

- Vaccines don't always work — sometimes they don't give you immunity.

- You can sometimes have a bad reaction to a vaccine (e.g. swelling, or maybe something more serious like a fever or seizures). But bad reactions are very rare.

Exam Tip
In the exam, you might get asked to 'evaluate' the pros and cons of vaccinations. This means giving a balanced account of both the advantages and the disadvantages, before trying to come up with an overall judgement.

Balancing the risks

Deciding whether to have a vaccination means balancing risks — the risk of catching the disease if you don't have a vaccine, against the risk of having a bad reaction if you do. As always, you need to look at the evidence.

> **Example**
>
> If you get measles (the disease), there's about a 1 in 15 chance that you'll get complications (e.g. pneumonia) — and about 1 in 500 people who get measles actually die. However, the number of people who have a problem with the vaccine is more like 1 in 1 000 000.

Figure 2: *A baby being given the MMR vaccine.*

Practice Question — Application

Q1 Whooping cough is a severe cough that can cause serious breathing difficulties in young babies.

In 2012, the US state of Washington declared a whooping cough epidemic. The Department of Health encouraged all adults to get booster vaccinations against the disease, to help protect babies who were too young to receive the vaccination.

a) Suggest how a whooping cough vaccination might work.

b) Explain how a large-scale vaccination of adults could help to protect babies who haven't been vaccinated.

- Know that painkillers and some other drugs can relieve the symptoms of a disease, but don't kill the pathogens.
- Understand how antibiotics can be used to treat disease.
- Understand that antibiotics (e.g. penicillin) are drugs used to kill bacteria.
- Understand that different antibiotics kill different bacteria and that antibiotics have no effect on viruses.
- Understand why it's hard to produce drugs to kill viruses.
- Know that the use of antibiotics has greatly reduced deaths from communicable diseases.
- Understand that antibiotic-resistant strains of bacteria can develop, and that this is a problem.
- Know that drugs were once extracted from plants and from microorganisms, including digitalis, aspirin and penicillin.
- Know that many new drugs are now synthesised by chemists working in pharmaceutical companies, but they may still begin with a plant chemical.

Specification References
4.3.1.8, 4.3.1.9

7. Fighting Disease — Drugs

There aren't vaccinations against every pathogen (not just yet, anyway) so you're still going to get ill sometimes. And that's when drugs come in...

Different types of drugs

Painkillers (e.g. aspirin) are drugs that relieve pain. However, they don't actually tackle the cause of the disease, they just help to reduce the symptoms. Other drugs do a similar kind of thing — reduce the symptoms without tackling the underlying cause. For example, lots of "cold remedies" don't actually cure colds — they have no effect on the cold virus itself.

Antibiotics (e.g. **penicillin**) work differently — they actually kill (or prevent the growth of) the bacteria causing the problem without killing your own body cells. Different antibiotics kill different types of bacteria, so it's important to be treated with the right one.

But antibiotics don't destroy viruses (e.g. flu or cold viruses). Viruses reproduce using your own body cells, which makes it very difficult to develop drugs that destroy just the virus without killing the body's cells.

The use of antibiotics has greatly reduced the number of deaths from communicable diseases caused by bacteria.

Example

During the First World War, nearly 20% of US soldiers who caught pneumonia (a bacterial infection) died as a result. During World War II, this figure dropped to less than 1% thanks to treatment with penicillin.

Antibiotic resistance

Bacteria can **mutate** — sometimes the mutations cause them to be resistant to (not killed by) an antibiotic.

Examples

- **MRSA** (methicillin-resistant *Staphylococcus aureus*) causes serious wound infections and is resistant to the powerful antibiotic, methicillin.

- Some strains of the bacteria that cause TB (a lung disease) are now resistant to several of the antibiotics that would normally be used to fight them.

If you have an infection, some of the bacteria might be resistant to antibiotics. This means that when you treat the infection, only the non-resistant strains of bacteria will be killed. The individual resistant bacteria will survive and reproduce, and the population of the resistant strain will increase. This is an example of **natural selection** (see page 235). This resistant strain could cause a serious infection that can't be treated by antibiotics.

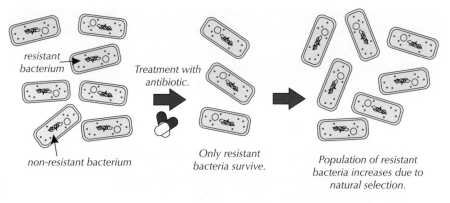

Figure 1: How antibiotic resistance develops.

Figure 2: A wound infected with MRSA.

Slowing down the development of antibiotic resistance

To slow down the rate of development of resistant strains, it's important for doctors to avoid over-prescribing antibiotics. So you won't get them for a sore throat, only for something more serious. It's also important that you finish the whole course of antibiotics and don't just stop once you feel better.

The origins of drugs

Plants produce a variety of chemicals to defend themselves against pests and pathogens. Some of these chemicals can be used as drugs to treat human diseases or relieve symptoms. A lot of our current medicines were discovered by studying plants used in traditional cures.

> **Examples**
>
> - Aspirin is used as a painkiller and to lower fever.
>   It was developed from a chemical found in willow.
>
> - Digitalis is used to treat heart conditions.
>   It was developed from a chemical found in foxgloves.

Some drugs were extracted from microorganisms.

> **Example**
>
> Alexander Fleming was clearing out some Petri dishes containing bacteria. He noticed that one of the dishes of bacteria also had mould on it and the area around the mould was free of the bacteria. He found that the mould (called *Penicillium notatum*) on the Petri dish was producing a substance that killed the bacteria — this substance was penicillin.

Tip: A Petri dish is a circular dish with a lid. Samples of bacteria can be grown in them on a layer of agar jelly.

These days, drugs are made on a large scale in the pharmaceutical industry — they're synthesised by chemists in labs. However, the process still might start with a chemical extracted from a plant.

> **Example**
>
> The World Health Organisation has a list of drugs that it considers to be essential for a basic health care system. In 2000, 11% of the 252 drugs were plant-based.

Tip: There's more about how drugs are developed on pages 137-138.

Practice Questions — Fact Recall

Q1 True or false?
Painkillers can be used to tackle the cause of an infection.

Q2 What are antibiotics? Give one example.

Q3 Why is it important to be treated with the right antibiotic for a particular infection?

Q4 Explain why it can be difficult to develop drugs that kill viruses.

Q5 Why is it important not to over-use antibiotics?

Q6 Which drug originates from willow?

Q7 Who discovered penicillin, and how was it discovered?

Practice Question — Application

Q1 Chloe is suffering from the flu, which is caused by a virus.

a) Explain why Chloe's doctor will not prescribe her antibiotics.

b) Chloe's flu is causing a headache. Chloe's doctor recommends taking a painkiller. Suggest why the painkiller will not help to clear Chloe's infection any quicker.

Tip: To answer part b), think about what the flu remedy will and won't do.

8. Developing Drugs

Before drugs make it onto the pharmacy shelves, they have to be tested...

Drug testing

New drugs are constantly being developed. But before they can be given to the general public, they have to go through a thorough testing procedure to make sure they are safe and effective. There are three main stages in drug testing — preclinical testing on human cells and tissues, preclinical testing on live animals, and clinical testing on human volunteers.

Preclinical trials

Cells and tissues

In preclinical testing, drugs are tested on human cells and tissues in the lab. However, you can't use human cells and tissues to test drugs that affect whole or multiple body systems, e.g. testing a drug for blood pressure must be done on a whole animal because it has an intact circulatory system.

Live animals

The next step in preclinical testing is to test the drug on live animals. This is to test **efficacy** (whether the drug works and produces the effect you're looking for), to find out about its **toxicity** (how harmful it is) and to find the best dosage (the concentration that should be given, and how often it should be given).

The law in Britain states that any new drug must be tested on two different live mammals. Some people think it's cruel to test on animals, but others believe this is the safest way to make sure a drug isn't dangerous before it's given to humans. Other people think that animals are so different from humans that testing on animals is pointless.

Clinical trials

If the drug passes the tests on animals then it's tested on human volunteers in a clinical trial.

First, the drug is tested on healthy volunteers. This is to make sure that it doesn't have any harmful side effects when the body is working normally. At the start of the trial, a very low dose of the drug is given and this is gradually increased.

If the results of the tests on healthy volunteers are good, the drugs can be tested on people suffering from the illness. The **optimum dose** is found — this is the dose of drug that is the most effective and has few side effects.

Placebos

To test how well the drug works, patients are randomly put into two groups. One is given the new drug, the other is given a **placebo** (a substance that's like the drug being tested but doesn't do anything). This is so the doctor can see the actual difference the drug makes — it allows for the placebo effect (when the patient expects the treatment to work and so feels better, even though the treatment isn't doing anything).

Learning Objectives:

- Understand why new medicinal drugs have to be tested before becoming available to the public (to check safety and effectiveness).
- Know that during drug trials, new drugs are tested for efficacy and toxicity, and to find the optimum dose.
- Be able to describe the process of preclinical testing of new drugs.
- Be able to describe what happens when drugs are tested in clinical trials.
- Know what the terms 'optimum dose', 'placebo' and 'double-blind trials' mean.

Specification Reference 4.3.1.9

Figure 1: *A piece of tissue from a human intestine being used in drug testing.*

Tip: A placebo is usually a tablet or an injection with no drug added.

Tip: People in the control group of a clinical trial should be similar to people in the treatment group, e.g. of a similar age, gender, etc. This helps to make sure the study is a fair test — see page 10 for more on making a study a fair test.

Tip: Peer review is when other scientists check that the work is valid and has been carried out rigorously — see page 2.

Example

A pharmaceutical company has developed a drug, Drug X, to help people with high blood cholesterol to lower their cholesterol level. The drug was tested on 1500 patients with high cholesterol. The patients were divided into two groups and over six months each patient had one tablet per day. One group had a tablet containing Drug X and the other group had a tablet without Drug X — the placebo.

Blind and double-blind trials

Clinical trials are **blind** — the patient in the study doesn't know whether they're getting the drug or the placebo. In fact, they're often **double-blind** — neither the patient nor the doctor knows until all the results have been gathered (see Figure 2). This is so the doctors monitoring the patients and analysing the results aren't subconsciously influenced by their knowledge.

	Blind trial	**Double-blind trial**
Does the **patient** know whether they're getting the drug or the placebo?	no	no
Does the **doctor** know whether the patient is getting the drug or the placebo?	yes	no

Figure 2: Table summarising blind and double-blind trials.

The results of drug testing and drug trials aren't published until they've been through peer review. This helps to prevent false claims.

The importance of drug testing

It's really important that drugs are tested thoroughly before being used to make sure they're safe. An example of what can happen when drugs are not thoroughly tested is the case of thalidomide...

Example

Thalidomide is a drug that was developed in the 1950s. It was intended as a sleeping pill, and was tested for that use. But later it was also found to be effective in relieving morning sickness in pregnant women.

Unfortunately, thalidomide hadn't been tested as a drug for morning sickness, and so it wasn't known that it could pass through the placenta and affect the fetus, causing abnormal limb development. In some cases, babies were born with no arms or legs at all. About 10 000 babies were affected by thalidomide, and only about half of them survived.

The drug was banned, and more rigorous testing procedures were introduced. More recently thalidomide has been used in the treatment of leprosy and other diseases, e.g. some cancers.

Figure 3: This baby was born with a deformed hand due to thalidomide.

Practice Questions — Fact Recall

Q1 What are drugs tested on in preclinical testing?

Q2 Give two things that drug testing aims to find out.

Q3 a) In a clinical trial, what type of volunteer is the drug tested on first
— healthy volunteers or people suffering from the illness?

b) Describe the dosage of drug that is first used in a clinical trial.

Q4 What is a placebo?

Q5 Briefly explain what is involved in a double-blind trial.

Exam Tip
If you're asked what a placebo is in the exam, remember that it's <u>not</u> a drug — this is because it doesn't actually do anything.

Practice Questions — Application

Q1 For each of the drugs below, suggest what would have been given as a placebo when that drug went through clinical trials.

a) a paracetamol capsule   b) a steroid inhaler

c) a cortisone injection

Q2 A new weight-loss pill has been developed called Drug X. The pill was tested in a double-blind clinical trial. It involved three groups of obese volunteers (50 per group), all of whom wanted to lose weight.
Each group member took a pill three times a day for a year, alongside diet and exercise. The first group took Drug X, the second group took a similar weight-loss pill already available (Drug Y) and the third group took a placebo. The average weight loss per person after one year is shown on the graph.

a) i) Would the doctors involved in this trial have known which patients were being given the placebo? Explain your answer.

ii) Suggest what could have been used as a placebo in this trial.

b) Why do you think Group 2 was included in the trial?

c) From these results, what can you conclude about Drug X? Use data from the graph to support your answer.

Exam Tip
When answering a question about a clinical trial in the exam, make sure you read all the information you're given. Here you need to have spotted that it's a double-blind trial — this will help you answer Q2 a) i).

Topic 3 Checklist — Make sure you know...

Communicable Disease

☐ That pathogens are microorganisms that cause communicable disease in plants or animals, and include bacteria, viruses, protists and fungi.

☐ That bacteria and viruses reproduce rapidly — bacteria can make you feel ill by producing toxins that damage cells, and viruses make you feel ill by reproducing inside cells and damaging them.

☐ That pathogens can be spread between people by water, air or by direct contact.

Viral Diseases

☐ That measles is caused by a virus, and that the symptoms are fever and a red skin rash — it is spread in droplets when people with the virus sneeze or cough.

☐ That if complications occur, measles can be fatal, and so most children have the measles vaccine.

☐ That HIV is spread by sexual contact or exchange of bodily fluids, and the first symptoms are flu-like.

☐ That at the early stage, HIV can be controlled with antiretroviral drugs.

☐ That HIV attacks the cells of the immune system — when the immune system is so damaged that it can no longer fight off other infections or cancers, HIV is called late stage HIV infection, or AIDS.

☐ That tobacco mosaic virus (TMV) affects many types of plants, including tomatoes, and causes leaves to become discoloured — this affects growth by preventing photosynthesis.

Fungal and Protist Diseases

☐ That rose black spot is a fungal plant disease that causes purple or black spots to develop on the leaves — the leaves sometimes then turn yellow and fall off.

☐ That changes to the leaves in rose black spot mean that photosynthesis is reduced, affecting growth.

☐ That rose black spot is spread in water or by the wind, and that it can be treated using fungicides and by removing and destroying the affected leaves.

☐ That malaria is caused by a protist that spends part of its life cycle in the mosquito host.

☐ That malaria causes recurring fever and can be fatal, but that its spread can be reduced by preventing the mosquitoes from breeding and by taking precautions to avoid being bitten (e.g. mosquito nets).

Bacteria Diseases and Preventing Disease

☐ That *Salmonella* bacteria cause food poisoning — fever, abdominal cramps, vomiting and diarrhoea.

☐ That *Salmonella* can be spread by eating contaminated food, and know how it can be controlled.

☐ That gonorrhoea is a bacterial sexually transmitted disease that causes pain when urinating and a yellow or green discharge from the genitals.

☐ That gonorrhoea can often no longer be treated with penicillin because of antibiotic resistance — it is now treated with other antibiotics and can be prevented by using condoms.

☐ That the spread of diseases can be reduced or prevented by being hygienic, destroying vectors, isolating infectious people, and by using vaccinations.

cont...

Fighting Disease

☐ That the skin, nose, trachea and bronchi, and the stomach have features to stop pathogens entering the body.

☐ That if pathogens do manage to enter the body, the immune system can attack them — white blood cells produce antibodies and antitoxins, and engulf pathogens by phagocytosis.

Fighting Disease — Vaccination

☐ How vaccinations work — dead or inactive pathogens are used to trigger the production of antibodies by white blood cells. If the same, live pathogen then enters the body, the white blood cells will rapidly mass-produce the right antibodies to kill it, so that the person doesn't get ill.

☐ That if enough people are immune to a certain pathogen, it can reduce the spread of the pathogen.

Fighting Disease — Drugs

☐ That many drugs (such as painkillers) reduce the symptoms of a disease but don't kill pathogens.

☐ That antibiotics (such as penicillin) are drugs that kill bacteria but don't destroy viruses.

☐ That antibiotics kill specific bacteria, so it's important to be treated with the right one.

☐ That viruses reproduce inside body cells, making it difficult to develop drugs against them.

☐ That the use of antibiotics has greatly reduced the number of deaths from communicable diseases caused by bacteria.

☐ That bacteria can mutate, leading to the development of antibiotic-resistant strains.

☐ That originally, drugs were extracted from plants and microorganisms (e.g. aspirin from willow, digitalis from foxgloves, and penicillin from mould).

☐ That drugs are now synthesised in labs, but that the process may still involve a plant chemical.

Developing Drugs

☐ That drugs have to be tested to make sure they are safe and effective.

☐ That during drug trials, new drugs are tested for efficacy and toxicity, and also to find the best dose.

☐ That new drugs are first tested in preclinical trials on human cells and tissues as well as on animals.

☐ That after preclinical testing, drugs are tested in clinical trials on healthy volunteers at low doses. They're then tested on ill volunteers to find the optimum dose of a drug (the dose the drug works best at).

☐ What a placebo is (a substance that's similar to the drug being tested but that doesn't do anything) and why they are used in clinical trials (to make sure the drug works).

☐ That in a double-blind trial, neither the doctors nor the volunteers know which volunteers have been given the drug and who has been given the placebo.

Exam-style Questions

1   A patient in a hospital has been diagnosed with malaria after returning from Kenya.

   1.1   Give **one** symptom of malaria.

(1 mark)

   1.2   Name the type of pathogen that causes malaria.

(1 mark)

   1.3   Another disease that can be caught in Kenya is typhoid.
           The patient was vaccinated against typhoid before his trip to Kenya.
           Outline how the typhoid vaccine can prevent someone from developing the disease.

(4 marks)

2   A garden centre has to keep their plants healthy and free from disease.
      The staff discover that a rose plant has been infected with rose black spot.

   2.1   What type of pathogen causes rose black spot?

(1 mark)

   2.2   Suggest how the disease may have been spread to the plant.

(2 marks)

   2.3   Suggest how the garden centre should treat the disease.

(3 marks)

3   Pathogens can enter the body in several ways.

   3.1   Outline how the stomach helps to defend the body against the entry of pathogens.

(1 mark)

   3.2   The human airways include the trachea and bronchi.
           Outline how the trachea and bronchi help to defend the body against pathogens.

(3 marks)

           Sometimes pathogens get past the body's defences.

   3.3   How can bacteria make people feel ill?

(1 mark)

   3.4   Name **one** disease in humans caused by bacteria.

(1 mark)

   3.5   The immune system responds to pathogens getting inside the body.
           Outline the immune system's response to bacteria inside the body.

(4 marks)

4   Measles is caused by a pathogen.

4.1   What is a pathogen?

(1 mark)

4.2   Name the type of pathogen that causes measles.

(1 mark)

The graph below shows the number of measles cases reported each year worldwide, along with the estimated vaccine coverage, from 1980 to 2014.

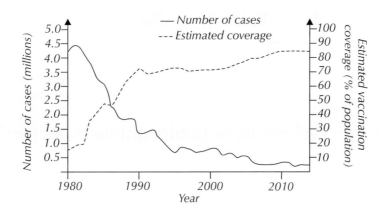

4.3   From the graph, estimate how many cases of measles there were in 1990.

(1 mark)

4.4   Describe the trends shown in the graph.
Use data from the graph to support your answer.

(4 marks)

4.5   Evaluate how far this data supports the case for vaccinating people against measles.

(3 marks)

5   A new drug is being developed.

5.1   Describe the difference between how drugs were made traditionally and how drugs are made these days.

(2 marks)

5.2   The new drug enters preclinical testing. Preclinical testing happens on cells and tissues, and it is sometimes done using live animals too.
Suggest why a drug designed to affect the absorption of nutrients from the small intestine into the bloodstream might be tested on live animals rather than just on cells and tissues.

(2 marks)

The drug then enters clinical trials.

5.3* Describe what happens at this stage.
Refer to placebos and double-blind testing in your answer.

(6 marks)

Learning Objectives:

- Know that energy is transferred to the chloroplasts of plants when they absorb light.
- Know that photosynthesis is endothermic.
- Be able to write the word equation for photosynthesis.
- Know the chemical symbols for carbon dioxide, water, oxygen and glucose.

Specification Reference 4.4.1.1

Tip: Exothermic reactions transfer energy to the surroundings and endothermic reactions transfer energy from the surroundings.

Figure 2: Microscope image of a plant cell. The green structures are chloroplasts.

Tip: Xylem is the tissue that transports water around a plant (see page 85).

Exam Tip
You should learn this photosynthesis equation — it could get you easy marks in the exam.

1. The Basics of Photosynthesis

Plants make their own food using energy from the Sun, a substance called chlorophyll, carbon dioxide from the air and water from the soil.

What is photosynthesis?

Photosynthesis is the process that produces 'food' in plants. The 'food' it produces is **glucose** (a sugar). Photosynthesis uses energy to change carbon dioxide and water into glucose and oxygen. Plants use this glucose for a number of things, such as making cell walls and proteins (see pages 146-147).

Where does photosynthesis happen?

Photosynthesis takes place in **chloroplasts** in green plant cells — they contain pigments like **chlorophyll** that absorb light. Energy is transferred to the chloroplasts from the environment by light. Photosynthesis is **endothermic** — this means energy is transferred from the environment in the process.

Photosynthesis happens in the leaves of all green plants — this is largely what the leaves are for. Figure 1 shows a cross-section of a leaf showing the four raw materials (carbon dioxide, water, light and chlorophyll) needed for photosynthesis.

Figure 1: Diagram of a cross-section through a leaf, showing the four raw materials required for photosynthesis.

Word equation

The word equation for photosynthesis is:

$$\text{carbon dioxide} + \text{water} \xrightarrow{\text{light}} \text{glucose} + \text{oxygen}$$

Symbol equation

There's a symbol equation for photosynthesis too:

$$6CO_2 + 6H_2O \xrightarrow{\text{light}} C_6H_{12}O_6 + 6O_2$$

Exam Tip
You don't need to know this equation for the exam, but you do need to know the individual symbols for carbon dioxide (CO_2), water (H_2O), glucose ($C_6H_{12}O_6$) and oxygen (O_2).

Practice Questions — Fact Recall

Q1 Which product produced by photosynthesis is 'food' for the plant?

Q2 Which gas is used in photosynthesis?

Q3 Which gas is produced by photosynthesis?

Q4 a) Name the parts of a plant cell that contain chlorophyll.

   b) What role does chlorophyll play in photosynthesis?

Q5 Write out the word equation for photosynthesis.

Q6 Name the chemical substance with the symbol $C_6H_{12}O_6$.

Practice Questions — Application

Q1 Three identical plants were grown for a week. They were treated in exactly the same way, except they each received different amounts of sunlight per day, as shown in this table:

Plant	Hours of sunlight received per day
A	3
B	7
C	10

The plants didn't have any source of light other than sunlight.

Which plant do you think will have produced the most glucose after one week? Explain your answer.

Q2 A scientist studied three different types of plant cell (taken from the same plant) under a microscope. She recorded the average number of chloroplasts she found in each type of cell, as shown in this table:

Type of plant cell	Average number of chloroplasts
1	20
2	0
3	51

Tip: Think about what the job of the chloroplasts is.

Suggest which type of plant cell (1-3) is likely to have the highest rate of photosynthesis. Explain your answer.

Learning Objectives:
- Know the ways that plants use the glucose produced during photosynthesis.
- Know that plants need nitrate ions from the soil, as well as glucose, to make proteins.

Specification Reference 4.4.1.3

2. How Plants Use Glucose

As you know, plants photosynthesise to make 'food' in the form of glucose. They make use of this glucose in a number of ways...

What is glucose used for?

During photosynthesis, plants convert carbon dioxide and water into glucose (see page 144). They use the glucose they produce for the following things:

1. Respiration

Plants use some of the glucose they make for respiration. Respiration is a process which occurs in all living organisms — it's where energy is released from the breakdown of glucose (see page 159).
Plants use this energy to convert the rest of the glucose into various other useful substances, which they can use to build new cells and grow. To produce some of these substances plants also need to gather a few minerals from the soil (e.g. nitrates — see below).

2. Making cellulose

Glucose is converted into **cellulose** for making strong cell walls (see page 24), especially in a rapidly growing plant. These cell walls support and strengthen the cells.

Figure 1: Microscope image of a plant cell wall made up of strands of cellulose.

3. Making amino acids

In plant cells, glucose is combined with **nitrate ions** (which are absorbed from the soil) to make **amino acids**. Amino acids are the building blocks which make up proteins. When amino acids are joined together in a particular sequence they make up a particular protein.

Tip: Plants use proteins for growth. If a plant has a nitrate ion deficiency it can't make as much protein, and so it will have stunted growth.

Storage of glucose

Glucose can be converted into other substances for storage:

Lipids

Plants can convert some of the glucose they produce into **lipids** (fats and oils). Plants store lipids in seeds.

Example

Sunflower seeds contain a lot of oil — we get cooking oil and margarine from them.

Starch

Plants can convert glucose into starch. Glucose is stored as starch so it's ready for use when photosynthesis isn't happening as much, like in the winter. In plants, starch is stored in roots, stems, seeds and leaves.

Example

Potato and parsnip plants store a lot of starch underground over the winter so a new plant can grow from it the following spring. We eat the swollen storage organs (see Figure 2).

Figure 2: *Potato plants that have just been dug up — the potatoes that we eat are starch stores for the plant.*

Starch is **insoluble** which makes it much better for storing than glucose — a cell with lots of glucose in would draw in loads of water and swell up.

> **Tip:** Water moves from regions of higher concentration of water to regions of lower concentration — this is known as osmosis (see page 48). A cell with lots of glucose would have a lower concentration of water than its surroundings, and so water would move in from outside by osmosis.

Practice Questions — Fact Recall

Q1 By what process do plants break down glucose in order to transfer energy to their cells?

Q2 What do plants use cellulose for?

Q3 What do plants absorb from the soil to make proteins with?

Q4 Glucose can be stored as starch in plants. How else is glucose stored?

Q5 Why is starch better for storage than glucose?

- Be able to explain how the rate of photosynthesis can be affected by temperature, the level of carbon dioxide, the light intensity, and also by the amount of chlorophyll in the plant.
- Be able to draw, read from and interpret graphs showing the effect of one limiting factor on the rate of photosynthesis.
- **H** Know that the factors that affect the rate of photosynthesis can interact.
- **H** Be able to interpret rate graphs that show two or three factors to identify which is the limiting factor.

Specification Reference 4.4.1.2

3. The Rate of Photosynthesis

Photosynthesis doesn't always happen at the same rate — factors such as light intensity, carbon dioxide level and temperature can all affect the rate.

Limiting factors in photosynthesis

The rate of photosynthesis is affected by the intensity of light, the volume of carbon dioxide (CO_2), and the temperature. All three of these things need to be at the right level to allow a plant to photosynthesise as quickly as possible. If any one of these factors is too high or too low, it will become the **limiting factor**. This just means it's the factor which is stopping photosynthesis from happening any faster.

Which factor is limiting at a particular time depends on the environmental conditions:

> **Examples**
>
> - At night there's much less light than there is during the day, so light intensity is usually the limiting factor at night.
>
> - In winter it's usually cold, so a low temperature is often the limiting factor.
>
> - If it's warm enough and bright enough, the amount of CO_2 is usually limiting.

The amount of chlorophyll can also be a limiting factor of photosynthesis.

> **Example**
>
> The amount of chlorophyll in a plant can be affected by disease (e.g. infection with the tobacco mosaic virus) or environmental stress, such as a lack of nutrients. These factors can cause chloroplasts to become damaged or to not make enough chlorophyll. This means the rate of photosynthesis is reduced because they can't absorb as much light.

Tip: Plants also need water for photosynthesis, but when a plant is so short of water that it becomes the limiting factor in photosynthesis, it's already in such trouble that this is the least of its worries.

Tip: There's more about tobacco mosaic virus on page 126.

Interpreting data on the rate of photosynthesis

You need to be able to interpret data showing how different factors affect the rate of photosynthesis.

1. Effect of light intensity

Light provides the energy needed for photosynthesis. As you can see from Figure 1, as the light level is raised, the rate of photosynthesis increases steadily — but only up to a certain point. Beyond that, it won't make any difference — as light intensity increases, the rate will no longer increase. This is because it'll be either the temperature or the carbon dioxide level which is now the limiting factor, not light.

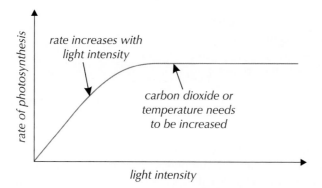

Figure 1: Graph showing how light intensity affects the rate of photosynthesis.

Exam Tip
You need to know how to plot a graph like this when given appropriate data — see p.18 if you need some tips. You also need to be able to read off values from graphs like this and explain what the data is showing, so make sure you really understand what these pages are talking about.

Remember, photosynthesis hasn't stopped when the graph levels off — it's just not increasing anymore.

In the lab you can change the light intensity by moving a lamp closer to or further away from your plant (see page 153 for this experiment). But if you just plot the rate of photosynthesis against "distance of lamp from the plant", you get a weird-shaped graph. To get a graph like the one above you either need to measure the light intensity at the plant using a light meter or do a bit of nifty maths with your results.

Figure 2: The number of bubbles produced in a set time can be counted to estimate the rate of photosynthesis, but a more accurate set-up can be seen on page 153.

2. Effect of carbon dioxide level

CO_2 is one of the raw materials needed for photosynthesis.
As with light intensity, the amount of CO_2 will only increase the rate of photosynthesis up to a point. After this the graph flattens out — as the amount of CO_2 increases, the rate no longer increases. This shows that CO_2 is no longer the limiting factor.

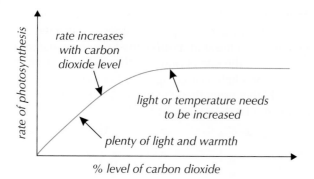

Figure 3: Graph showing how carbon dioxide level affects the rate of photosynthesis.

As long as light and CO_2 are in plentiful supply then the factor limiting photosynthesis must be temperature.

Tip: If you're investigating the rate of photosynthesis using a plant in water, you can increase the CO_2 level by dissolving sodium hydrogencarbonate in the water. This gives off carbon dioxide.

3. Effect of temperature

Enzymes are proteins which increase the speed of chemical reactions in living things — so enzymes increase the rate of photosynthesis in plant cells. The speed at which enzymes work is affected by temperature.

Tip: You can read more about enzymes on pages 109-111.

Usually, if the temperature is the limiting factor in photosynthesis it's because it's too low — the enzymes needed for photosynthesis work more slowly at low temperatures. But if the plant gets too hot, the enzymes it needs for photosynthesis and its other reactions will be damaged. This happens at about 45 °C (which is pretty hot for outdoors, although greenhouses can get that hot if you're not careful). Figure 4 shows the effect of temperature on the rate of photosynthesis.

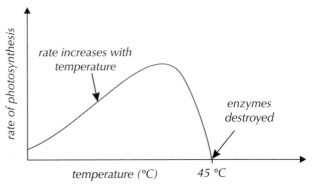

Figure 4: *Graph showing how temperature affects the rate of photosynthesis.*

4. Graphs with more than one limiting factor   Higher

You could get a graph that shows more than one limiting factor on the rate of photosynthesis.

Exam Tip H
Make sure you get to grips with interpreting graphs like this — they could come up in the exam. Just look at what factors the graph shows, and look at how they're affecting the line that shows the rate of photosynthesis. There's a question on page 152 to practise with.

Example 1 — **Higher**

Figure 5 shows how the rate of photosynthesis is affected by light intensity and temperature. At the start, both of the lines show that as the light intensity increases, the rate of photosynthesis increases steadily. But the lines level off when light is no longer the limiting factor. The line at 25 °C levels off at a higher point than the one at 15 °C, showing that temperature must have been a limiting factor at 15 °C.

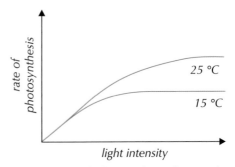

Figure 5: *Graph showing how photosynthesis is affected by light intensity and temperature.*

Example 2 — Higher

Figure 6 shows how the rate of photosynthesis is affected by light intensity and CO_2 concentration. Again, both the lines level off when light is no longer the limiting factor. The line at the higher CO_2 concentration of 0.4% levels off at a higher point than the one at 0.04%. This means CO_2 concentration must have been a limiting factor at 0.04% CO_2. The limiting factor here isn't temperature because it's the same for both lines (25 °C).

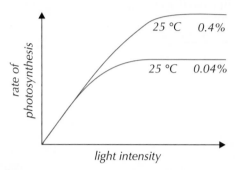

Figure 6: *Graph showing how photosynthesis is affected by light intensity and CO_2 concentration.*

Practice Questions — Fact Recall

Q1 The rate of photosynthesis is affected by limiting factors.

   a) What is meant by a 'limiting factor' of photosynthesis?

   b) Give three environmental conditions that can affect the rate of photosynthesis.

Q2 True or false? The rate of photosynthesis can be affected by the amount of chlorophyll in the leaves.

Practice Questions — Application

Q1 Complete the table to show what is most likely to be the limiting factor of photosynthesis in the environmental conditions listed.

Environmental conditions	Most likely limiting factor
Outside on a cold winter's day.	
In an unlit garden at 1:30 am, in the UK, in summer.	
On a windowsill on a warm, bright day.	

Q2 Peter was investigating the rate of photosynthesis in pondweed. He put equally sized samples of pondweed from the same plant in two separate flasks containing different solutions. The solution in flask A had a lower carbon dioxide concentration than the solution in flask B. Peter put the flasks an equal distance away from a light source and gradually increased the intensity of the light throughout the experiment. He kept both flasks at a constant temperature of 25 °C. During the experiment Peter measured the amount of gas produced in each flask using a gas syringe. His results are shown on the graph:

Exam Tip H
μmoles/m²/s is a unit used to measure light intensity. Don't panic if you see unfamiliar units in the exam — just focus on what the axis is showing you, e.g. here it's light intensity.

a) Peter thinks that the limiting factor before point X in his experiment is light. Why does he think this?

b) Both graphs level off. Suggest why Flask A levels off at a lower point than Flask B. Explain your answer.

4. Investigating Photosynthesis Rate

So you've seen a graph showing how light intensity affects the rate of photosynthesis back on page 149, but you also need to know how you'd actually get the data for that graph.

Investigating the rate of photosynthesis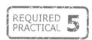

To investigate the effect of different light intensities on the rate of photosynthesis, you need to be able to measure the rate. One way to do this involves an aquatic plant, such as Canadian pondweed. The rate at which the pondweed produces oxygen corresponds to the rate at which it's photosynthesising — the faster the rate of oxygen production, the faster the rate of photosynthesis.

Here's how the experiment works:

A source of white light is placed at a specific distance from the pondweed. You should then leave the pondweed for a couple of minutes to adjust to the new light intensity before starting the experiment. When you're ready to start, the pondweed is left to photosynthesise for a set amount of time. As it photosynthesises, the oxygen released will collect in the capillary tube.

At the end of the experiment, the syringe is used to draw the gas bubble in the tube up alongside a ruler and the length of the gas bubble is measured. This is proportional to the volume of O_2 produced.

Learning Objectives:
- Be able to investigate how light intensity affects the rate of photosynthesis, using an aquatic plant (Required Practical 5).
- Be able to calculate the rate of photosynthesis.

Specification Reference 4.4.1.2

Tip: Make sure you do a risk assessment before you start this investigation, so that you carry it out safely. E.g. there's a slight risk of infection from the pond water, so make sure you wash your hands after handling the pondweed and cover up any cuts.

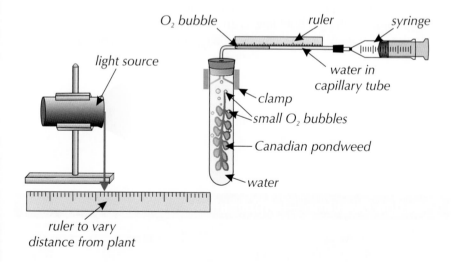

Figure 1: *Diagram showing the experimental set up used to measure the rate of photosynthesis in water plants.*

Figure 2: *Pondweed giving off oxygen bubbles as a by-product of photosynthesis.*

The experiment is repeated twice with the light source at the same distance and the mean volume of O_2 produced is calculated. Then the whole experiment is repeated with the light source at different distances from the pondweed.

Tip: Taking repeat readings and calculating a mean reduces the effect of random errors, and will make your results more precise — see page 13.

WORKING SCIENTIFICALLY

Controlling variables

In this experiment, you're investigating the effect of different light intensities on the rate of photosynthesis — the light intensity is the **independent variable**. The **dependent variable** (the variable you're measuring) is the amount of oxygen produced, which is represented by the length of the bubble.
You have to try to keep all the other variables constant, so that it's a fair test.

Tip: The independent variable is the variable that you change in an experiment — see p. 10.

WORKING SCIENTIFICALLY

Examples

- If your plant's in a flask, keep the flask in a water bath to help keep the temperature constant.

- There's not much you can do to keep the carbon dioxide level constant — you may just have to use a large container for your plant, and do the experiments as quickly as you can, so that the plant doesn't use up too much of the carbon dioxide in the container.

Tip: The variables in this experiment include all of the limiting factors of photosynthesis.

Calculating the rate of photosynthesis

You can compare the results at different light intensities by giving the rate of photosynthesis as the length of the bubble per unit time, e.g. cm/min.

To calculate the rate, just divide the total length of the bubble by the time taken to produce it.

Tip: For more on designing investigations and controlling variables see pages 9-11.

Example

MATHS SKILLS

A student measured the amount of gas produced by a piece of pondweed by collecting it in a capillary tube. After 5 minutes, the gas bubble was 25 mm long. Calculate the rate of photosynthesis. Give your answer in cm/min.

- First, convert 25 mm into cm:
$$25 \div 10 = 2.5 \text{ cm}$$

- Then divide the length by the time taken:
$$\text{Rate} = 2.5 \text{ cm} \div 5 \text{ min} = \textbf{0.5 cm/min}$$

Tip: Alternatively, you could work out the rate as the volume of oxygen per unit time (e.g. cm^3/min), but this requires a bit more maths to find the volume of the bubble first.

Tip: When you're working out a rate, you should always be dividing by time.

Practice Question — Application

Q1 A student set up an experiment to investigate the rate of photosynthesis using a piece of Canadian pondweed.

She placed the pondweed in a test tube of water, and measured the bubble of oxygen that formed in a capillary tube, as shown in the diagram.

In 3 minutes, the pondweed produced a bubble of oxygen in the capillary tube that was 25 mm long. Calculate the rate of photosynthesis for the pondweed. Give your answer in cm/min, to 1 significant figure.

5. The Inverse Square Law   Higher

This can be a bit tricky to get your head around, but stick with it...

What is the inverse square law?

In the experiment on page 153, when the lamp is moved away from the pondweed, the amount of light that reaches the pondweed decreases. You can say that as the distance increases, the light intensity decreases. In other words, distance and light intensity are **inversely proportional** to each other.

However, it's not quite as simple as that. It turns out that light intensity decreases in proportion to the square of the distance. This is called the **inverse square law** and is written out like this:

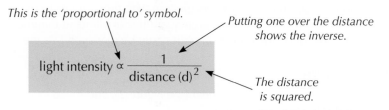

This is the 'proportional to' symbol.

Putting one over the distance shows the inverse.

$$\text{light intensity} \propto \frac{1}{\text{distance (d)}^2}$$

The distance is squared.

The inverse square law means that if you halve the distance, the light intensity will be four times greater and if you third the distance, the light intensity will be nine times greater. Likewise, if you double the distance, the light intensity will be four times smaller and if you treble the distance, the light intensity will be nine times smaller.

You can use $1/d^2$ as a measure of light intensity.

Example — Higher

Use the inverse square law to calculate the light intensity when the lamp is 10 cm from the pondweed.

- Use the formula $\frac{1}{d^2}$:

  $$\text{light intensity} = \frac{1}{d^2}$$

- Fill in the values you know — you're given the distance, so put that in.

  $$\text{light intensity} = \frac{1}{10^2}$$

- Calculate the answer.

  $$\frac{1}{10^2} = 0.01 \text{ a.u.}$$

Practice Question — Application

Q1 A student is carrying out an experiment to study the effect of light intensity on the rate of photosynthesis. He positions a lamp at different distances from samples of pondweed.
Use the inverse square law to calculate the light intensity when the lamp is positioned:

  a) 15 cm from the pondweed,   b) 30 cm from the pondweed.

Learning Objectives:
- **H** Know what inverse proportion is.
- **H** Know that the inverse square law links light intensity and distance.
- **H** Understand how to use the inverse square law.

Specification Reference 4.4.1.2

Tip: H If two variables are proportional to each other, when one variable changes, the other will change at the same rate. Inverse proportion just means that as one variable increases, the other decreases at the same rate.

Tip: H a.u. stands for arbitrary units.

- H Understand that the temperature, light intensity and carbon dioxide concentration in a plant's environment can be managed artificially in order to increase the rate of photosynthesis and therefore increase the profit made from the plants.

Specification Reference
4.4.1.2

6. Artificially Controlling Plant Growth   Higher

As you've read on the last few pages, different factors affect the rate of photosynthesis. Farmers and other plant growers can use this knowledge to try to increase the rate of growth in their plants.

Greenhouses

If you know the ideal conditions for photosynthesis, then you can create an environment which maximises the rate of photosynthesis, which in turn maximises the rate of plant growth (plants use some of the glucose produced by photosynthesis for growth — see page 146). The most common way to artificially create the ideal environment for plants is to grow them in a greenhouse. Commercial growers (people who grow plants to make money, such as farmers) often grow large quantities of plants in commercial greenhouses. The following conditions can easily be managed in a greenhouse:

Figure 1: *Lettuces growing in a commercial greenhouse.*

1. Temperature

Greenhouses help to trap the Sun's heat (see Figure 2), and make sure that the temperature doesn't become limiting.

Figure 2: *Greenhouses trap the Sun's heat.*

Temperature can be controlled in other ways too:

> **Example** — **Higher**
> - In winter, a farmer might use a heater in their greenhouse to keep the temperature at the ideal level.
> - In summer, greenhouses could get too hot, so farmers might use shades and ventilation to cool things down.

2. Light

Light is always needed for photosynthesis, so farmers often supply artificial light after the Sun goes down to give their plants more quality photosynthesis time.

Figure 3: *Lamps in greenhouses supply light so plants can continue to photosynthesise at night.*

3. Carbon dioxide concentration

Farmers can also increase the level of carbon dioxide in the greenhouse. A fairly common way is to use a paraffin heater to heat the greenhouse. As the paraffin burns, it makes carbon dioxide as a by-product.

4. General health of plants

Keeping plants enclosed in a greenhouse also makes it easier to keep them free from pests and diseases. The farmer can add fertilisers to the soil as well, to provide all the minerals needed for healthy growth.

Greenhouse costs

Controlling the conditions in a greenhouse costs money — but if the farmer can keep the conditions just right for photosynthesis, the plants will grow much faster and a decent crop can be harvested much more often, which can then be sold.

It's important that a farmer supplies just the right amount of heat, light, etc. — enough to make the plants grow well, but not more than the plants need, as this would just be wasting money.

Interpreting data on artificial environments

In the exam you could be given some data about controlling photosynthesis in artificial environments (like greenhouses) and asked questions about it.

Example — **Higher**

A farmer normally grows his plants outside when the average air temperature is between 9 and 11 °C. The farmer wants to increase the growth rate of his plants, so he is considering getting a greenhouse. He finds some data on how temperature affects the rate of photosynthesis for the type of plants he grows. This is shown in the graph:

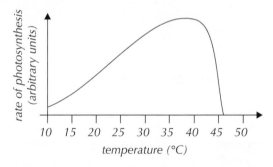

You could be asked to evaluate the benefits of growing plants in an artificial environment...
By looking at the graph you can see that the plants could photosynthesise faster if they were grown at temperatures higher than the average temperatures outside. If the farmer had a greenhouse he could control the temperature the plants were kept at, therefore increasing their rate of photosynthesis and growth. However, he would have to weigh up the cost of buying and running a greenhouse against this increased rate of growth.

You could be asked to make suggestions based on data from the graph...
For instance, you could be asked to suggest the best temperature for the farmer to keep his plants at and to explain why. Based on the graph, suggesting 37 °C would be a good idea, as this is the minimum temperature at which the rate of photosynthesis is highest. Keeping them at temperatures higher than this would just be a waste of money.

Exam Tip H
If you get a question like this in the exam, remember that the aim of commercial farming is to make money. Farmers try to create conditions to increase photosynthesis (and therefore growth) but at a minimum cost.

Practice Questions — Fact Recall

Q1 Explain why some farmers grow plants in an artificial environment.

Q2 Farmers can control the light and temperature in a greenhouse. Give one other condition they can control in a greenhouse.

Practice Question — Application

Tip: In the exam you might see experiments using rate of plant growth or increase in plant mass as an indirect way of measuring the rate of photosynthesis. This is because some of the glucose produced by photosynthesis is used for growth in plants (see page 146).

Q1 A farmer grew the same type of plant in two greenhouses, A and B. He used a paraffin heater in Greenhouse A and an electric heater in Greenhouse B. Electric heaters don't release any carbon dioxide, whereas carbon dioxide is released when paraffin is burnt.

For 8 weeks the farmer recorded the average height of the plants in each greenhouse. He also monitored the temperature in both greenhouses. Plants in both greenhouses were exposed to the same amount of light and given the same amount of water and nutrients. His results are shown below:

a) i) What was the average growth rate per week for the plants in Greenhouse A?

   ii) What was the average growth rate per week for the plants in Greenhouse B?

b) What factor do you think is responsible for the difference between the average growth rates of the plants in Greenhouse A compared to Greenhouse B. Explain your answer.

Tip: If you're stuck on part b, have a look back at the pages on limiting factors of photosynthesis (pages 148-151).

c) The farmer is trying to decide which type of heater to use on a permanent basis. Other than the effect on growth rate, suggest what else the farmer will need to consider when choosing a heater.

7. Aerobic Respiration

*We, and other organisms, need energy to do... well... everything really.
This energy comes from the reactions of respiration.*

Respiration and enzymes

The chemical reactions that occur inside cells are controlled by enzymes.
All of the reactions involved in respiration are catalysed by enzymes.
These are really important reactions, as respiration transfers the energy
that the cell needs to do just about everything — this energy is used for
all living processes.

Respiration is not breathing in and breathing out, as you might think.
Respiration is the process of transferring energy from the breakdown of
glucose — and it goes on in every cell in your body continuously.

Respiration happens in plants too. All living things respire.
It's how they release energy from their food.

> Respiration is the process of transferring energy
> from glucose, which goes on in every cell.

Respiration is **exothermic** — it transfers energy to the environment.

What is aerobic respiration?

Aerobic respiration is respiration using oxygen. It's the most efficient way
to transfer energy from glucose. Aerobic respiration goes on all the time in
plants and animals.

Most of the reactions in aerobic respiration happen inside cell structures
called **mitochondria** (see page 23).

Word equation

You need to learn the overall word equation for aerobic respiration:

> glucose + oxygen → carbon dioxide + water

Symbol equation

There's a symbol equation for aerobic respiration too:

$$C_6H_{12}O_6 + 6O_2 \rightarrow 6CO_2 + 6H_2O$$

Learning Objectives:

- Know that all the energy needed for cellular processes is supplied by respiration.
- Know that respiration is the process of transferring energy from glucose, which occurs continuously in living cells.
- Know that respiration is an exothermic reaction.
- Know that respiration can take place aerobically (with oxygen) in cells to transfer energy from glucose.
- Know the word equation for aerobic respiration.
- Know the chemical symbols for glucose, oxygen, carbon dioxide and water.
- Know how organisms use the energy transferred from respiration.

Specification Reference
4.4.2.1

Tip: You can also have anaerobic respiration, which happens without oxygen, but that doesn't transfer nearly as much energy as aerobic respiration — see page 161.

Tip: You don't need to know this symbol equation, but you do need to recognise the symbols — lucky for you, they're the same as the ones you need to know for photosynthesis (see page 145).

Energy from respiration

Organisms use the energy transferred by respiration to fuel all sorts of processes. You need to know about the following ways in which an organism may use energy from respiration:

Figure 1: *Animals, including humans, need energy from respiration to contract their muscles and move.*

1. Organisms use energy to build up larger molecules from smaller ones (like proteins from amino acids).

2. Animals use energy to allow their muscles to contract (which in turn allows them to move about).

3. Mammals and birds use energy to keep their body temperature steady (unlike other animals, mammals and birds keep their bodies constantly warm).

Practice Questions — Fact Recall

Q1 What is aerobic respiration?

Q2 Aerobic respiration is an exothermic reaction.
What does this mean?

Q3 Write the chemical symbols for the products of aerobic respiration.

Q4 Give three ways in which mammals use energy from respiration.

Practice Question — Application

Q1 This diagram shows the equation for aerobic respiration.

Glucose + $\boxed{A}$ → carbon dioxide + $\boxed{B}$

a) What is A in the equation?

b) What is B in the equation?

Exam Tip
Make sure you know the word equation for aerobic respiration off by heart, as it can get you easy marks in the exam.

8. Anaerobic Respiration

When you're exercising hard, aerobic respiration isn't always enough to keep you going. Don't worry though, your body has another trick up its sleeve...

What is anaerobic respiration?

When you do vigorous exercise and your body can't supply enough oxygen to your muscles, they start doing anaerobic respiration as well as aerobic respiration.

"Anaerobic" just means "without oxygen". It's the incomplete breakdown of glucose, making **lactic acid**. Here's the word equation for anaerobic respiration in muscle cells:

$$glucose \rightarrow lactic\ acid$$

Anaerobic respiration does not transfer nearly as much energy as aerobic respiration. This is because glucose isn't fully oxidised (because it doesn't combine with oxygen). So, anaerobic respiration is only useful in emergencies, e.g. during exercise when it allows you to keep on using your muscles for a while longer.

Oxygen debt

After resorting to anaerobic respiration, when you stop exercising you'll have an "oxygen debt". An oxygen debt is the amount of extra oxygen your body needs after exercise. In other words, you have to "repay" the oxygen that you didn't get to your muscles in time, because your lungs, heart and blood couldn't keep up with the demand earlier on.

This means you have to keep breathing hard for a while after you stop, to get more oxygen into your blood, which is transported to the muscle cells.

Removing lactic acid `Higher`

The extra oxygen that 'repays' the oxygen debt is needed to react with the lactic acid in the muscles to form harmless carbon dioxide and water. You can define oxygen debt like this:

> Oxygen debt is the amount of extra oxygen the body needs after exercise to react with the build up of lactic acid and remove it from the cells.

The pulse and breathing rate stay high whilst there are high levels of lactic acid and carbon dioxide to deliver more oxygen to the cells and take away the carbon dioxide.

Your body also has another way of coping with the high level of lactic acid — the blood that enters your muscles transports the lactic acid to the liver. In the liver, the lactic acid is converted back to glucose.

Learning Objectives:

- Know that respiration can take place anaerobically (without oxygen) in cells to transfer energy from glucose.

- Know that anaerobic respiration in muscle cells produces lactic acid, and be able to write the word equation for this.

- Know that in anaerobic respiration, glucose doesn't get fully oxidised, which means that not as much energy is transferred as in aerobic respiration.

- Know that anaerobic respiration in muscle cells produces an oxygen debt which must be repaid after exercise.

- **H** Be able to define oxygen debt.

- **H** Know how lactic acid is removed from the muscles.

- Know the word equation for anaerobic respiration in plant and yeast cells.

- Know that anaerobic respiration in yeast cells is called fermentation, and that the process has economic importance in bread and alcoholic drink production.

- Be able to compare aerobic and anaerobic respiration in terms of the need for oxygen, the products and how much energy is transferred.

Specification References
4.4.2.1, 4.4.2.2

Anaerobic respiration in plants and yeast

Tip: Yeast are single-celled organisms.

Anaerobic respiration in plants and yeast is slightly different. Plants and yeast cells can respire without oxygen too, but they produce ethanol (alcohol) and carbon dioxide instead of lactic acid.

Word equation

You need to learn the overall word equation for anaerobic respiration in plants and yeast cells:

$$\text{glucose} \rightarrow \text{ethanol} + \text{carbon dioxide}$$

Fermentation

Tip: Bread and alcoholic drinks make a lot of money, so yeast plays an important part in the economy.

Anaerobic respiration in yeast cells is called **fermentation**. In the food and drinks industry, fermentation by yeast is of great value because it's used to make bread and alcoholic drinks, e.g. beer and wine. In bread-making, it's the carbon dioxide from fermentation that makes bread rise. In beer and wine-making, it's the fermentation process that produces alcohol.

Figure 1: *Bread dough being left to rise in an industrial vat.*

Comparing aerobic and anaerobic respiration

You need to be able to compare aerobic and anaerobic respiration.

	Aerobic respiration	Anaerobic respiration
Is oxygen needed?	yes	no
What products are made?	CO_2 and water	lactic acid (muscles) / CO_2 and ethanol (plants & yeast)
How much energy is transferred?	A large amount.	A small amount.

Practice Questions — Fact Recall

Q1 Explain when the body uses anaerobic respiration.

Q2 Explain what an oxygen debt is.

Q3 How does the liver help to get rid of lactic acid?

Q4 Give the word equation for anaerobic respiration in yeast.

Q5 a) What is anaerobic respiration in yeast cells also known as?

b) Give two industrial uses of this reaction.

9. Exercise

When we exercise we need to get more glucose and oxygen to our muscles for respiration. The body has some clever ways of doing this...

Energy for exercise

Muscle cells use oxygen to transfer energy from glucose (aerobic respiration — see page 159), which is used to contract the muscles.

When you exercise, some of your muscles contract more frequently than normal so you need more energy. This energy comes from increased respiration. The increase in respiration in your cells means you need to get more oxygen into them. For this to happen, the blood has to flow at a faster rate. Therefore physical activity:

- increases your breathing rate and breath volume to meet the demand for extra oxygen.

- increases your heart rate (the speed at which the heart pumps) to make your blood flow more quickly, delivering more oxygen and glucose to cells for respiration, and taking more carbon dioxide away.

When you do really vigorous exercise (like sprinting) your body can't supply oxygen to your muscles quickly enough, so they start respiring anaerobically (see page 161). This is not the best way to transfer energy from glucose because lactic acid builds up in the muscles, which gets painful. Long periods of exercise also cause **muscle fatigue** — the muscles get tired and then stop contracting efficiently.

Recovery period

After anaerobic exercise stops, there will be an "oxygen debt". Heart rate and breathing rate stay higher than normal for a while after exercise whilst the oxygen debt is being paid back. This is known as the recovery period — see Figure 1.

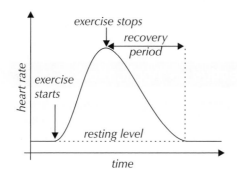

Figure 1: *Graph showing how a person's heart rate changes during exercise.*

Learning Objectives:
- Know that the body needs to react to provide more energy during exercise.
- Be able to describe how the heart rate, breathing rate and breath volume change during exercise to get more oxygen to the muscles.
- Know that long periods of exercise can cause muscle fatigue, where the muscles get tired and stop contracting efficiently.

Specification Reference 4.4.2.2

Tip: Remember, lactic acid is formed from the incomplete oxidation of glucose.

Exam Tip
In the exam you might be given some data on heart rate or breathing rate during exercise and asked to say what is happening and why. So make sure you learn this page really well.

Tip: The heart rate at resting level is just your heart rate when you're not exercising.

Figure 2: A person having their breathing rate and heart rate recorded during exercise.

Tip: You can also take a pulse from the side of the neck.

Tip: Beats per minute (bpm) is a unit used for measuring heart rate.

Tip: There's more about random error on page 13.

Investigating the effect of exercise

You can measure breathing rate by counting breaths, and heart rate by taking the pulse.

Example

To take a pulse, place two fingers on the inside of the wrist (see Figure 3) and count the number of beats in 1 minute. You can also count the number of beats in 30 seconds and then double it.

You could take your pulse after:

- sitting down for 5 minutes,

- then after 5 minutes of gentle walking,

- then again after 5 minutes of slow jogging,

- then again after running for 5 minutes,

and plot your results in a bar chart.

Figure 3: Taking a pulse.

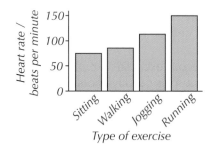

Figure 4: Results from reading the heart rate after different activities.

Your heart rate will increase the more intense the exercise is, as your body needs to get more oxygen to the muscles and take more carbon dioxide away from the muscles.

To reduce the effect of any random errors on your results, do it as a group and plot the average heart rate for each exercise.

Practice Question — Application

Q1 Charlotte is working out on the cross trainer machine at the gym. As she's running, her heart rate increases from 80 to 146 bpm. Describe two other responses her body will have to the physical demands of running.

10. Metabolism

Metabolism is going on all of the time, so it's worthwhile knowing about it. That, and it could come up in your exam too...

What is metabolism?

In a cell there are lots of chemical reactions happening all the time, which are controlled by **enzymes**. Many of these reactions are linked together to form bigger reactions:

In some of these reactions, larger molecules are made from smaller ones. Overall these reactions are **endothermic** (they take in energy from the environment).

> **Examples**
>
> - Lots of small glucose molecules are joined together in reactions to form starch (a storage molecule in plant cells), glycogen (a storage molecule in animal cells) and cellulose (a component of plant cell walls).
>
> - Lipid molecules are each made from one molecule of glycerol and three fatty acids.
>
> - Glucose is combined with nitrate ions to make amino acids, which are then made into proteins.

In other reactions, larger molecules are broken down into smaller ones. Overall these reactions are **exothermic** (they transfer energy to the environment). For example:

> **Examples**
>
> - Glucose is broken down in respiration. Respiration transfers energy to power all the reactions in the body that make molecules.
>
> - Excess protein is broken down in a reaction to produce urea. Urea is then excreted in urine.

The sum (total) of all of the reactions that happen in a cell or the body is called its metabolism.

Practice Questions — Fact Recall

Q1 What does a lipid molecule consist of?

Q2 What is formed when glucose combines with nitrate ions?

Q3 What component of urine is produced from the breakdown of excess protein?

Q4 What is meant by metabolism?

Learning Objectives:

- Know that the processes in metabolism use energy transferred by respiration and are controlled by enzymes.
- Be able to give examples of reactions involved in metabolism, including ones where larger molecules are made from smaller ones, and where larger molecules are broken down into smaller ones.
- Be able to explain how smaller molecules (glucose, amino acids, fatty acids and glycerol) are important in the formation and breakdown of larger ones (carbohydrates, proteins and lipids).
- Know that the sum of all of the reactions that happen in a cell, or in the body, is called its metabolism.

Specification Reference 4.4.2.3

Tip: Enzymes are biological catalysts — see page 109.

Topic 4 Checklist — Make sure you know...

The Basics of Photosynthesis

☐ That energy is transferred to chloroplasts when they absorb light for photosynthesis.

☐ That photosynthesis is an endothermic reaction because energy is transferred from the environment.

☐ The word equation for photosynthesis: carbon dioxide + water $\xrightarrow{\text{light}}$ glucose + oxygen

☐ The chemical symbols for carbon dioxide (CO_2), water (H_2O), oxygen (O_2) and glucose ($C_6H_{12}O_6$).

How Plants Use Glucose

☐ That plants use glucose produced during photosynthesis in many ways, including for respiration, to make cellulose for cell walls, to make amino acids for protein synthesis.

☐ That proteins in plants are made by combining glucose with nitrate ions from the soil to make amino acids, which are then joined together to form proteins.

☐ That glucose from photosynthesis can be converted to fats, oils or insoluble starch for storage.

The Rate of Photosynthesis

☐ How the rate of photosynthesis can be affected by temperature, the level of carbon dioxide, light intensity, or by the amount of chlorophyll in the plant and know that any of these factors can be the limiting factor (that stops photosynthesis from happening).

☐ How to draw, read from and interpret graphs that show the rate of photosynthesis linked to one limiting factor.

☐ H That the factors that affect the rate of photosynthesis can interact, and be able to work out which is the limiting factor from a graph that shows more than one factor.

Investigating Photosynthesis Rate

☐ How to investigate how light intensity affects the rate of photosynthesis of an aquatic plant (Required Practical 5), and how to calculate the rate of photosynthesis (e.g. by dividing the length of the bubble produced by the time taken to produce it).

The Inverse Square Law

☐ H That inverse proportion is when one variable increases as the other decreases at the same rate.

☐ H That the inverse square law is an example of inverse proportion that links together light intensity and distance between the light source and a plant, and be able to use it.

Artificially Controlling Plant Growth

☐ H That in greenhouses, the factors that affect the rate of photosynthesis can be controlled to increase the rate of photosynthesis, which in turn increases the profit made from the plants.

☐ H How to interpret data that relates to controlling the conditions in a greenhouse.

cont...

Aerobic Respiration

☐ That respiration is an exothermic reaction because it transfers energy to the environment, and that it transfers all the energy needed for living processes.

☐ That aerobic respiration is the process of transferring energy from glucose using oxygen, and that it occurs continuously in living cells.

☐ The word equation for aerobic respiration: glucose + oxygen → carbon dioxide + water

☐ The chemical symbols for glucose ($C_6H_{12}O_6$), oxygen (O_2), carbon dioxide (CO_2) and water (H_2O).

☐ That the energy transferred from respiration is used by organisms to make larger molecules from smaller ones, for muscle contraction and to keep warm.

Anaerobic Respiration

☐ That muscles will start to respire anaerobically (without oxygen) if they can't get enough oxygen to respire aerobically, and that this involves the incomplete oxidation of glucose, which forms lactic acid: glucose → lactic acid. Anaerobic respiration transfers less energy than aerobic respiration.

☐ That an oxygen debt occurs after anaerobic respiration in muscle cells — you have to 'repay' the oxygen you didn't manage to get to your muscles in time.

☐ [H] That lactic acid is removed from the body by being carried by the blood to the liver (where it's turned back into glucose), or by reacting with oxygen. An oxygen debt is the amount of extra oxygen needed to react with and remove lactic acid from muscle cells after exercise.

☐ The word equation for anaerobic respiration in plants and yeast: glucose → ethanol + carbon dioxide

☐ That anaerobic respiration in yeast cells is called fermentation, and that this process has economic importance in the bread and alcohol industries.

☐ The differences between aerobic and anaerobic respiration, including whether they need oxygen, what products are made, and how much energy is transferred.

Exercise

☐ That during exercise, there is an increased demand for energy.

☐ That breathing rate and breath volume increase during exercise to get more oxygen into the body, and a person's heart rate increases during exercise so that blood flow to their muscles increases.

☐ That long periods of exercise can cause muscle fatigue, where the muscles don't contract efficiently.

Metabolism

☐ That enzymes control the reactions of metabolism, which use energy transferred by respiration.

☐ That metabolism includes reactions that build up larger molecules from smaller ones, and reactions that break down larger molecules into smaller ones.

☐ How glucose, amino acids, fatty acids and glycerol are important in the formation and breakdown of carbohydrates, proteins and lipids.

☐ That metabolism is the sum of every reaction in a cell or the body.

Exam-style Questions

1   Tim read the following information in a science magazine:

> You can measure the rate of photosynthesis in plants by doing the following:
>
> Cut discs from a plant leaf and put them in a 0.2% sodium hydrogencarbonate solution (which serves as a source of carbon dioxide). Put the solution and leaf discs in a syringe and then remove all the air from the syringe — this removes any gases out of the air spaces in the leaf, which will cause the leaf discs to sink.
>
> Then put the syringe containing the leaf discs under a light source. As the leaf discs photosynthesise, their cells produce oxygen. The oxygen will fill the air spaces in the leaf — with enough oxygen in the air spaces they'll begin to float. You can use the time this takes as a measure of the rate of photosynthesis.

1.1   Where in a plant cell does photosynthesis take place?

(1 mark)

1.2   Complete the word equation for photosynthesis:

carbon dioxide + ... ⟶ glucose + oxygen

(1 mark)

Tim decided to use the method to investigate the effect of light intensity on the rate of photosynthesis. He conducted the experiment at three different light intensities. For each light intensity he cut 10 equally sized discs from a leaf, and set up the experiment as described in the magazine. He then timed how long it took for all of the leaf discs to float to the surface in the syringe. His results are shown in this table:

Light intensity	Time it took for all discs to float (minutes)
A	18
B	9
C	11

1.3   Which light intensity do you think was the highest, A, B or C? Explain your answer.

(2 marks)

1.4   Tim thinks that if he keeps increasing the light intensity, he will keep increasing the rate of photosynthesis. Is he right? Explain your answer.

(3 marks)

1.5   Tim conducts the experiment again using light intensity A. This time he uses a solution containing 0.8% sodium hydrogen carbonate. Do you think it will take more or less than 18 minutes for all of the discs to float? Explain your answer.

(2 marks)

1.6*   The process of photosynthesis produces glucose.
         Describe as fully as you can how this glucose may be used by a plant.

(6 marks)

2 A student wants to find out how his heart rate changes during exercise. The exercise he chooses is to run on a running machine. He records his heart rate before the run, then again after five minutes of running. He repeats the exercise three times.

His results are shown in this table:

Time of record	Heart rate (beats per minute)		
	1st go	2nd go	3rd go
At rest, before run	72	71	72
After 5 minutes of running	151	163	154

2.1 Calculate the student's mean heart rate at the end of his runs.

(2 marks)

Respiration gives the student energy to contract his muscles and run.

2.2 As the student was running, his heart rate increased from its resting level. Explain why.

(2 marks)

2.3 Give **two** other ways the student's body will use energy from respiration.

(2 marks)

3 A scientist is investigating the reactions of aerobic and anaerobic respiration.

3.1 What is the word equation for aerobic respiration?

(4 marks)

3.2 In a cell, energy is stored in a molecule called ATP. The scientist conducts an experiment to find out how much ATP each type of respiration forms per glucose molecule.

His results are shown in this table:

Type of respiration	Number of ATP molecules released per glucose molecule
Aerobic	32
Anaerobic	2

Using the table, describe and explain the difference in the amount of energy transferred by aerobic and anaerobic respiration.

(2 marks)

- Understand that the internal conditions in the body must be carefully controlled so that cells and enzymes can function properly.

- Know what homeostasis means.

- Know that control systems can include nervous or chemical responses.

- Know that there are control systems in the human body that regulate body temperature, blood glucose concentration and water content.

- Know that a control system includes receptors, a coordination centre and effectors.

- Know that changes in the environment (stimuli) are detected by receptors.

- Know that information travels from receptors to coordination centres, which coordinate a response.

- Know that effectors respond to bring a system back to its normal level.

Specification Reference
4.5.1

Tip: The optimum level is just the level that enables the body to work at its best — e.g. the body has an optimum level of water and temperature.

1. Homeostasis

The internal conditions in the body must be kept constant — this stops cell damage that could happen if we didn't keep on top of things. Luckily there are some clever systems in place to keep everything plodding along steadily.

What is homeostasis?

The conditions inside your body need to be kept steady, even when the external environment changes. This is really important because your cells need the right conditions in order to function properly, including the right conditions for enzyme action (see pages 110-111). Homeostasis is the way in which everything is kept at the right level.

> Homeostasis is the regulation of the conditions inside your body (and cells) to maintain a stable internal environment, in response to changes in both internal and external conditions.

You have loads of automatic **control systems** in your body that regulate your internal environment — these include both nervous and hormonal (chemical) communication systems. The conditions in your internal environment that need regulating include:

Examples

- Body temperature.
- Blood glucose content (see pages 184-185).
- Water content of the body.

All your automatic control systems are made up of three main components which work together to maintain a steady condition — cells called **receptors**, **coordination centres** (including the brain, spinal cord and pancreas) and **effectors** (muscles or glands — see page 172).

Stimuli and negative feedback

A change in your environment that you might need to respond to is called a **stimulus** (the plural is 'stimuli'). A stimulus can be light, sound, touch, pressure, pain, chemical, or a change in position or temperature.

The receptors of an automatic control system detect a stimulus when the level of something (e.g. water or temperature) is too high or too low. They then send this information to the coordination centre, which processes the information and organises a response from the effectors. The effectors respond to counteract the change — bringing the level back to its optimum. The mechanism that restores the **optimum level** is called a **negative feedback mechanism** — see Figure 1 on the next page.

level brought back to optimum

negative feedback loop

Figure 1: *A negative feedback mechanism.*

Tip: A negative feedback system responds when a level changes from its optimum point, in order to bring the level back to optimum. It's a continuous, looping process.

The effectors will just carry on producing the responses for as long as they're stimulated by the coordination centre. This might cause the opposite problem — making the level change too much (away from the ideal). Luckily the receptors detect if the level becomes too different and negative feedback starts again, so the level is kept at its optimum. This process happens without you thinking about it — it's all automatic.

Example

Body temperature is usually kept within 0.5 °C above or below 37 °C.

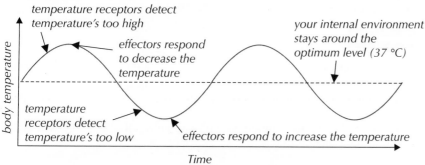

temperature receptors detect temperature's too high

effectors respond to decrease the temperature

your internal environment stays around the optimum level (37 °C)

temperature receptors detect temperature's too low

effectors respond to increase the temperature

body temperature

Time

Figure 2: *Control of body temperature via negative feedback.*

Practice Questions — Fact Recall

Q1 Define homeostasis.

Q2 Give two examples of conditions in your internal environment that need regulating and maintaining.

Q3 What is a stimulus?

Q4 Name the part of an automatic control system that receives information about a stimulus and organises a response.

Practice Question — Application

Q1 The water content of the body is monitored by a control system. If it gets too low, a negative feedback mechanism is triggered. Briefly outline the stages in this negative feedback system.

- Know that the nervous
  system allows humans
  to respond to their
  environment and
  coordinate their
  behaviour.
- Know that information
  from receptors travels
  via neurones as
  electrical impulses to
  the central nervous
  system (CNS), where
  the response of the
  effectors (muscles
  contracting or glands
  secreting hormones)
  is coordinated.
- Know that the CNS
  consists of the brain
  and spinal cord.
- Be able to explain
  how the structure of
  the nervous system
  is adapted to its
  functions.
- Know the path that
  a nervous impulse
  takes in response to
  a stimulus: stimulus –
  receptor – coordinator
  – effector – response
- Be able to read from
  and interpret tables,
  charts and graphs
  containing data
  about nervous system
  function.

Specification Reference
4.5.2

2. The Nervous System

Next up, an overview of the nervous system...

What is the nervous system?

Organisms need to respond to **stimuli** (changes in the environment) in order to survive. A single-celled organism can just respond to its environment, but the cells of multicellular organisms need to communicate with each other first. So as multicellular organisms evolved, they developed nervous and hormonal communication systems.

Your nervous system is what allows you to react to your surroundings. It also allows you to coordinate your behaviour. It's made up of all the **neurones** (nerve cells) in your body — there's more on these on the next page.

Receptors

Receptors are the cells that detect stimuli. There are many different types of receptors, such as:

> **Examples**
>
> - Taste receptors on the tongue.
> - Sound receptors in the ears.
> - Smell receptors in the nose.
> - Light receptors in the eyes.

Receptors can form part of larger, complex organs, e.g. the retina of the eye is covered in light receptor cells.

The central nervous system (CNS)

The central nervous system (CNS) is where all the information from the receptors is sent, and where reflexes (see p. 175) and actions are coordinated.

In vertebrates (animals with backbones) this consists of the brain and spinal cord only (see Figure 1). In mammals, the CNS is connected to the body by sensory neurones and motor neurones. Neurones transmit information as electrical impulses to and from the CNS. This happens very quickly.

Effectors

'Instructions' from the CNS are sent along neurones to **effectors**. Effectors are **muscles** or **glands** which respond to nervous impulses and bring about a response to a stimulus. Muscles and glands respond to nervous impulses in different ways:

- Muscles contract.
- Glands secrete chemical substances called hormones (see page 181).

Different types of neurone

Different types of neurone are involved in the transfer of information to and from the CNS — see the next page.

Figure 1: *Scan of the head and neck. The brain and upper spinal cord can be seen in orange/red.*

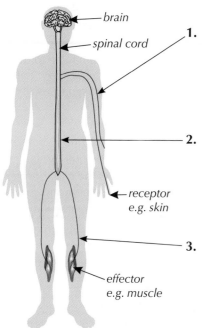

1. Sensory neurones
The neurones that carry information as electrical impulses from the receptors in the sense organs to the central nervous system.

2. Relay neurones
The neurones that carry electrical impulses from sensory neurones to motor neurones. They are found in the central nervous system.

3. Motor neurones
The neurones that carry electrical impulses from the central nervous system to the effectors.

Exam Tip
The exam isn't just a test of what you know — it's also a test of how well you can apply what you know. For instance, you might have to take what you know about a human and apply it to a horse (e.g. sound receptors in its ears send information to the brain via sensory neurones). The key is not to panic — just think carefully about the information that you are given.

The transmission of information to and from the CNS is summarised in Figure 2:

Figure 2: *Flow diagram showing the transmission of information to and from the CNS.*

Exam Tip
In your exam, you might need to read off values related to nervous system function from a table, graph or chart, or explain what the data is showing. Remember to always check any units or graph scales carefully to avoid throwing away marks.

Practice Questions — Fact Recall

Q1 Which type of effector secretes hormones?

Q2 A sensory neurone is a type of neurone.
Name two other types of neurone.

Practice Question — Application

Q1 A dog hears a cat moving in the garden, so runs towards it.

a) i) What is the stimulus in this situation?

ii) What detects the stimulus in this situation?

iii) What name is given to the type of neurone that transmits information about the stimulus to the central nervous system?

The dog's brain sends an impulse to the dog's muscles which act as an effector.

b) i) What type of neurone transmits information from the central nervous system to an effector?

ii) How do the dog's muscles respond to the nerve impulse?

Exam Tip
Make sure you know which type of neurone transfers information to which place in the nervous system — it's easy to get the different types of neurones confused and they often come up in exams.

Learning Objectives:
- Know the structure and function of a synapse.
- Know that reflexes are fast, automatic responses to stimuli that don't involve the conscious brain.
- Understand the importance of reflex reactions.
- Know the order of events in a simple reflex arc and be able to explain how the structures of a reflex arc are related to their function.

Specification Reference
4.5.2

3. Synapses and Reflexes

Reflexes are rapid responses to stimuli that happen without you having to think about them — they're automatic. The neurones involved in a reflex aren't all joined together though — they have gaps between them called synapses.

Synapses

The connection between two neurones is called a synapse. The nerve signal is transferred by chemicals which diffuse (move) across the gap. These chemicals then set off a new electrical signal in the next neurone. This is shown in Figure 1.

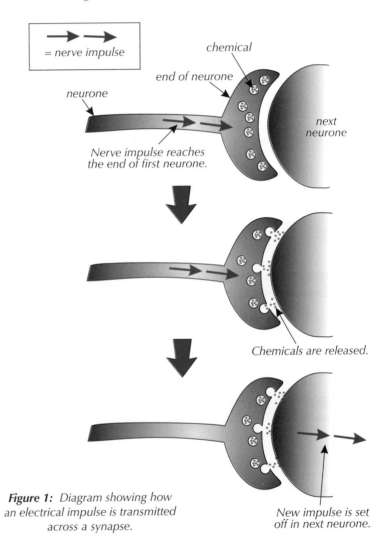

Figure 1: Diagram showing how an electrical impulse is transmitted across a synapse.

Figure 2: A synapse viewed under a microscope. The neurones are shown in green. The red dots contain the chemicals that diffuse between the neurones.

Neurones deliver information really quickly because the signal is transmitted by electrical impulses. Synapses slow down the transmission of a nervous impulse because the diffusion of chemicals across the gap takes time (it's still pretty fast though).

Reflexes

Reflexes are fast, automatic responses to certain stimuli. They bypass your conscious brain completely when a quick response is essential — your body just gets on with things. Reflexes can reduce your chance of being injured, although they have other roles as well.

Tip: 'Automatic' means done without thinking.

Examples

- If someone shines a bright light in your eyes, your pupils automatically get smaller. This means that less light gets into your eyes, which stops them getting damaged.

- Adrenaline is a hormone (see p. 199), which gets your body ready for action. If you get a shock, your body releases adrenaline automatically — it doesn't wait for you to decide that you're shocked.

- The knee-jerk reflex helps maintain posture and balance. Doctors test this reflex by tapping just below the knee with a small hammer. This stimulates pressure receptors, making a muscle in the upper leg contract, which causes the lower leg to rise up.

Figure 3: The knee-jerk reflex. Doctors often use this test to see if a patient's reflexes are working properly.

Reflex arcs

The passage of information in a reflex (from receptor to effector) is called a reflex arc. The neurones in reflex arcs go through the spinal cord or through an unconscious part of the brain. Here are the main stages in a reflex arc:

1. When a stimulus is detected by receptors, impulses are sent along a sensory neurone to a relay neurone in the CNS.

2. When the impulses reach a synapse between the sensory neurone and the relay neurone, they trigger chemicals to be released (see previous page). These chemicals cause impulses to be sent along the relay neurone.

3. When the impulses reach a synapse between the relay neurone and a motor neurone, the same thing happens. Chemicals are released and cause impulses to be sent along the motor neurone.

4. The impulses then travel along the motor neurone to the effector (which is usually a muscle).

5. If the effector is a muscle, it will respond to the impulse by contracting. If it's a gland, it will secrete a hormone.

Because you don't have to think about the response (which takes time) a reflex is quicker than normal responses. Figure 4 summarises a reflex arc:

Tip: Flick back to page 173 for more on sensory, relay and motor neurones.

Tip: Remember, electrical impulses pass between the different neurones via diffusion of chemicals at the synapse. They don't just jump between the neurones.

Figure 4: Block diagram of a reflex arc.

Tip: The important things to remember about reflexes are that they're <u>automatic</u> (you don't have to think about them) and <u>rapid</u> (so they're often able to prevent or reduce the chance of injury).

Example

If a bee stings a person's finger, the reflex response is that the hand moves away from the source of pain. Here's the pathway taken by this reflex arc:

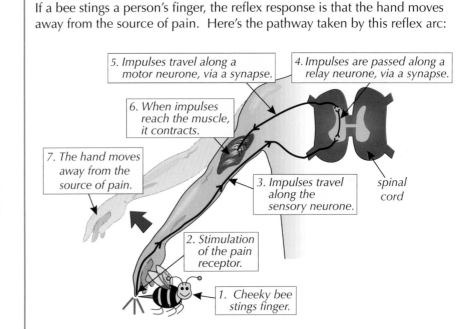

5. Impulses travel along a motor neurone, via a synapse.

4. Impulses are passed along a relay neurone, via a synapse.

6. When impulses reach the muscle, it contracts.

7. The hand moves away from the source of pain.

3. Impulses travel along the sensory neurone.

spinal cord

2. Stimulation of the pain receptor.

1. Cheeky bee stings finger.

Practice Questions — Fact Recall

Q1 How do nerve impulses travel between two neurones?

Q2 What is a reflex?

Q3 Do reflex arcs travel through conscious parts of the brain?

Q4 What neurone comes after the sensory neurone in a reflex arc?

Q5 If the effector in a reflex arc is a muscle, what will the response of that reflex arc be?

Exam Tip
Questions on reflex arcs are quite common in the exam. Make sure you know the general pathway they take really well, and you'll be able to apply it to any reflex response you're given.

Practice Question — Application

Q1 David steps on a drawing pin and immediately pulls his foot up off the pin.

a) What is the stimulus in this response?

b) What is the effector in this response? How does it respond?

c) Complete the pathway taken by this reflex arc.

Stimulus → Receptor → Sensory neurone...

4. Investigating Reaction Time

The time it takes to react to a stimulus depends on how quickly the message travels from the receptor to the effector, via the central nervous system. This is called the reaction time, and it varies from person to person.

What is reaction time?

Reaction time is the time it takes to respond to a stimulus — it's often less than a second. It can be affected by factors such as age, gender or drugs.

Measuring reaction time

REQUIRED PRACTICAL **6**

You need to know how to investigate the effect of a factor on a person's reaction time.

Example

Caffeine is a drug that can speed up a person's reaction time. The effect of caffeine on reaction time can be measured. You will need another person for this experiment — this is the person whose reaction time will be tested. You will provide the stimulus. Here's what to do:

1. The person being tested should sit with their arm resting on the edge of a table (this should stop them moving their arm up or down during the test).

2. Hold a ruler vertically between their thumb and forefinger. Make sure that the zero end of the ruler is level with their thumb and finger. Then let go without giving any warning.

3. The person being tested should try to catch the ruler as quickly as they can — as soon as they see it fall.

4. Reaction time is measured by the number on the ruler where it's caught (see Figure 1) — the further down it's caught (i.e. the higher the number), the slower their reaction time.

Figure 1: A person catching a ruler in a drop test.

5. Repeat the test several times then calculate the mean distance that the ruler fell.

The person being tested should then have a caffeinated drink (e.g. 300 ml of cola). After ten minutes, repeat steps 1–5.

Learning Objectives:

- Be able to investigate how a factor affects reaction time (Required Practical 6).

- Be able to convert between reaction time data shown in a graph and in numerical form.

Specification Reference 4.5.2

Tip: The type of stimulus (e.g. whether you see, hear or touch it) can also affect reaction time.

Tip: Remember to do a risk assessment for this experiment. There are some examples of things you need to think about on the next page.

Tip: It's possible to work out the reaction time in seconds by popping the mean distance (in cm) into this formula:

$$\text{time} = \sqrt{\frac{\text{mean distance}}{490}}$$

But you don't need to learn this formula.

Tip: Reaction times can be plotted on a graph to show possible relationships, e.g.:

concentration of caffeine (mg/dm³)

Make sure you know how to read off data from a graph like this, as well as how to draw one using reaction time data (see page 18).

Controlling variables

If you're carrying out the investigation on the previous page, you need to control any variables to make sure that it's a fair test.

Examples

- You should use the same person to catch the ruler each time.

- That person should always use the same hand to catch the ruler.

- The ruler should always be dropped from the same height.

- You should make sure that the person being tested has not had any caffeine (or anything else that may affect their reaction time) before the start of the experiment.

Tip: For more about variables, see page 10.

Safety issues

Testing reaction times seems simple enough, but there are still some important safety points you need to think about for this experiment. For example, any drinks need to be consumed outside of the lab, away from any chemicals or other hazards. Also, too much caffeine can cause unpleasant side-effects, so the person being tested should avoid drinking any more caffeine for the rest of the day after the experiment is completed.

Measuring reaction time using a computer

Simple computer tests can also be used to measure reaction time.

Example

The person being tested has to click the mouse (or press a key) as soon as they see a stimulus on the screen, e.g. a box change colour.

Computers can give a more precise reaction time because they remove the possibility of human error from the measurement. As the computer can record the reaction time in milliseconds, it can also give a more accurate measurement.

Using a computer can also remove the possibility that the person can predict when to respond — using the ruler test, the catcher may learn to anticipate the drop by reading the tester's body language.

Figure 2: *The person clicks the mouse as quickly as they can when they see the stimulus on the computer screen.*

Practice Questions — Application

Q1 A particular drug stops some of the chemical that transfers across a synapse from reaching the next neurone. Suggest what effect this drug would have on a person's reaction time.

Q2 a) Describe how you could use a ruler to investigate a person's reaction time.

b) Suggest two factors that could be tested to investigate their effect on reaction time.

Topic 5a Checklist — Make sure you know...

Homeostasis

☐ That internal conditions within the body need to be carefully controlled to maintain the optimum environment for enzymes and cell function.

☐ That homeostasis is the regulation of the conditions inside your body (and cells) to maintain a stable internal environment, in response to changes in both internal and external conditions.

☐ That internal conditions, including body temperature, blood glucose level and water content, are regulated by nervous and hormonal control systems.

☐ That a control system includes: cells called receptors that detect stimuli (changes in the environment), a coordination centre (e.g. the brain, spinal cord or pancreas) that receives and processes information from receptors and organises a response, and effectors (muscles or glands) that produce a response to restore the system back to its normal level.

The Nervous System

☐ That the nervous system allows humans to respond to changes in the environment (stimuli) and to coordinate their behaviour.

☐ That information from receptors travels as electrical impulses via neurones to the CNS (which consists of the brain and spinal cord), where a response is coordinated.

☐ That muscles respond to impulses by contracting, and glands respond by secreting hormones.

☐ How the nervous system is adapted to its functions.

☐ How to read from tables, charts and graphs containing data about nervous system function, and how to interpret this data.

Synapses and Reflexes

☐ That the connections between neurones are called synapses and that a nerve signal is transferred across a synapse by chemicals that diffuse across the gap.

☐ That reflexes are fast, automatic responses involving sensory neurones, synapses, relay neurones and motor neurones, and that they don't involve the conscious brain.

☐ That reflex reactions reduce the chance of being injured by providing a quick response to stimuli.

☐ That in a simple reflex, stimuli are detected by receptors and transmitted to the central nervous system (CNS) as nervous impulses via sensory neurones. The impulses are then transferred via a relay neurone in the CNS to a motor neurone, which sends impulses to an effector. The effector then produces a response.

Investigating Reaction Time

☐ How to investigate how a factor, e.g. caffeine, affects reaction time (Required Practical 6).

☐ How to convert between reaction time data shown in a graph and its numerical form, and how to draw a graph to display reaction time data.

Exam-style Questions

1   A scientist conducted an experiment on reaction time.

Subjects had an electrode placed on their upper arm to detect when their muscle contracted. The subjects were asked to place their finger on a metal disc, which gave out a small electric shock at random. This shock caused the muscle in the upper arm to contract.

The scientist measured reaction time as the time it took between the initiation of the shock and the contraction of the muscle in the upper arm.

The diagram shows the pathway taken in this reflex response.

1.1   What is the effector in this response?

(1 mark)

1.2   Name the neurone labelled **A** in the diagram.

(1 mark)

1.3   The average reaction time measured during the experiment was 0.024 s.

After he had recorded their reaction times, the scientist gave the subjects a drug which is known to increase the amount of chemical released at the synapses. He then repeated the experiment.

What do you think would happen to the average reaction time after administration of the drug? Explain your answer.

(2 marks)

1.4   Reflexes often help to protect us from injury.
Suggest and explain **two** features of reflexes that help them do this.

(4 marks)

1. Hormones

Along with the nervous system, hormones allow us to react to changes in the environment and in our bodies in order to keep everything ticking over nicely. Hormones are secreted by the glands of the endocrine system.

What are hormones?

Hormones are chemical molecules released directly into the blood to regulate bodily processes. They are carried in the blood plasma (the liquid part of the blood) to other parts of the body, but only affect particular cells in particular organs (called **target organs**). Hormones control things in organs and cells that need constant adjustment.

Here's a definition of hormones:

> Hormones are chemical messengers which travel in the blood to activate target cells.

The endocrine system

Hormones are produced in (and secreted by) various glands, called endocrine **glands**. These glands make up the endocrine system.

The endocrine system uses hormones to react to changes in the environment or changes inside the body.

Endocrine glands

There are many glands in the endocrine system, including:

- The pituitary gland — this produces many hormones that regulate body conditions. It is sometimes called the 'master gland' because these hormones act on other glands, directing them to release hormones that bring about change.

- The pancreas — this produces insulin, which is used to regulate the blood glucose level (see page 184).

- The thyroid — this produces thyroxine, which is involved in regulating things like the rate of metabolism, heart rate and temperature (see p. 198).

- The adrenal glands — these produce adrenaline, which is used to prepare the body for a 'fight or flight' response (see page 199).

Learning Objectives:
- Know that hormones are chemical molecules which are secreted into the bloodstream.
- Know that hormones are carried in the blood to their target organs, where they have an effect.
- Know that glands secrete hormones.
- Know that the endocrine system is made up of glands.
- Understand why the pituitary gland is sometimes called the 'master gland'.
- Know where certain endocrine glands are found in the body.
- Know that hormonal responses are slower but last longer than nervous impulses.

Specification Reference 4.5.3.1

Figure 1: *Scan of the brain. The pituitary gland (green structure) is circled in white.*

- The ovaries (females only) — these produce oestrogen, which is involved in the menstrual cycle (see pages 189-191).

- The testes (males only) — these produce testosterone, which controls puberty and sperm production in males (see page 189).

Exam Tip
In the exam, you might be asked to point out where a certain gland is found in the body, or be asked to name a gland from its location.

Exam Tip
These are the glands you need to learn for the exam. There are loads more glands in the body though, each doing its own thing.

Tip: Testis is the singular of testes.

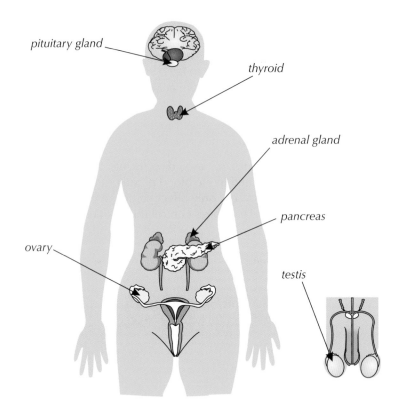

Figure 2: Diagram showing the location of some of the endocrine glands.

Comparing nerves and hormones

Tip: There's more about the nervous system on pages 172-173.

As hormones are carried in the blood, they tend to travel around the body relatively slowly (compared to nervous impulses anyway). They also tend to have relatively long-lasting effects. Hormones and nerves do similar jobs in the body, but with a few differences. These are summarised in Figure 3.

Nerves	Hormones
Fast action	Slower action
Act for a short time	Act for a long time
Acts on a very precise area	Acts in a more general way

Figure 3: Table summarising the differences between nerves and hormones.

If you're not sure whether a response is nervous or hormonal, have a think...

▪ If the response is really quick, it's probably nervous.
Some information needs to be passed to effectors really quickly (e.g. pain signals, or information from your eyes telling you about a car heading your way), so it's no good using hormones to carry the message — they're too slow.

▪ If a response lasts for a long time, it's probably hormonal.
For example, when you get a shock, a hormone called adrenaline is released into the body (causing the fight-or-flight response, where your body is hyped up ready for action). You can tell it's a hormonal response (even though it kicks in pretty quickly) because you feel a bit wobbly for a while afterwards.

Practice Questions — Fact Recall

Q1 How are hormones carried around the body?

Q2 True or false? Hormones affect all organs.

Q3 What are hormones secreted from?

Q4 Name a hormone secreted from the ovaries.

Q5 Which produces a faster response — nerves or hormones?

Exam Tip
Try to learn to spell difficult words like 'pituitary'. It'll help to make sure the examiner knows what you're talking about.

- Know that the pancreas monitors and controls blood glucose level.

- Know that the pancreas produces insulin when the blood glucose level gets too high and understand how insulin reduces the blood glucose level.

- Know that excess glucose is stored as glycogen in liver and muscle cells.

- **H** Understand how glucagon from the pancreas increases the blood glucose level when it's too low, as part of a negative feedback cycle with insulin.

- Know what Type 1 diabetes is and understand why it can result in the blood glucose level being too high.

- Know how Type 1 diabetes can be controlled.

- Know what Type 2 diabetes is and why it can result in the blood glucose level being too high.

- Know that being obese increases a person's risk of getting Type 2 diabetes.

- Know how Type 2 diabetes can be controlled.

- Be able to compare Type 1 and Type 2 diabetes.

- Be able to read from and interpret graphs showing the effect of insulin on blood glucose concentration.

Specification Reference
4.5.3.2

2. Controlling Blood Glucose

Your blood glucose level needs to carefully regulated. This is done with the help of hormones produced by the pancreas. However, if things don't work quite as they should, it can result in a condition called diabetes...

Glucose concentration of the blood

Glucose is a type of sugar. Throughout the day the blood glucose level varies:

> **Examples**
>
> - Eating foods containing carbohydrate puts glucose into the blood from the digestive system.
>
> - The normal metabolism of cells removes glucose from the blood.
>
> - Vigorous exercise removes much more glucose from the blood.

Hormonal control of blood glucose

The level of glucose in the blood must be kept steady. Changes in the blood glucose level are monitored by the **pancreas**. The pancreas produces hormones which help to control the blood glucose level.

Insulin

Insulin is a hormone produced by the pancreas. It decreases the blood glucose level when it gets too high. Here's what happens:

1. After a meal containing carbohydrate, a person's blood glucose level rises. This rise is detected by the pancreas.

2. The pancreas responds by producing insulin, which is secreted into the blood.

3. Insulin causes body cells to take up more glucose from the blood. Cells in the liver and muscles can take up glucose and convert it into a storage molecule called **glycogen**.

4. This causes the blood glucose level to fall.

This process is shown in Figure 1.

4. Blood glucose reduced.

1. Blood with too much glucose.

liver

3. Glucose moves from blood into liver and muscle cells.

pancreas

insulin

2. Insulin secreted by pancreas.

Figure 1: *Diagram showing the role of insulin in the control of blood glucose.*

Glucagon Higher

Glucagon is another hormone produced by the pancreas. It increases the blood glucose level when it gets too low. Here's what happens:

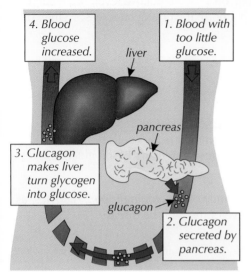

4. Blood glucose increased.

1. Blood with too little glucose.

liver

pancreas

3. Glucagon makes liver turn glycogen into glucose.

glucagon

2. Glucagon secreted by pancreas.

Figure 2: *Diagram showing the role of glucagon in the control of blood glucose.*

1. If a person's blood glucose level decreases, the fall is detected by the pancreas.

2. The pancreas responds by producing glucagon, which is secreted into the blood.

3. Glucose can be stored in the muscles and liver as glycogen (see previous page). Glucagon causes the glycogen to be converted back into glucose, which enters the blood.

4. This causes the blood glucose level to rise.

This process is shown in Figure 2.

Exam Tip H
The words 'glucagon' and 'glycogen' look and sound very similar. You need to make sure you get the spelling of these words spot on in the exam. E.g. if you write 'glycogon' the examiner won't know whether you mean glucagon or glycogen so you won't get the marks.

Tip: H Glucagon works with insulin to control blood glucose level in a negative feedback cycle — together they keep blood glucose around its optimum. (See pages 170-171 for more on negative feedback.)

Type 1 diabetes

Type 1 diabetes is a condition where the pancreas produces little or no insulin. The result is that a person's blood glucose can rise to a level that can kill them.

Controlling Type 1 diabetes

Type 1 diabetes needs to be controlled in the following ways:

1. **Insulin therapy** — this usually involves injecting insulin into the blood. People with Type 1 diabetes usually have several injections of insulin throughout the day, which are likely to be at mealtimes. Insulin injections make sure glucose is removed from the blood quickly once the food has been digested. This stops the level of glucose in the blood from getting too high and is a very effective treatment.

   The amount of insulin that needs to be injected depends on the person's diet and how active they are, since these things will affect their blood glucose level.

2. **Limit the intake of foods rich in simple carbohydrates** — i.e. sugars (which cause the blood glucose level to rise rapidly). People with Type 1 diabetes are also advised to spread their intake of starchy carbohydrates (e.g. pasta, rice, bread, etc.) throughout the day and to pick varieties of these foods that are absorbed more slowly (so they don't cause such a sharp rise in the blood glucose level).

3. **Regular exercise** — this helps to lower the blood glucose level as the increased metabolism of cells during exercise removes more glucose from the blood.

Tip: Remember, insulin <u>reduces</u> blood glucose level.

Figure 3: *A person injecting insulin.*

Tip: Insulin can't be taken in a pill or tablet — the enzymes in the stomach completely destroy it before it reaches the bloodstream. That's why it's normally injected.

Tip: Prolonged periods of high blood glucose levels can cause damage to organs such as the eyes, heart and kidneys, resulting in long-term health problems.

Insulin used to be extracted from the pancreases of pigs or cows, but now human insulin is made by genetic engineering. This human insulin doesn't cause adverse reactions in patients, like animal insulin did.

Insulin injections help to control a person's blood glucose level, but it can't be controlled as accurately as having a normal working pancreas, so they may still have long-term health problems.

Type 2 diabetes

Type 2 diabetes is a condition where a person becomes resistant to their own insulin. They still produce insulin, but their body's cells don't respond properly to the hormone. This can also cause a person's blood glucose level to rise to a dangerous level.

Being overweight can increase your chance of developing Type 2 diabetes, as obesity is a major risk factor in the development of the disease.

Exam Tip
In the exam you might be asked to compare Type 1 and Type 2 diabetes. It might help to draw a table comparing the two. You could include what they are and how they can be controlled.

Controlling Type 2 diabetes

Type 2 diabetes can be controlled in the following ways:

1. **Eating a carbohydrate-controlled diet** — this includes controlling a person's intake of simple carbohydrates to avoid sudden rises in glucose.

2. **Regular exercise** — this helps to lower the blood glucose level.

Modern treatment options

There are some new treatment options available, and some currently being researched, for people with Type 1 diabetes:

1. Diabetics can have a pancreas transplant. A successful operation means they won't have to inject themselves with insulin again. But as with any organ transplant, your body can reject the tissue. If this happens you have to take costly immunosuppressive drugs (drugs that suppress the immune system), which often have serious side-effects.

2. Modern research into artificial pancreases and stem cell research may mean the elimination of organ rejection, but there's a way to go yet.

Tip: You covered stem cells on page 38. They have the ability to turn into a range of different cell types. It's possible that stem cells could be made into pancreatic cells and used to replace the faulty insulin-producing cells in Type 1 diabetics.

Testing for diabetes

At a high blood glucose level, glucose begins to move into the urine. This means diabetes can be tested for by looking for glucose in a urine sample. A blood test for glucose can then confirm the diagnosis. The blood test is more reliable as it gives the current level of glucose in the blood (urine samples can be hours old), and can detect a high level of glucose when the level is not yet high enough for glucose in the urine.

Interpreting blood glucose level graphs

The changes in a person's blood glucose level over time can be shown by a graph. The shape of the graph can vary, depending on whether the person has diabetes — see Figure 4. You need to be able to explain what graphs like this are showing.

Example

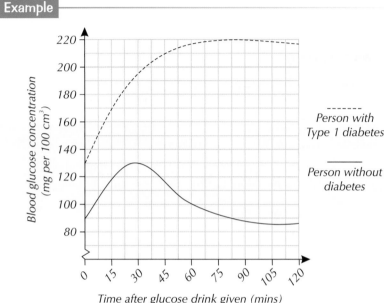

Figure 4: Graph showing the change in blood glucose concentration over time after consuming a glucose drink for a person with Type 1 diabetes and a person without diabetes.

Here's what Figure 4 is showing:

Person without diabetes

In the initial 30 minutes after consuming the glucose drink, their blood glucose concentration rises from 90 mg/100 cm³ to 130 mg/100 cm³. After 30 minutes, their blood glucose concentration begins to fall. This is because as the glucose level rises above normal, the pancreas responds by releasing insulin into the blood. The insulin causes body cells to take up the glucose.

After about 80 minutes, the blood glucose concentration is back to its normal level of 90 mg/100 cm³, so the pancreas stops releasing insulin. However, the blood glucose concentration then falls slightly below normal — this is due to some insulin still remaining in the blood.

Person with Type 1 diabetes

After the person with Type 1 diabetes consumes the glucose drink, their blood glucose concentration rises higher than that of the person without diabetes, from 130 mg/100 cm³ to 220 mg/100 cm³. Their glucose level then remains high.

This is because their pancreas produces little or no insulin in response to the rising amount of glucose in the blood, so they are not able to control their blood glucose level.

Tip: If the blood glucose concentration rises high then decreases slowly, the person may be resistant to insulin — this is Type 2 diabetes. E.g.:

Their pancreas is producing insulin but it's not having the proper effect on the body cells.

Tip: There is a time delay between the release of insulin and the reduction of blood glucose concentration. This is because the insulin first needs to travel in the blood to its target cells.

Tip: **H** As the glucose level falls below normal, the pancreas responds by releasing glucagon into the blood. Glucagon works to bring the blood glucose back up to its normal level.

Practice Questions — Fact Recall

Q1 Where in the body is the hormone insulin produced?

Q2 What effect does insulin have on the body's cells?

Q3 Where in the body is the hormone glucagon produced?

Q4 How does glucagon increase blood glucose levels?

Q5 What is Type 1 diabetes?

Q6 Give two ways Type 2 diabetes can be controlled.

Practice Question — Application

Exam Tip
If you are given a graph on blood glucose level in the exam, it's a good idea to look at it carefully and try to work out what it is showing before you start answering the questions. It sounds obvious, but if you just jump straight in you might miss something important.

Q1 In a study, a hormone was injected into a subject while their blood glucose level was monitored. The results are shown in the graph.

a) What hormone do you think was injected?
Explain your answer.

b) i) Name the other main hormone that affects the blood glucose level.

   ii) What do you think would happen to the blood glucose level if this hormone had been injected instead? Explain your answer.

3. Puberty and the Menstrual Cycle

Hormones secreted by the ovaries and the pituitary gland are responsible for controlling the changes that occur during a woman's menstrual cycle.

Puberty

At puberty, your body starts releasing sex hormones that trigger off secondary sexual characteristics (such as the development of facial hair in men and breasts in women) and cause eggs to mature in women.

- In men, the main reproductive hormone is **testosterone**. It's produced by the testes and stimulates sperm production.

- In women, the main reproductive hormone is **oestrogen**. It's produced by the ovaries. As well as bringing about physical changes, oestrogen is also involved in the menstrual cycle.

The menstrual cycle

The menstrual cycle is the monthly sequence of events in which the female body releases an egg and prepares the uterus (womb) in case it receives a fertilised egg. The menstrual cycle has four stages:

Figure 1: *Diagram showing the four stages of the menstrual cycle.*

- **Stage 1**
  Day 1 is when menstruation (bleeding) starts.
  The uterus lining breaks down for about four days.

- **Stage 2**
  The lining of the uterus builds up again, from day 4 to day 14, into a thick spongy layer full of blood vessels, ready to receive a fertilised egg.

- **Stage 3**
  An egg is released from the ovary at day 14. This is called **ovulation**.

- **Stage 4**
  The wall is then maintained for about 14 days, until day 28. If no fertilised egg has landed on the uterus wall by day 28, the spongy lining starts to break down again and the whole cycle starts again.

Learning Objectives:
- Know that reproductive hormones promote secondary sexual characteristics at puberty.
- Know that testosterone, produced in the testes, is the main male reproductive hormone and that it stimulates sperm production.
- Know that oestrogen, produced in the ovaries, is the main female reproductive hormone and that it is involved in the menstrual cycle.
- Know that an egg is released from the ovary roughly every 28 days and that this is known as ovulation.
- Know that hormones are involved in controlling the menstrual cycle.
- Know how follicle stimulating hormone (FSH), luteinising hormone (LH), oestrogen and progesterone are involved in the menstrual cycle.
- **H** Be able to explain how FSH, LH, oestrogen and progesterone interact to control the menstrual cycle.
- **H** Be able to read from and explain graphs showing changing hormone levels during the menstrual cycle.

Specification Reference
4.5.3.3

Figure 2: *A microscope image showing an egg (pink oval) being released from an ovary (brown).*

Hormonal control of the menstrual cycle

You need to know about four hormones that are involved in the menstrual cycle:

- **Follicle stimulating hormone (FSH)**
  FSH causes an egg to mature in one of the ovaries, in a structure called a follicle.

- **Luteinising hormone (LH)**
  LH stimulates the release of an egg at day 14 (ovulation).

- **Oestrogen** and **progesterone**
  These hormones are involved in the growth and maintenance of the uterus lining.

Exam Tip
Make sure you don't talk about egg 'production' or 'development' if you're asked about the menstrual cycle in the exam. Eggs already exist in a woman's ovaries at birth. FSH causes these eggs to <u>mature</u> and LH (see next page) causes them to be <u>released</u>.

Hormonal interaction in the menstrual cycle `Higher`

The levels of the four hormones above fluctuate throughout the cycle (see Figure 3). They also interact with each other to promote or inhibit the release of other hormones.

Exam Tip `H`
In the exam you might be asked to interpret a graph like the one in Figure 3. It might look confusing at first, but if you get your head around what each of the four hormones does, it should start to make more sense. A graph is a really useful way to visualise how the hormones interact when controlling the cycle.

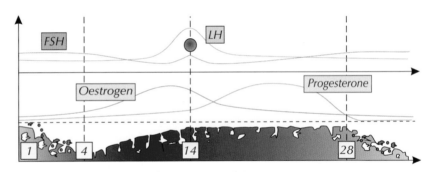

Figure 3: *Diagram showing hormonal changes during the menstrual cycle*

1. **FSH** is produced in the pituitary gland and causes an egg to mature in an ovary. It also stimulates the ovaries to produce oestrogen.

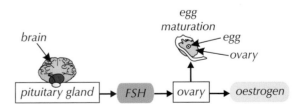

Figure 4: *Diagram showing the role of FSH in the menstrual cycle.*

2. **Oestrogen** is produced in the ovaries and causes the lining of the uterus to grow. It also stimulates the release of LH (which causes the release of an egg) and inhibits the release of FSH.

Tip: **H** The inhibition of FSH by oestrogen makes sure that no more eggs mature during that month's cycle.

Figure 5: *Diagram showing the role of oestrogen in the menstrual cycle.*

3. **LH** is produced by the pituitary gland and stimulates the release of an egg at day 14 (ovulation).

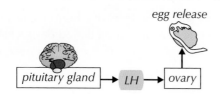

Figure 6: *Diagram showing the role of LH in the menstrual cycle.*

4. **Progesterone** is produced in the ovaries by the remains of the follicle after ovulation. It maintains the lining of the uterus during the second half of the cycle. When the level of progesterone falls, the lining breaks down. Progesterone also inhibits the release of LH and FSH.

Figure 7: *Diagram showing the role of progesterone in the menstrual cycle.*

Levels of FSH, LH, oestrogen and progesterone change throughout the menstrual cycle. So the change in the level of one hormone can be used to predict the change in the level of another hormone:

Exam Tip **H**
In the exam, you might be tested on how the hormones in the menstrual cycle interact by being shown a graph — don't worry, just apply what you know about the effects of each hormone.

Example — Higher

FSH stimulates the ovaries to produce oestrogen, so if the FSH level rises, you'd expect the oestrogen level to rise too. The increasing oestrogen level will then inhibit FSH release, causing the FSH level to drop.

Q1 Name the main female reproductive hormone.

Q2 Give one effect that testosterone has on the male body.

Q3 What effect does FSH have on an egg in the menstrual cycle?

Q4 What is the function of LH?

Q5 Which hormones inhibit the release of FSH?

Q6 Which two glands secrete the hormones that control the menstrual cycle?

Practice Question — Application

Q1 The graph below shows the level of a hormone measured in the bloodstream of one woman during her 28 day menstrual cycle.

Tip: **H** Think about what happens around the middle of the menstrual cycle.

a) Which hormone do you think is shown on the graph? Give a reason for your answer.

b) Where is the hormone you gave in part a) produced?

c) The graph below shows the level of the same hormone measured in another woman during her 28 day menstrual cycle. This woman is struggling to have children. Suggest why this might be.

Tip: **H** Both graphs are drawn to the same scale.

4. Contraceptives

Some of the hormones involved in the menstrual cycle can be used to decrease a woman's fertility and are used in a range of different contraceptives.

Reducing fertility

Contraceptives are used to prevent pregnancy. The hormones oestrogen and progesterone can be taken by women to reduce their **fertility** (their ability to get pregnant) and so are often used as contraceptives.

Oestrogen

Oestrogen can be used to prevent egg release. This may seem kind of strange (since naturally oestrogen helps stimulate the release of eggs — see page 191). But if oestrogen is taken every day to keep the level of it permanently high, it inhibits FSH production, and after a while egg maturation and therefore egg release stop and stay stopped.

Progesterone

Progesterone also reduces fertility, e.g. by stimulating the production of thick cervical mucus which prevents any sperm getting through and reaching an egg. It can inhibit egg maturation and therefore the release of an egg too.

Oral contraceptives

The pill is an oral contraceptive (it can be taken by mouth to decrease fertility). The first version (known as the combined oral contraceptive pill) was made in the 1950s and contained high levels of oestrogen and progesterone.

However, there were concerns about a link between oestrogen in the pill and side effects like blood clots. The pill now contains lower doses of oestrogen so has fewer side effects.

There's also a progesterone-only pill — it has fewer side effects than the combined pill and is just as effective.

There are both positives and negatives associated with using the pill:

Benefits of the combined oral contraceptive pill

- The pill's over 99% effective at preventing pregnancy.
- It's also been shown to reduce the risk of getting some types of cancer.

Problems with the combined oral contraceptive pill

- It isn't 100% effective — there's still a very slight chance of getting pregnant.
- It can cause side effects like headaches, nausea, irregular menstrual bleeding, and fluid retention.
- It doesn't protect against STDs (sexually transmitted diseases).

Learning Objectives:
- Understand that hormonal and non-hormonal methods can be used to control fertility.
- Understand how hormonal methods of contraception work, including oral contraceptives, skin patches, implants, injections and intrauterine devices.
- Understand how non-hormonal methods of contraception work, including barrier methods, spermicidal agents, intrauterine devices, surgery and abstinence.
- Be able to evaluate methods of contraception.

Specification Reference 4.5.3.4

Figure 1: *The contraceptive pill is used to reduce fertility, decreasing the risk of pregnancy.*

Tip: Oral contraceptives are sometimes called birth-control pills.

Figure 2: *The contraceptive patch gets attached to the skin.*

Skin patches, implants and injections

- The contraceptive patch contains oestrogen and progesterone (the same as the combined pill). It's a small (5 cm × 5 cm) patch that's stuck to the skin. Each patch lasts one week.

- The contraceptive implant is inserted under the skin of the arm. It releases a continuous amount of progesterone, which stops the ovaries releasing eggs, makes it hard for sperm to swim to the egg and stops any fertilised egg implanting in the uterus. An implant can last for three years.

- The contraceptive injection also contains progesterone. Each dose lasts 2 to 3 months.

Barrier methods

Non-hormonal barrier forms of contraception are designed to stop the sperm from getting to the egg.

- Condoms are worn over the penis during intercourse to prevent the sperm entering the vagina. There are also female condoms that are worn inside the vagina. Condoms are the only form of contraception that will protect against sexually transmitted diseases.

- A diaphragm is a shallow plastic cup that fits over the cervix (the entrance to the uterus) to form a barrier. It has to be used with spermicide (a substance that disables or kills sperm). Spermicide can be used alone as a contraceptive, but it's not as effective as when used with a diaphragm.

Tip: When a diaphragm is used correctly with spermicide, it's 92-96% effective at preventing pregnancy (so between 4 and 8 women out of 100 that use this method will still become pregnant each year). Spermicide used by itself is only about 70-80% effective. Male condoms are the most effective barrier method at 98%.

Intrauterine devices

An intrauterine device (IUD) is a T-shaped device that is inserted into the uterus to kill sperm and prevent implantation of a fertilised egg. There are two main types — plastic IUDs that release progesterone and copper IUDs that prevent the sperm surviving in the uterus.

Surgical methods

Sterilisation involves cutting or tying the fallopian tubes (which connect the ovaries to the uterus) in a female, or the sperm duct (the tube between the testes and penis) in a male. This is a permanent procedure. However, there is a very small chance that the tubes can rejoin.

Tip: As with oral contraceptives, there are benefits and problems with all of the methods on this page. The contraceptive that is most suitable will differ based on the individual.

Natural methods

Pregnancy may be avoided by finding out when in the menstrual cycle the woman is most fertile and avoiding sexual intercourse on those days. It's popular with people who think that hormonal and barrier methods are unnatural, but it's not very effective. The only way to be completely sure that sperm and egg don't meet is to not have intercourse — this is abstinence.

Practice Questions — Fact Recall

Q1   Explain the function of oestrogen in the combined contraceptive pill.

Q2   Apart from oestrogen, what hormone is found in the combined pill?

Q3   Name one of the barrier methods of controlling fertility.

5. Increasing Fertility `Higher`

Scientific advances in understanding how hormones affect fertility have led to many infertile women being able to have babies. Read on for more...

Increasing fertility

Hormones can be taken by women to increase their fertility. For example, some women have an FSH level that is too low to cause their eggs to mature. This means that no eggs are released and the women can't get pregnant.

The hormones FSH and LH can be injected by these women to stimulate egg maturation and release in their ovaries. These 'fertility drugs' can help a lot of women to get pregnant when previously they couldn't. They are often used during **IVF** too — see below.

Problems with fertility drugs

Using fertility drugs like FSH and LH has its problems:

- They don't always work — some women may have to use the treatment many times, which can be expensive.

- Too many eggs could be stimulated, resulting in unexpected multiple pregnancies (twins, triplets, etc.).

In vitro fertilisation (IVF)

IVF is a process that can be used to help couples who are having difficulty having children.

IVF involves the following steps:

1. FSH and LH are given to the woman to stimulate the maturation of multiple eggs.

2. Eggs are then collected from the woman's ovaries.

3. The eggs are fertilised in a lab using the man's sperm.

4. The fertilised eggs then grow into embryos (small balls of cells) in a laboratory incubator.

5. Once the embryos have formed, one or two of them are transferred to the woman's uterus. Transferring more than one improves the chance of pregnancy.

This is summarised in Figure 1.

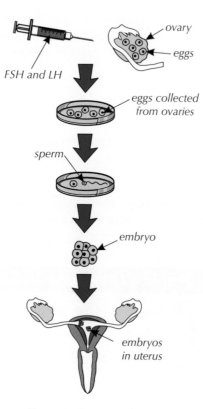

Figure 1: Diagram showing the steps involved in IVF.

FSH and LH → ovary, eggs → eggs collected from ovaries → sperm → embryo → embryos in uterus

Learning Objectives:

- **H** Understand how hormones can be used to treat infertility, including the use of FSH and LH in 'fertility drugs' for women.
- **H** Understand the steps involved in *in vitro* fertilisation (IVF).
- **H** Know about the disadvantages of using IVF to control fertility.

Specification Reference 4.5.3.5

Tip: **H** Flick back to page 190 for a reminder of what the hormones FSH and LH do.

Tip: **H** As well as being hard work, having multiple births puts a bigger stress on the mother and embryos' health during pregnancy.

Tip: **H** IVF treatment can also involve a technique called Intra-Cytoplasmic Sperm Injection (ICSI), where the sperm is injected directly into an egg. It's useful if the man has a very low sperm count.

Figure 2: An embryo ready for transfer into a uterus.

Tip: H These pros and
cons must be taken into
consideration by the
patients being treated for
infertility but also by the
doctor who is treating
them.

The pros and cons of IVF

The main benefit of IVF is that it can give an infertile couple a child — a pretty
obvious benefit. However there are negative sides to the treatment:

- Multiple births can happen if more than one embryo grows into a baby
  — these are risky for the mother and babies (there's a higher risk of
  miscarriage, stillbirth...).

- The success rate of IVF is low — the average success rate in the UK
  is about 26%. This makes the process incredibly stressful and often
  upsetting, especially if it ends in multiple failures.

- As well as being emotionally stressful, the process is also physically
  stressful for the woman. Some women have a strong reaction to the
  hormones — e.g. abdominal pain, vomiting, dehydration.

*Figure 3: A light microscope
image of the fertilisation
of a human egg using
a micro-needle.*

Tip: H You find can out
more about microscopy
on page 25.

Developments in microscopy

Advances in microscope techniques have helped to improve
the techniques (and therefore the success rate) of IVF.

- Specialised micro-tools (see Figure 3) have been developed to use on the
  eggs and sperm under the microscope. They're also used to remove single
  cells from the embryo for genetic testing (to check that it is healthy —
  see page 225).

- More recently, the development of time-lapse imaging (using a
  microscope and camera built into the incubator) means that the growth of
  the embryos can be continuously monitored to help identify those that are
  more likely to result in a successful pregnancy.

Social and ethical issues

The process of IVF often results in unused embryos that are
eventually destroyed. Because of this, some people think it is
unethical because each embryo is a potential human life.

The genetic testing of embryos before implantation also raises ethical issues
as some people think it could lead to the selection of preferred characteristics,
such as gender or eye colour.

Practice Questions — Fact Recall

Q1 Why is a mother given FSH and LH as the first stage of IVF treatment?

Q2 What is the next step after egg collection in IVF?

Q3 Give two downsides of using IVF treatment.

Q4 Give one reason why a person may believe that IVF is unethical.

Practice Question — Application

Q1 The table shows some data about women aged 18-34 undergoing IVF in the UK in 2013 and 2014 using their own fresh eggs.

Year	Number of embryo transfers during IVF	Number of IVF pregnancies
2013	17 892	
2014	17 765	7768

a) Calculate the percentage of embryo transfers that resulted in pregnancy for 18-34 year olds undergoing IVF in 2014.

b) The percentage of embryo transfers that resulted in pregnancy for 18-34 year olds undergoing IVF in 2013 was 41.74%. Calculate the number of these embryo transfers that resulted in pregnancy.

c) The average multiple pregnancy rate of women undergoing IVF in 2014 in the UK with their own fresh eggs was 15.7%. The multiple pregnancy rate of normal pregnancies was lower than this. Give a reason why this might be.

Tip: H IVF can be done using a woman's own fresh eggs (eggs freshly collected from the woman), frozen eggs (eggs which have been extracted at an earlier date and frozen until needed), or using eggs from another woman.

Exam Tip H
Read any data given to you carefully. In this question, make sure you're using the correct numbers from the table.

Learning Objectives:

- **H** Know that thyroxine is a hormone produced in the thyroid gland.
- **H** Understand the role thyroxine plays in metabolism, growth and development.
- **H** Understand how thyroxine is controlled by negative feedback to keep it at the right level in the blood.
- **H** Know that adrenaline is a hormone produced at times of fear and stress in the adrenal glands.
- **H** Understand the role adrenaline plays in the 'flight or fight' response.

Specification Reference 4.5.3.6

6. Thyroxine and Adrenaline Higher

Adrenaline and thyroxine are both pretty useful hormones for us humans.

Thyroxine

Thyroxine is a hormone released by the **thyroid gland**, which is found in the neck.

It plays an important role in regulating the basal metabolic rate — the speed at which chemical reactions in the body occur while the body is at rest. It is also important for loads of processes in the body, such as stimulating protein synthesis for growth and development.

Thyroxine is released in response to thyroid stimulating hormone (TSH), which is released from the pituitary gland.

Negative feedback

As you know from page 170, when the levels of certain substances in the body go above or below a normal level, the body triggers responses that help to bring these levels back into a normal range. This is called negative feedback.

A negative feedback system keeps the amount of thyroxine in the blood at the right level (see Figure 1).

- When the level of thyroxine in the blood is higher than normal, the secretion of TSH from the pituitary gland is inhibited (stopped). This reduces the amount of thyroxine released from the thyroid gland, so the level in the blood falls back towards normal.

- When the level of thyroxine in the blood is lower than normal, the secretion of TSH from the pituitary gland is stimulated (started up) again. This increases the amount of thyroxine released from the thyroid gland, so the level in the blood rises back towards normal.

Tip: **H** You can think about negative feedback working like a thermostat — if the temperature gets too low, the thermostat will turn the heating on, then if the temperature gets too high, it'll turn the heating off again.

Exam Tip **H**
In the exam you could be asked to interpret graphs like Figure 1. Even if they look different, just apply your understanding of negative feedback to help you work out what the diagram is showing you.

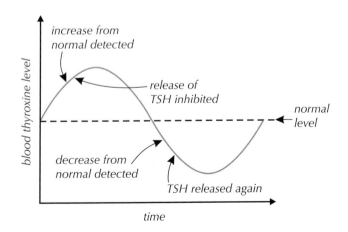

Figure 1: Graph showing how the level of thyroxine in the blood is controlled by negative feedback.

Adrenaline

Adrenaline is a hormone released by the **adrenal glands** (found just above the kidneys — see the diagram on page 182).

It is released in response to stressful or scary situations. Your brain detects fear or stress and sends nervous impulses to the adrenal glands, which respond by secreting adrenaline. Adrenaline gets the body ready for 'fight or flight' by triggering mechanisms that increase the supply of oxygen and glucose to cells in the brain and muscles. For example, it increases heart rate.

Practice Questions — Fact Recall

Q1 Give two roles of thyroxine in the body.

Q2 Name the glands that release adrenaline.

Practice Question — Application

Q1 Pierre is surprised when a dog jumps up at him.
His heart starts to beat faster.

a) Name the hormone that has caused this response.

b) Explain the purpose of this response.

Topic 5b Checklist — Make sure you know...

The Endocrine System

☐ That hormones are chemical molecules which travel in the blood to activate target organs.

☐ That hormones are secreted by glands (e.g. the pituitary gland), and that glands make up the endocrine system.

☐ That the pituitary gland is called the 'master gland' because it releases hormones that act on other glands to stimulate the release of other hormones.

☐ Where the pituitary gland, pancreas, thyroid, adrenal glands, ovaries and testes are found in the body.

☐ That hormones have a slower action than nerve impulses but the effects last longer.

Controlling Blood Glucose

☐ That the pancreas monitors and controls the glucose level of the blood.

☐ That the pancreas produces insulin if blood glucose gets too high — insulin decreases the blood glucose level by causing body cells to take up more glucose from the blood.

☐ That any extra glucose that is not immediately needed by the body is stored as glycogen in liver and muscle cells.

☐ H That the pancreas produces glucagon if blood glucose gets too low — glucagon increases the blood glucose level by causing body cells to convert glycogen into glucose which then enters the blood.

☐ That Type 1 diabetes is a condition where the pancreas produces little to no insulin and that it can be controlled by insulin therapy, eating a carbohydrate-controlled diet and taking regular exercise.

☐ That Type 2 diabetes is a condition where the body's cells don't respond to insulin, and that obesity is a risk factor.

☐ That Type 2 diabetes can be controlled eating a carbohydrate-controlled diet and taking regular exercise.

☐ The differences between the causes and treatments of Type 1 and Type 2 diabetes.

☐ How to read from and interpret graphs that show the effect of insulin on the blood glucose concentration of a person with or without diabetes.

Puberty and the Menstrual Cycle

☐ That sex hormones trigger the development of secondary sexual characteristics during puberty.

☐ That testosterone (produced in the testes) is the main male reproductive hormone and it stimulates sperm production.

☐ That oestrogen (produced in the ovaries) is the main female reproductive hormone and it is involved in the menstrual cycle.

☐ That an egg is released from the ovary approximately every 28 days and that this is called ovulation.

☐ The roles that four hormones (follicle stimulating hormone (FSH), luteinising hormone (LH), oestrogen and progesterone) have in the menstrual cycle.

cont...

☐ H How FSH, LH, oestrogen and progesterone interact to control the menstrual cycle, including the stimulation and inhibition of the release of other hormones.

☐ H How to read from and interpret graphs that show the changing levels of FSH, LH, oestrogen and progesterone during the menstrual cycle.

Contraceptives

☐ That hormonal and non-hormonal methods can be used to control fertility.

☐ How hormonal methods of contraception work, including how oral contraceptives, skin patches, implants, injections and intrauterine devices use oestrogen and/or progesterone to reduce fertility.

☐ How non-hormonal methods of contraception work, including barrier methods, spermicidal agents, intrauterine devices, surgery and abstinence.

☐ How to evaluate different methods of contraception, using their advantages and disadvantages.

Increasing Fertility

☐ H That hormones can be used to treat infertility, e.g. the use of fertility drugs involving FSH and LH.

☐ H The steps involved in IVF and how the process increases the chance of pregnancy.

☐ H That although IVF can give a couple a child, it has disadvantages — it can cause multiple births (which are risky), the success rate is low, and it is emotionally and physically stressful.

Thyroxine and Adrenaline

☐ H That thyroxine is produced in the thyroid gland and helps regulate basal metabolic rate and stimulates protein synthesis for growth and development.

☐ H How negative feedback is used to control the levels of thyroxine in the blood.

☐ H That adrenaline is produced in the adrenal glands and prepares the body for 'fight or flight'.

1 Kaye has recently been diagnosed with Type 1 diabetes.

1.1 Which of the following statements about Type 1 diabetes is true?

    A People with Type 1 diabetes are advised to eat a high sugar diet.

    B Type 1 diabetes allows the blood glucose concentration to get too high.

    C Type 1 diabetes is caused by the liver and stomach failing to produce vital hormones.

    D Type 1 diabetes is directly caused by the overproduction of testosterone.

(1 mark)

Kaye's doctor prescribed her hormone injections to control her condition.

1.2 Name the hormone that the injections will contain.

(1 mark)

1.3 Explain why injecting this hormone can be an effective treatment for Type 1 diabetes.

(3 marks)

1.4 In cases where a patient has particularly poor control over their Type 1 diabetes, a pancreas transplant is sometimes recommended by doctors.

Suggest why a pancreas transplant may be a suitable treatment for Type 1 diabetes but not for Type 2 diabetes.

(3 marks)

1.5 Outline and explain the treatment for Type 2 diabetes.

(4 marks)

2 The diagram below shows how the stages of the menstrual cycle affect the uterus lining.

Some people choose to use a 'natural' method of contraception where they avoid sexual intercourse when the woman is most fertile.

2.1 Based on the diagram above and your knowledge, between which of the days labelled would a couple using this method of contraception avoid sexual intercourse?

(1 mark)

2.2 Suggest **one** advantage and **one** disadvantage of this method of contraception.

(2 marks)

The combined pill is an oral contraceptive that contains oestrogen.
This hormone inhibits FSH production.

2.3 Outline how the inhibition of FSH production prevents pregnancy.

(1 mark)

2.4 Oral contraceptives are not the only type of hormonal contraception available.
Give **three** other methods of hormonal contraception.

(3 marks)

3 Thyroxine is an important hormone of the endocrine system.

3.1 In which of the following glands of the endocrine system is thyroxine produced?

A pituitary   **B** ovary   **C** thyroid   **D** pancreas

(1 mark)

3.2* Describe how the level of thyroxine in the blood is kept at its optimum.

(4 marks)

One role of thyroxine is the regulation of the basal metabolic rate.
Basal metabolic rate can be given as the number of calories burned at rest
in a certain time.

3.3 A man's basal metabolic rate is 1860 kcal/day.
How many calories does he burn at rest during six hours?

(2 marks)

4 A couple are struggling to fall pregnant.
They have decided to try *in vitro* fertilisation (IVF).

4.1 Name the **two** hormones that will be given to the mother during the first stage of IVF.

(2 marks)

4.2 As part of the IVF process, eggs are removed from the mother's ovaries.
Explain why this needs to be done.

(2 marks)

4.3 Two embryos may be implanted into the mother's uterus, rather than just one.
Explain why.

(1 mark)

4.4 Evaluate the use of IVF as a way of becoming pregnant.

(4 marks)

Learning Objectives:

- Know that genetic material is made up from DNA.
- Know that DNA is found in the nucleus of cells, and that it is found in chromosomes.
- Be able to explain the term 'chromosome'.
- Be able to describe the structure of DNA — it is a polymer and has two strands which are coiled together in a double helix shape.
- Be able to explain that a gene is a small section of DNA, and that each one codes for a specific chain of amino acids.
- Know that specific chains of amino acids make specific proteins.
- Know what is meant by the term 'genome'.
- Know why understanding the human genome is a really important tool.

Specification Reference 4.6.1.3

Tip: You might remember learning about genes and chromosomes on pages 33-34 — however, there's a bit more you need to know now.

Tip: Amino acids are the building blocks that make up proteins.

1. DNA

DNA is a pretty important molecule because it's what makes us unique. Therefore it's really important that you learn all about it...

Chromosomes and DNA

DNA stands for deoxyribonucleic acid. It's the chemical that all of the genetic material in a cell is made up from. It contains coded information — basically all the instructions to put an organism together and make it work. So it's what's in your DNA that determines what inherited characteristics you have.

DNA is found in the nucleus of animal and plant cells, in really long structures called **chromosomes**. The DNA is coiled up to form the 'arms' of the chromosome. Chromosomes normally come in pairs.

DNA is a polymer — a large molecule built from a chain of smaller molecules. As you can see from Figure 1, DNA is made up of two strands coiled together in the shape of a **double helix**.

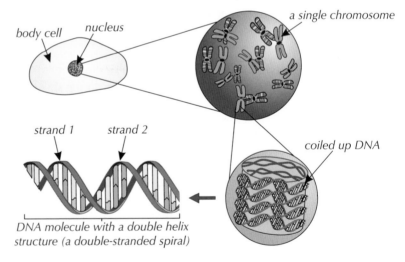

DNA molecule with a double helix structure (a double-stranded spiral)

Figure 1: Diagram showing the structure of DNA and where it is found in a cell.

Genes and proteins

A **gene** is a small section of DNA found on a chromosome. Each gene codes for (tells the cells to make) a particular sequence of amino acids which are put together to make a specific **protein**. Only 20 amino acids are used, but they make up thousands of different proteins. Genes simply tell cells in what order to put the amino acids together.

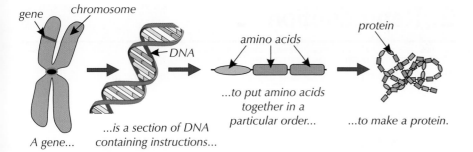

Figure 2: Diagram showing how a gene codes for a protein.

Tip: Another way of saying a gene contains the instructions for a protein is to say a gene 'codes for' a protein.

DNA also determines what proteins the cell produces, e.g. haemoglobin, keratin. That in turn determines what type of cell it is, e.g. red blood cell, skin cell.

Genomes

You need to know the definition of **genome**:

A genome is the entire set of genetic material in an organism.

Scientists have worked out the complete human genome. Understanding the human genome is a really important tool for science and medicine for many reasons.

Tip: A huge research project called the Human Genome Project mapped out the genes that make up human chromosomes.

Examples

- It allows scientists to identify genes in the genome that are linked to different types of disease.

- Knowing which genes are linked to inherited diseases could help us to understand them better and could help us to develop effective treatments for them.

- Scientists can look at genomes to trace the migration of certain populations of people around the world. All modern humans are descended from a common ancestor who lived in Africa, but humans can now be found all over the planet. The human genome is mostly identical in all individuals, but as different populations of people migrated away from Africa, they gradually developed tiny differences in their genomes. By investigating these differences, scientists can work out when new populations split off in a different direction and what route they took.

Figure 3: Analysis of human chromosomes during the Human Genome Project.

Practice Questions — Fact Recall

Q1 Where in a cell is DNA found?

Q2 What are chromosomes made up of?

Q3 Explain why DNA molecules are described as a double helix.

Q4 How does a gene help a cell to make a specific protein?

Q5 What is meant by the term 'genome'?

- Be able to explain the term 'gamete'.

- Know that gametes are produced by meiosis.

- Know that in animals, the gametes are sperm and egg cells.

- Know that in sexual reproduction, male and female gametes are fused.

- Know that in sexual reproduction, genetic information from the mother and father is mixed, which leads to variation in the offspring.

- Know that in flowering plants, the gametes are pollen and egg cells.

- Know that in asexual reproduction there is only one parent, and the offspring are genetical identical to the parent (clones).

- Know that asexual reproduction happens by mitosis, and that identical cells are made.

- Know that in asexual reproduction, gametes do not fuse and genetic information isn't mixed.

Specification References
4.6.1.1, 4.6.1.4

Figure 3: *A sperm (shown in blue) fertilising an egg (shown in yellow) as seen under a microscope.*

2. Reproduction

Organisms make more of themselves through reproduction.
There are two types: sexual and asexual. You need to know about both.

Sexual reproduction

Sexual reproduction is where genetic information from two organisms (a father and a mother) is combined to produce offspring which are genetically different to either parent.

Gametes

In sexual reproduction the mother and father produce gametes (sex cells) by meiosis (see page 208) — e.g. egg and sperm cells in animals (see Figure 1). In humans, each gamete contains 23 chromosomes — half the number of chromosomes in a normal cell. (Instead of having two of each chromosome, a gamete has just one of each.)

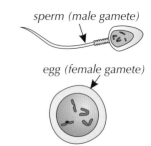

Figure 1: *The sperm and egg cells.*

Fertilisation

The egg (from the mother) and the sperm cell (from the father) fuse together to form a cell with the full number of chromosomes (half from the father, half from the mother). The fusion of gametes is known as fertilisation (see Figure 2).

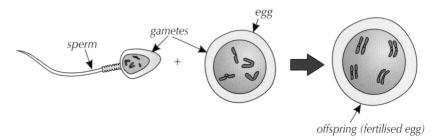

Figure 2: *Diagram showing fertilisation.*

This is why the offspring inherits features from both parents — it's received a mixture of chromosomes from its mum and its dad (and it's the chromosomes that decide how you turn out). This mixture of genetic information produces variation in the offspring. Pretty cool, eh.

Here's the main thing to remember about sexual reproduction:

> Sexual reproduction involves the fusion of male and female gametes. Because there are two parents, the offspring contain a mixture of their parents' genes and are genetically different to their parents.

Flowering plants can reproduce in this way too. They also have egg cells, but their version of sperm is known as pollen.

Asexual reproduction

In asexual reproduction there's only one parent so the offspring are genetically identical to that parent. Asexual reproduction happens by mitosis — an ordinary cell makes a new cell by dividing in two (see pages 35-36). The new cell has exactly the same genetic information (i.e. genes) as the parent cell — it's called a clone.

Here's the main thing to remember about asexual reproduction:

Figure 4: *A single-celled organism called a 'sea sparkle' undergoing asexual reproduction.*

> In asexual reproduction there's only one parent.
> There's no fusion of gametes, no mixing of chromosomes and no genetic variation between parent and offspring. The offspring are genetically identical to the parent — they're **clones**.

Bacteria, some plants and some animals reproduce asexually.

Practice Questions — Fact Recall

Q1   Are gametes produced by meiosis or by mitosis?

Q2   Name the male and female gametes in humans.

Q3   How many parents are there in asexual reproduction?

Practice Question — Application

Q1   For each of the following examples, write down whether it's a case of sexual or asexual reproduction, and explain your answer.

   a) A single-celled amoeba splits in two to form two genetically identical offspring.

   b) Gametes from a male pea plant are crossed with gametes from a female pea plant to produce genetically varied offspring.

   c) A lion and a tiger mate to produce an animal known as a 'liger'. The liger shares features with both its parents.

   d) A single Brahminy blind snake lays a batch of unfertilised eggs. The offspring that hatch are clones of the mother snake.

Tip: To answer these questions, you need to think about the main differences between sexual and asexual reproduction — look back at the green summary boxes if you need clues.

- Know that meiosis produces gametes with only half the normal number of chromosomes, and that when gametes fuse at fertilisation, the full number of chromosomes is restored.
- Know that meiosis only happens in the reproductive organs.
- Be able to recall what happens when a cell divides in meiosis to form genetically different gametes (sperm or egg cells).
- Know that when gametes fuse during fertilisation, the cell that's created divides by mitosis to produce more cells, which start to differentiate as the embryo develops.

Specification Reference 4.6.1.2

Tip: The genetic information is stored in DNA — see page 204.

Figure 2: *Microscope image showing pairs of chromosomes being pulled apart during the first division in meiosis.*

3. Meiosis

You met mitosis back on pages 35-36. Meiosis is another type of cell division. It only happens in the cells of the reproductive organs — it produces gametes.

Gamete production

As you know from page 206, gametes only have one copy of each chromosome, so that when gamete fusion takes place, you get the right amount of chromosomes again (two copies of each).

To make gametes which only have half the original number of chromosomes, cells divide by meiosis. This process involves two cell divisions. In humans, it only happens in the reproductive organs (the ovaries in females and testes in males).

Meiosis

Meiosis produces cells which have half the normal number of chromosomes. Here are the steps involved in meiosis:

1. Before the cell starts to divide, it duplicates its genetic information, forming two armed chromosomes — one arm of each chromosome is an exact copy of the other arm. After replication, the chromosomes arrange themselves into pairs.

2. In the first division in meiosis the chromosome pairs line up in the centre of the cell.

3. The pairs are then pulled apart so each new cell only has one copy of each chromosome. Some of the father's chromosomes (shown in blue) and some of the mother's chromosomes (shown in red) go into each new cell.

4. In the second division, the chromosomes line up again in the centre of the cell. The arms of the chromosomes are pulled apart.

5. You get four gametes, each with only a single set of chromosomes in it. Each of the gametes (sperm or egg cells) is genetically different from the others because the chromosomes all get shuffled up during meiosis and each gamete only gets half of them, at random.

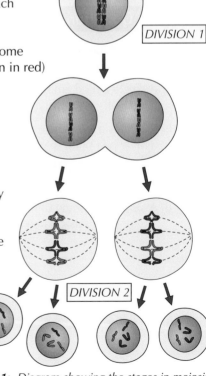

Figure 1: *Diagram showing the stages in meiosis.*

Embryo development

After two gametes have fused during fertilisation, the resulting new cell divides by mitosis to make a copy of itself. Mitosis repeats many times to produce lots of new cells in an embryo. As the embryo develops, these cells then start to differentiate (see page 30) into the different types of specialised cell that make up a whole organism.

Tip: There's loads on mitosis on pages 35-36.

Practice Questions — Fact Recall

Q1 How many sets of chromosomes do gametes contain?

Q2 Where are gametes produced?

Q3 How many cell divisions occur in meiosis?

Q4 How many new cells are produced when a cell divides by meiosis?

Q5 True or False? Gametes are all genetically identical.

Q6 Following fertilisation, how does the resulting cell grow?

Practice Questions — Application

Q1 Different animals have different numbers of chromosomes in their body cells and in their gametes, as shown in the table:

Type of animal cell	Number of chromosomes
Dog body cell	78
Cat egg cell	19
Horse sperm cell	32

Using your knowledge and the information provided in the table, suggest:

a) how many chromosomes there are in a dog sperm cell.

b) how many chromosomes there are in the body cell of a cat.

c) how many chromosomes there are in a horse egg cell.

Q2 Mary thinks that after the first division in meiosis, cells will have half a set of chromosomes. Why does this not happen when a cell divides by meiosis?

Exam Tip
The words 'mitosis' and 'meiosis' look and sound very similar. Make sure that you know how to spell each one. You won't gain marks in the exam if the examiner can't tell which type of cell division you are talking about.

Topic 6a Checklist — Make sure you know...

DNA

☐ That DNA makes up all of the genetic material in cells, and that it's found in the nucleus.

☐ That DNA is found in really long structures called chromosomes.

☐ The structure of DNA — that DNA is a polymer, and that it's made up of two strands coiled together to form a double helix.

☐ That a gene is a small section of DNA, and that each gene in DNA codes for a particular sequence of amino acids which are put together to make a particular protein.

☐ That a genome is the entire set of genetic material in an organism.

☐ That understanding the human genome is important because it means that scientists can link genes to particular diseases, understand and treat inherited disorders effectively, and also trace the migration patterns of human populations.

Reproduction

☐ That gametes are sex cells and are made by meiosis, and that in animals, the gametes are sperm and egg cells.

☐ That in sexual reproduction, male and female gametes fuse together.

☐ That in sexual reproduction, genetic information from the male and female gametes is mixed, which results in variation in the offspring.

☐ That in flowering plants, the gametes are egg cells and pollen.

☐ That in asexual reproduction, there is only one parent, so offspring that are genetically identical to the parent are produced (called clones).

☐ That asexual reproduction happens by mitosis, and produces identical cells.

☐ That in mitosis, there's no fusing of gametes and no mixing of genetic material, which means that there is no variation in the offspring.

Meiosis

☐ That meiosis produces gametes that have half the normal chromosome number, and so when fertilisation happens, the cell that is produced has the full number of chromosomes again.

☐ That in humans, meiosis only happens in the reproductive organs (the ovaries and testes).

☐ That during meiosis, the cell first duplicates its genetic material before dividing twice to produce four gametes.

☐ That each of the gametes produced during meiosis is genetically different because the chromosomes all get shuffled up during meiosis and each gamete only gets half of them, at random — so meiosis produces genetically different cells being formed.

☐ That after fertilisation, the cell that's created divides by mitosis over and over again to produce lots of new cells which differentiate as the embryo develops.

Exam-style Questions

1   A farmer selects a male pig and a female pig and breeds them together.
       Figure 1 shows the process.

Figure 1

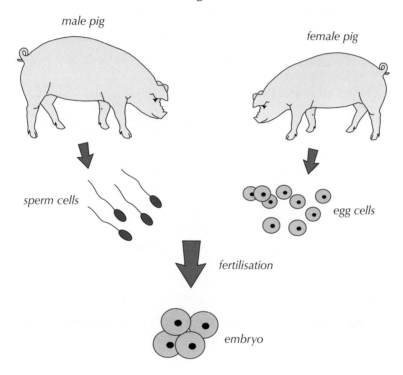

1.1   Is the reproduction shown in **Figure 1** an example of sexual or asexual reproduction?
       Give a reason for your answer.

       (1 mark)

1.2   The pigs that are born as a result of this process will share characteristics with
       both the male pig and the female pig. Explain why.

       (2 marks)

1.3   The sperm cells are gametes.
       Explain why it is important that the sperm cells only have one set of chromosomes.

       (1 mark)

1.4   What type of cell division occurs in the embryo in order for it to grow?

       (1 mark)

2   The Human Genome Project was a major genetics project that revealed the genes in the human body.

2.1   Outline what is meant by the term 'human genome'.

(1 mark)

2.2   Give **two** reasons why research into the human genome is important.

(2 marks)

3   **Figure 2** shows an animal cell.

Figure 2

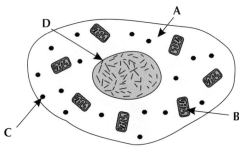

3.1   Which of the labels, A-D, on **Figure 2** shows where DNA strands are found in an animal cell?

(1 mark)

3.2   Which one of the following sentences is correct?

A   DNA is made up of amino acids joined together.
B   DNA is found in a triple helix shape.
C   DNA determines the characteristics you inherit.
D   DNA is always found in single strands.

(1 mark)

3.3   Describe the structure of a DNA molecule.

(3 marks)

3.4*   The genetic material in animal cells exists in the form of genes and chromosomes.

Describe what is meant by these terms and outline how they are linked with each other.

(4 marks)

3.5   Gametes contain genetic material in the form of DNA.
Name the type of cell division used to make gametes.

(1 mark)

1. X and Y Chromosomes

We all know that there are loads of differences between males and females. It's all to do with two little chromosomes — X and Y.

Sex chromosomes

There are 23 pairs of chromosomes in every human body cell. Of these, 22 are matched pairs of chromosomes — these just control your characteristics. The 23rd pair are labelled XY or XX. They're the two chromosomes that decide your sex — whether you turn out male or female.

Males have an **X** and a **Y** chromosome: **XY**
The Y chromosome causes male characteristics.

Females have **two X** chromosomes: **XX**
The XX combination allows female characteristics to develop.

When making sperm, the X and Y chromosomes from the original male cell are drawn apart in the first division of meiosis (see page 208) for more on meiosis). There's a 50% chance each sperm cell gets an X chromosome and a 50% chance it gets a Y chromosome (see Figure 1).

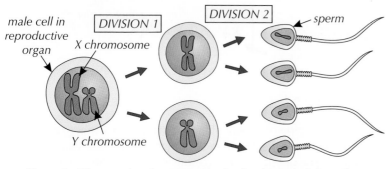

Figure 1: *Diagram showing sperm production by meiosis in males.*

A similar thing happens when making eggs. But the original cell has two X chromosomes (as it's from a female), so all the eggs end up with one X chromosome (see Figure 2).

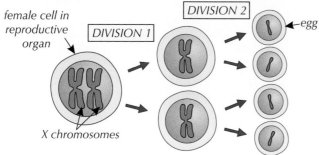

Figure 2: *Diagram showing egg production by meiosis in females.*

Learning Objectives:

- Know that there are 23 pairs of chromosomes found in ordinary human body cells and that 22 of these pairs just control characteristics.

- Know that the genes which determine sex are carried on the 23rd pair of chromosomes — the sex chromosomes.

- Know that females have two of the same sex chromosome (XX) whereas males have two different sex chromosomes (XY).

- Be able to complete and interpret genetic diagrams to show sex inheritance.

- Be able to understand probability in terms of the outcome of a genetic cross.

- Be able to express the outcome of a genetic cross using ratios or direct proportion.

- **H** Be able to construct genetic diagrams.

Specification References
4.6.1.4, 4.6.1.6

Figure 3: *Here's what the sex chromosomes actually look like. The Y chromosome (shown in blue) is smaller than the (pink) X chromosome.*

Exam Tip
Most genetic diagrams you'll see in exams concentrate on a gene, instead of a chromosome. But the principle's the same. Don't worry — there are loads of other examples on pages 218-224.

Tip: Only one of these possible combinations would actually happen for any one offspring.

Sex inheritance and genetic diagrams

At fertilisation, the sperm fertilises the egg, and the chromosomes from the gametes combine, forming a new individual with the correct number of chromosomes (see page 206). Whether the individual is male or female depends on the combination of sex chromosomes it receives — this is sex inheritance.

Genetic diagrams can be used to show sex inheritance. They are just models that are used to show all the possible genetic outcomes when you cross together different genes or chromosomes.

Interpreting genetic diagrams

You need to be able to interpret genetic diagrams showing sex inheritance.

Examples

Figure 4 is a type of genetic diagram called a Punnett square, showing sex inheritance. The pairs of letters in the middle show the possible combinations of the gametes.

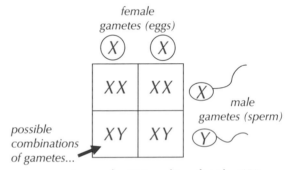

...two males (XY) and two females (XX).

Figure 4: *Punnett square showing sex inheritance.*

Figure 5 is another type of genetic diagram showing sex inheritance. It looks a bit more complicated than a Punnett square, but it shows exactly the same thing. The possible combinations of gametes are shown in the bottom circles.

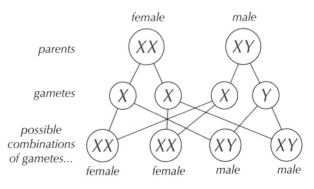

Figure 5: *Genetic diagram showing sex inheritance.*

You can use genetic diagrams to find the probability of any offspring inheriting either combination of sex chromosomes. (You can also use them to find the probability of offspring inheriting a certain characteristic — see pages 218-224.)

Probability is a measure of how likely something is to happen. In maths, the probability of a certain event happening is written as a number between 0 (impossible) and 1 (certain). It can also be written as a fraction or a percentage.

Example

Both Figure 4 and Figure 5 show two XX results and two XY results, so there's an equal probability of getting a boy or a girl. This can be written as a 50:50 ratio, which is the same as 1:1. Alternatively, you could say the probability of getting a boy is 1 in 2, 50%, 0.5 or ½.

Constructing genetic diagrams `Higher`

You can construct genetic diagrams to show sex inheritance.

Example 1 — **Higher**

Drawing a Punnett square to show sex inheritance in humans.

1. First, draw a grid with four squares.

2. Put the possible gametes (eggs or sperm) from one parent down the side, and those from the other parent along the top.

3. Then in each middle square you fill in the letters from the top and side that line up with that square — the pairs of letters in the middle show the possible combinations of the gametes.

Figure 7 shows these steps:

Figure 7: How to draw a Punnett square to show sex inheritance in humans.

Tip: Don't forget that this 50:50 ratio is only a probability at each pregnancy. If you had four kids they could all be boys.

Tip: There's more about ratios on page 297.

Figure 6: Having lots of sons doesn't increase the chances of having a daughter in the next pregnancy. There's still a 50:50 chance of having a boy or a girl at each pregnancy.

Example 2 — Higher

Drawing a different type of genetic diagram to show sex inheritance in humans.

1. Draw two circles at the top of the diagram to represent the parents. Put the female sex chromosomes in one and the male sex chromosomes in the other.

female parent   *male parent*

XX   XY

Tip: 🄷 Remember, one gamete from the female combines with one gamete from the male during fertilisation. It's quite easy to get confused, so check you aren't drawing lines that put both the male's gametes or both the female's gametes into the same circle.

2. Draw two circles below each of the parent circles to represent the possible gametes. Put a single chromosome from each parent in each circle. Draw lines to show which chromosomes come from each parent.

female parent   *male parent*

XX   XY

X   X   X   Y

3. One gamete from the female combines with one gamete from the male during fertilisation, so draw criss-cross lines to show all the possible ways the X and Y chromosomes could combine.

female parent   *male parent*

4. Then write the possible combinations of gametes in the bottom circles.

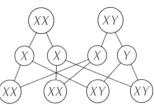

female parent   *male parent*

XX   XY

X   X   X   Y

XX   XX   XY   XY

Practice Questions — Fact Recall

Q1 How many of the 23 pairs of human chromosomes determine sex?

Q2 True or False? All sperm cells carry the Y chromosome.

Practice Questions — Application

Rachael and her husband Luca are expecting their first child.

Q1 Complete this genetic diagram to show the possible combinations of sex chromosomes that the baby could have.

Q2 What is the probability that their child will be a boy?

Q3 Draw a Punnett square to show the possible combinations of sex chromosomes that Rachael and Luca's baby could have.

Rachael   *Luca*

XX   XY

X   X   X   Y

female   *female*   *male*   *male*

2. Alleles and Genetic Diagrams

The next few pages are all about how our genes determine our characteristics...

Genes and characteristics

What genes (see p. 204) you inherit control what characteristics you develop. Different genes control different characteristics. Most characteristics are controlled by several genes interacting. However, some characteristics are controlled by a single gene.

> **Examples**
>
> - Mouse fur colour — see Figure 1.
>
> - Red-green colour blindness in humans.

Figure 1: *Two mice with different coloured fur.*

What are alleles?

All genes exist in different versions called alleles. Gametes only have one allele, but all the other cells in an organism have two — one on each chromosome in a pair (see Figure 2). This is because we inherit half of our alleles from our mother and half from our father. In genetic diagrams, letters are usually used to represent alleles.

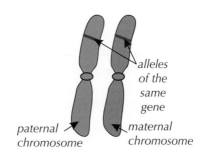

Figure 2: *Diagram showing two alleles for the same gene.*

For characteristics controlled by a single gene, if an organism has two alleles for that particular gene that are the same, then it's **homozygous** for that trait. If its two alleles for a particular gene are different, then it's **heterozygous**. If the two alleles are different, only one can determine what characteristic is present. The allele for the characteristic that's shown is called the **dominant** allele (use a capital letter for dominant alleles — e.g. 'C'). The other one is called **recessive** (and you show these with small letters — e.g. 'c').

For an organism to display a recessive characteristic, both its alleles must be recessive (e.g. cc). But to display a dominant characteristic the organism can be either CC or Cc, because the dominant allele overrules the recessive one if the plant/animal/other organism is heterozygous.

Your **genotype** is the combination of alleles you have, e.g. you could have the genotype Bb for hair colour. Your alleles work at a molecular level (by coding for slightly different proteins — see page 204) to determine what characteristics you have — your **phenotype**, e.g. brown eyes, blonde hair, etc.

Learning Objectives:

- Know that most characteristics are controlled by several genes but some characteristics are controlled by just one gene — e.g. fur colour in mice and red-green colour blindness in humans.

- Be able to explain the terms 'allele', 'homozygous', heterozygous', 'dominant' and 'recessive'.

- Understand that if two different alleles of the same gene are present, then the allele for the characteristic displayed is dominant, and the allele for the characteristic that isn't displayed is recessive.

- Know that two recessive alleles are needed for a recessive characteristic to be displayed.

- Be able to explain the terms 'genotype' and 'phenotype'.

- Know that your genotype determines your phenotype.

- Be able to complete and interpret genetic diagrams showing single gene inheritance.

- Be able to express the outcome of a single gene cross using ratios or direct proportion.

- **H** Be able to construct genetic diagrams and use them to predict what will happen in single gene crosses.

Specification Reference
4.6.1.4

Single gene inheritance

Characteristics that are determined by a single gene can be studied using **single gene crosses**. This is where you cross two parents to look at just one characteristic. In the exam they could ask you about the inheritance of any characteristic controlled by a single gene, as the principle's always the same.

Tip: 'Cross' just means 'breed together'.

Genetic diagrams of single gene inheritance

Genetic diagrams allow you to see how certain characteristics are inherited. The inheritance of round or wrinkly peas from pea plants is an example of single gene inheritance and can be shown using genetic diagrams.

Figure 3: The peas produced by pea plants can either be wrinkly (left) or round (right).

Tip: In this example, a plant producing wrinkly peas must be homozygous recessive (it must have 'rr' alleles). However, a plant producing round peas could be homozygous dominant or heterozygous — it can have two possible combinations of alleles — RR or Rr.

Example 1

The gene which causes wrinkly peas is recessive, so you can use a small 'r' to represent it. Round peas are due to a dominant gene, which you can represent with a capital 'R'. If you cross one pea plant which produces wrinkly peas (rr) and one that produces round peas (in this case RR), all of the offspring will produce round peas — but they'll have the alleles Rr.

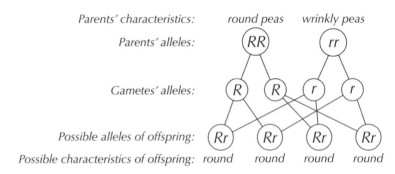

You can also show this genetic cross in a Punnett square:

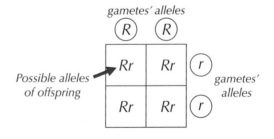

You need to be able to use genetic diagrams to predict and explain the outcomes of single gene crosses between individuals for lots of different combinations of alleles. The outcomes are given as ratios and can be used to work out the probability of having offspring with a certain characteristic.

A 3:1 ratio in the offspring

A cross could produce a 3:1 ratio of certain characteristics in the offspring. On the next page there's an example showing that this would happen if two of the heterozygous offspring from Example 1 were crossed.

Example 2

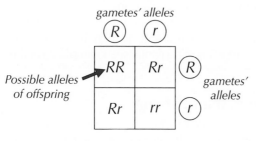

Parents' characteristics: round peas   round peas

Parents' alleles: Rr   Rr

Gametes' alleles: R   r   R   r

Possible alleles of offspring: RR   Rr   Rr   rr

Possible characteristics of offspring: round   round   round   wrinkly

Again, this cross can be shown in a Punnett square:

gametes' alleles

R   r

	R	r
R	RR	Rr
r	Rr	rr

Possible alleles of offspring

gametes' alleles

This cross gives a 3:1 ratio of plants producing round peas to plants producing wrinkly peas. This means there's a 1 in 4, 25%, 0.25 or ¼ chance of any new pea plant having wrinkly peas. Remember that "results" like this are only probabilities — they don't say definitely what'll happen.

All the offspring are the same

More than one cross could result in all of the offspring showing the same characteristic. Here you have to do some detective work to find out what's gone on:

Example 3

If you cross a homozygous pea plant that produces round peas (so has two dominant alleles — RR), with a homozygous pea plant that produces wrinkly peas (rr), all the offspring will be heterozygous (Rr), so produce round peas:

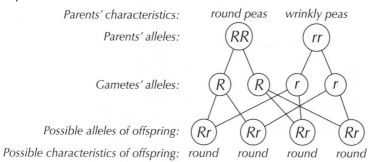

Parents' characteristics: round peas   wrinkly peas

Parents' alleles: RR   rr

Gametes' alleles: R   R   r   r

Possible alleles of offspring: Rr   Rr   Rr   Rr

Possible characteristics of offspring: round   round   round   round

This means there's a 100% probability of any new pea plant having round peas.

But, if you crossed a homozygous pea plant that produces round peas (RR), with a heterozygous pea plant that produces round peas (so has a dominant

Exam Tip
In the exam you might be given the results of a breeding experiment and asked to say whether a characteristic is dominant or recessive. To figure it out, look at the ratios of the characteristic in different generations. For example, in Example 2 here the 3:1 ratio of round to wrinkly peas shows that the round allele is dominant.

Exam Tip
A 3:1 ratio of plants producing round peas to plants producing wrinkly peas means there's a 1 in 4 chance of a new plant having wrinkly peas, not a 1 in 3 chance — it's an easy mistake to make, so be careful when you're talking about proportions and probabilities.

Tip: You can see a Punnett square showing this cross in Example 1 on the previous page.

and a recessive allele — Rr), you would also only get offspring that produce round peas:

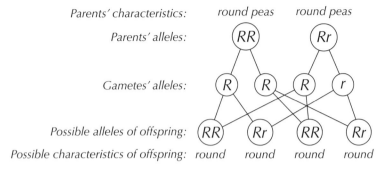

Parents' characteristics: round peas · round peas
Parents' alleles: RR · Rr
Gametes' alleles: R · R · R · r
Possible alleles of offspring: RR · Rr · RR · Rr
Possible characteristics of offspring: round · round · round · round

Tip: You know the drill by now — here's the Punnett square showing this cross:

	R	R
R	RR	RR
r	Rr	Rr

To find out which cross you'd done, you'd have to breed the offspring together and see what kind of ratio you got — then you'd have a good idea. If it was a 3:1 ratio of round to wrinkly in the offspring, it's likely that you originally had RR and rr plants (see Example 2 on the previous page).

A 1:1 ratio in the offspring

Next up is an example of when a cross produces a 1:1 ratio in the offspring — half the offspring are likely to show one characteristic and half are likely to show another characteristic. This time we're using cats with long and short hair. (Peas are a bit dull...)

Example

A cat's long hair is caused by a dominant allele 'H'. Short hair is caused by a recessive allele 'h'. A heterozygous cat with long hair (Hh) was bred with a homozygous cat with short hair (hh):

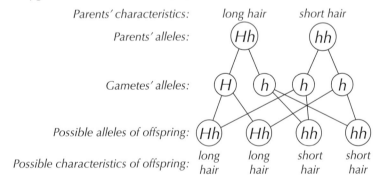

Parents' characteristics: long hair · short hair
Parents' alleles: Hh · hh
Gametes' alleles: H · h · h · h
Possible alleles of offspring: Hh · Hh · hh · hh
Possible characteristics of offspring: long hair · long hair · short hair · short hair

Here's the Punnett square for this cross:

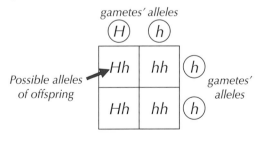

gametes' alleles

	H	h
h	Hh	hh
h	Hh	hh

Possible alleles of offspring

gametes' alleles

This is a 1:1 ratio, which gives a 50% probability of a new cat being born to these parents having long hair.

Exam Tip
Half the offspring of this cross are homozygous recessive — their genotype is 'hh', which produces a short-haired phenotype. The other half are heterozygous — their genotype is 'Hh', producing a long-haired phenotype. Get used to using terms such as 'homozygous', 'heterozygous', 'dominant', 'recessive' 'genotype' and 'phenotype' now — it'll really help you out in the exams.

Constructing genetic diagrams   Higher

You need to be able to construct genetic diagrams for single gene crosses.

Example 1 — Higher

Drawing a Punnett square to show a cross between a pea plant with round peas (Rr) and a pea plant with wrinkly peas (rr).

1. First, draw a grid with four squares.

2. Put the possible alleles from one parent down the side, and those from the other parent along the top.

3. Then in each middle square you fill in the letters from the top and side that line up with that square — the pairs of letters in the middle show the possible combinations of the alleles.

The steps are shown here:

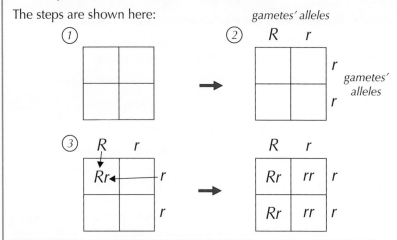

> **Tip:** H Constructing the genetic diagrams shown on this page is just the same as constructing the sex inheritance diagrams on pages 215-216 — the only difference is that you are showing alleles here rather than chromosomes.

Example 2 — Higher

Drawing a genetic diagram to show a cross between a pea plant with wrinkly peas (rr) and a pea plant with round peas (RR).

1. Draw two circles at the top of the diagram to represent the parents. Put the round genotype in one and the wrinkly genotype in the other.

2. Draw two circles below each of the parent circles to represent the possible gametes. Put a single allele from each parent in each circle.

3. One gamete from the female combines with one gamete from the male during fertilisation, so draw criss-cross lines to show all the possible ways the alleles could combine.

4. Then write the possible combinations of alleles in the offspring in the bottom circles.

These steps are illustrated here:

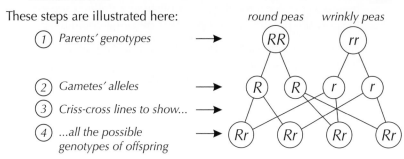

Practice Questions — Fact Recall

Q1　Give an example of a characteristic controlled by a single gene.

Q2　Explain what is meant by each of these terms:

　　a) alleles

　　b) homozygous

　　c) dominant allele

　　d) phenotype

Practice Questions — Application

Q1　A female cat has the genotype Ss. 'S' is the allele for spots and is dominant. 's' is the allele for no spots and is recessive.

　　a) Is the cat homozygous or heterozygous for the spot allele?

　　b) What genotype would a cat without spots have?

　　c) What other possible genotype could a spotty cat have?

Q2　Charlotte has some guinea pigs with rough coats and some guinea pigs with smooth coats. The allele for a rough coat is represented by 'R'. The allele for a smooth coat is represented by 'r'. The rough coat allele is dominant to the smooth coat allele. She crosses a rough coated guinea pig (RR) with a smooth coated guinea pig (rr). Here is a genetic diagram of the cross:

Parents' characteristics:　*female*　*male*　*smooth coat*　*rough coat*

Parents' alleles:　rr　RR

Gametes' alleles:　r　r　R　R

Possible alleles of offspring:　Rr　Rr　Rr　Rr

　　a) What type of coat will the offspring have?

　　b) i)　Charlotte breeds two guinea pigs together that are both heterozygous for a rough coat. Construct a Punnett square to show the possible genotypes their offspring could have.

　　　ii) From the Punnett square, what is the probability of the offspring having a smooth coat?

Exam Tip H
Make sure you read exam questions carefully to avoid throwing away easy marks. For example, in Q2 you're asked to construct a Punnett square — if you were asked this question in the exam and you produced a different type of genetic diagram you wouldn't get all the marks available to you.

3. Inherited Disorders

It's not just an organism's characteristics that can be passed on to its offspring — some disorders can be too. These are known as inherited disorders.

What are inherited disorders?

Inherited disorders are disorders that are caused by a faulty allele, which can be passed on to an individual's offspring. You need to know about two inherited disorders — **cystic fibrosis** and **polydactyly**.

Cystic fibrosis

Cystic fibrosis is an inherited disorder of the cell membranes. It results in the body producing a lot of thick sticky mucus in the air passages (which makes breathing difficult) and in the pancreas.

The allele which causes cystic fibrosis is a recessive allele, carried by about 1 person in 25. Because it's recessive, people with only one copy of the allele won't have the disorder — they're known as **carriers** (they carry the faulty allele, but don't have any symptoms).

For a child to have the disorder, both parents must be either carriers or have the disorder themselves. There's a 1 in 4 chance of a child having the disorder if both parents are carriers. This is shown in Figure 1, where 'f' is used for the recessive cystic fibrosis allele.

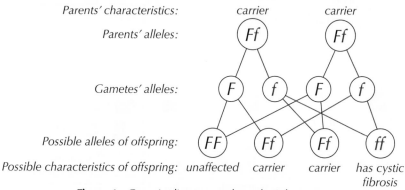

Figure 1: *Genetic diagram to show the inheritance of cystic fibrosis from two carriers.*

Polydactyly

Polydactyly is an inherited disorder where a baby's born with extra fingers or toes (see Figure 2). It doesn't usually cause any other problems so isn't life-threatening.

The disorder is caused by a dominant allele and so can be inherited if just one parent carries the defective allele. The parent that has the defective allele will have the condition too since the allele is dominant.

Learning Objectives:

- Know that some disorders are inherited, due to certain alleles being passed on to offspring.
- Know that cystic fibrosis is an inherited disorder affecting the cell membranes.
- Understand that people will only have cystic fibrosis if both their parents possess the faulty allele because it's a recessive disorder.
- Know that polydactyly is an inherited disorder that results in a person having extra fingers or toes.
- Understand that people will have polydactyly if only one parent has the allele because it is a dominant disorder.
- Be able to interpret family trees.
- Appreciate the economic, social and ethical issues surrounding the screening of embryos.

Specification References
4.6.1.4, 4.6.1.5

Figure 2: *X ray of a hand with an extra finger. This person has polydactyly.*

There's a 50% chance of a child having the disorder if one parent has the polydactyly allele. This is shown in Figure 3, where 'D' is used for the dominant polydactyly allele.

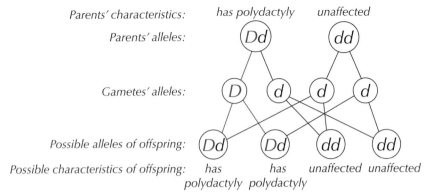

Figure 3: Genetic diagram to show the inheritance of polydactyly from a person with the condition and an unaffected individual.

Tip: Remember that there are no carriers for polydactyly. If you carry the faulty gene then you will be affected because the disorder is caused by a dominant allele, so you only need one copy to have the disorder.

Family trees

In genetics, a family tree is a diagram that shows how a characteristic (or disorder) is inherited in a group of related people. In the exam you might be asked to interpret a family tree.

Exam Tip
In the exam you might get a family tree showing the inheritance of a dominant allele — in this case there won't be any carriers shown.

Example

Here is a family tree for cystic fibrosis:

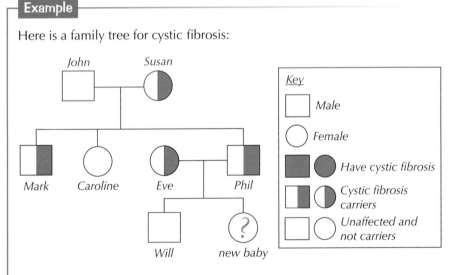

From the family tree, you can tell that:

1. The allele for cystic fibrosis isn't dominant because plenty of the family carry the allele but don't have the disorder.

2. There is a 25% chance that Eve and Phil's new baby will have the disorder and a 50% chance that it will be a carrier, as Eve and Phil are carriers but are unaffected. This is because the case of the new baby is just the same as in the genetic diagram on the previous page — so the baby could be unaffected (FF), a carrier (Ff) or have cystic fibrosis (ff).

Exam Tip
A good way to work out a family tree is to write the genotype of each person onto it.

Embryonic screening

Embryonic screening is a way of detecting inherited disorders, such as cystic fibrosis, in embryos. There are different methods used to do this:

1. **Pre-implantation genetic diagnosis (PGD).** During IVF, embryos are fertilised in a laboratory, and then implanted into the mother's womb. Before being implanted, it's possible to remove a cell from each embryo and analyse its genes (see Figure 4) — this is called pre-implantation genetic diagnosis (PGD). Embryos with 'healthy' alleles would be implanted into the mother — the ones with 'faulty' alleles destroyed.

2. **Chorionic villus sampling (CVS).** CVS is usually carried out between 10 and 13 weeks of pregnancy. It involves taking a sample of cells from part of the placenta and analysing their genes. The part of the placenta that's taken and the embryo develop from the same original cell — so they have the same genes. If the embryo is found to have an inherited disorder, the parents can decide whether or not to terminate (end) the pregnancy.

Figure 4: *A single cell being extracted from an embryo in order to be screened for inherited disorders.*

> **Tip:** The placenta is an organ that attaches the embryo to the lining of the womb. It provides the developing embryo with nutrients and takes away waste.

Issues surrounding embryonic screening

There is a huge debate raging about embryonic screening. Here's why:

Arguments for screening

- It helps to stop people suffering from certain inherited disorders.
- Treating disorders costs the Government (and the taxpayers) a lot of money, so screening embryos could reduce healthcare costs.
- During IVF, most of the embryos are destroyed anyway — PGD just ensures that the selected one is healthy.
- If an inherited disorder is diagnosed through CVS, parents don't have to have a termination — but it does give them the choice.

Arguments against screening

- There may come a point where everyone wants to screen their embryos so they can pick the most 'desirable' one, e.g. they want a blue-eyed, blond-haired, intelligent boy.
- It implies that people with genetic problems are 'undesirable' — this could increase prejudice.
- After PGD, the rejected embryos are destroyed — they could have developed into humans, so some people think destroying them is unethical.
- There's a risk that CVS could cause a miscarriage. And if an inherited disorder is diagnosed through CVS, it could lead to a termination (abortion).
- Screening embryos is expensive.

> **Tip:** There are laws to stop embryonic screening going too far. At the moment, parents can't even select their baby's sex (unless it's for health reasons).

Many people think that screening isn't justified for inherited disorders that don't affect a person's health:

> **Example**
>
> Polydactyly causes a physical disfigurement but it isn't life-threatening, so lots of people don't agree with screening for it. In comparison, conditions such as cystic fibrosis are potentially life-threatening and so more people agree to screening for them.

> **Exam Tip**
> You could be given some data about screening for inherited disorders in the exam, and then asked questions about it. You'll just need to read the information given to you carefully, and apply what you know.

Practice Questions — Fact Recall

Q1 What subcellular structure does cystic fibrosis affect?

Q2 Is cystic fibrosis caused by a dominant or recessive allele?

Q3 Why would an embryo be screened before it is inserted into the mother's uterus during IVF?

Practice Questions — Application

Q1 If 'f' represents the recessive allele for cystic fibrosis and 'F' represents the dominant allele:

a) give the alleles a carrier of cystic fibrosis would have.

b) give the alleles that a person with cystic fibrosis would have.

Q2 The family tree below shows the inheritance of the inherited disorder polydactyly in a family.

Using the family tree, answer the following questions:

a) From the diagram, how do you know that the allele for polydactyly is dominant?

b) If the new baby was a girl with polydactyly, what symbol would she have on the family tree?

For the following questions, use 'D' to represent the allele for polydactyly and 'd' to represent the allele for an unaffected person.

c) Give the genotype of the following individuals:

   i) Clark   ii) Kate

d) Kate and Aden are having a baby.

   i) Draw a Punnett square to show the inheritance of polydactyly from Kate and Aden.

   ii) What is the probability the new baby will have polydactyly?

Exam Tip
Sometimes you can't tell a person's genotype from looking straight at the family tree and the key — you might need to do a bit of detective work and figure out the genotypes of other people on the tree.

Topic 6b Checklist — Make sure you know...

X and Y Chromosomes

☐ That 22 of the 23 pairs of chromosomes in a human body cell are just responsible for controlling your characteristics and the 23rd pair of chromosomes carry the genes that determine sex. The 23rd pair of chromosomes are called sex chromosomes — females have two X sex chromosomes and males have an X sex chromosome and a Y sex chromosome.

☐ How to complete and interpret genetic diagrams to show sex inheritance.

☐ How to use probability to predict the likelihood of a result of a genetic diagram, and how to express the results of a genetic diagram using ratios or direct proportion.

☐ ▣ How to construct genetic diagrams to show sex inheritance.

Alleles and Genetic Diagrams

☐ That most characteristics are controlled by several genes, but some are controlled by just one gene — e.g. fur colour in mice and red-green colour blindness in humans.

☐ That all genes exist in different forms called alleles, and that if an organism has two alleles for a gene that are the same then it is homozygous. If the two alleles are different then it's heterozygous.

☐ That if an individual is heterozygous for a characteristic, the allele for the characteristic that is displayed is dominant, and the other allele is recessive. You need to be homozygous recessive for a recessive characteristic to be displayed.

☐ That your genotype is the combination of alleles you have (e.g. Gg, bb) and that these alleles work at the molecular level to determine your phenotype — the characteristics that you have (e.g. blue eyes, blonde hair).

☐ That single gene inheritance is where the alleles of a single gene control a characteristic.

☐ How to complete and interpret genetic diagrams showing the inheritance of a single gene for all combinations of dominant and recessive alleles.

☐ How to express the results of a single gene cross (a cross between two parents that looks at just one characteristic inherited by a single gene) as a ratio or a directly proportional relationship.

☐ ▣ How to construct genetic diagrams to predict the results of single gene crosses.

Inherited Disorders

☐ That inherited disorders result from faulty alleles, which can be passed onto an individual's offspring.

☐ That cystic fibrosis is an inherited disorder of the cell membranes caused by a recessive allele, meaning that both parents of a person with cystic fibrosis must have the faulty allele for that person to inherit the condition. If a person inherits just one allele for cystic fibrosis, they will be a carrier.

☐ That polydactyly is an inherited disorder where people have extra fingers and toes, and it's caused by a dominant allele, meaning that anyone who inherits a single polydactyly allele from one of their parents will have the condition.

☐ How to interpret family trees (diagrams showing how a characteristic is inherited in a group of related people).

☐ What the economic, social and ethical issues surrounding embryonic screening are and be able to form opinions regarding these given relevant information.

Exam-style Questions

1 In a certain type of plant, the allele which causes a tall plant is dominant (T) and the allele which causes a dwarf plant is recessive (t). What would the genotype be for a dwarf plant?

    A   TT

    B   Tt

    C   tt

    D   tT

(1 mark)

2 Polydactyly is an example of an inherited disorder.

2.1 What effect does polydactyly have on a person?

(1 mark)

2.2 If 'D' represents the allele for polydactyly and 'd' represents the allele for an unaffected person, give the possible genotype(s) of a person with polydactyly.

(1 mark)

2.3 Greg is homozygous for the polydactyly allele. Which of the following shows Greg's genotype?

    A   DD

    B   dd

    C   Dd

    D   dDd

(1 mark)

2.4 Greg's parents are both heterozygous for the polydactyly allele.

Draw a Punnett square and identify any offspring with polydactyly.
Write the ratio of affected to unaffected offspring.

(4 marks)

3 Kaye and Mark are expecting a baby.

3.1 Complete the sex inheritance Punnett square in **Figure 1** for Kaye and Mark's baby.

Kaye's gametes

Figure 1

	X	
X	XX	

Mark's gametes

(2 marks)

3.2 Kaye and Mark have found out that they are expecting a baby boy. What combination of sex chromosomes will the baby have?

(1 mark)

3.3 Kaye has dimples in her cheeks, but Mark does not.
The presence of dimples is thought to be caused by a dominant allele represented by the letter **D**. The recessive allele is represented by the letter **d**.
Kaye is heterozygous for the dimples gene.

What is the probability that the baby will have dimples?

Draw a genetic diagram to show the possible inheritance of the dimples gene by the baby. Identify the phenotype of each possible outcome.

(5 marks)

4 Family trees can show the inheritance of characteristics, such as cystic fibrosis.

Figure 2 is a family tree showing the inheritance of cystic fibrosis in a family.

Figure 2

4.1 What is cystic fibrosis?

(2 marks)

4.2 Is Gareth heterozygous or homozygous for the cystic fibrosis allele?
Explain your answer.

(1 mark)

4.3 Bex and Tony have a child with cystic fibrosis. However, Bex doesn't have cystic fibrosis. Therefore, what combination of alleles must Bex have for the cystic fibrosis gene? Explain your answer.

(3 marks)

4.4 Bex and Tony are considering having another child.
They want to use *in vitro* fertilisation (IVF) so that they can select an embryo without cystic fibrosis to be implanted into Bex's womb. The remaining embryos that aren't implanted will be destroyed.

Give **two** reasons why some people are against this use of embryonic screening.

(2 marks)

4.5 Looking at the family tree, could Ivana and Tam have a child with cystic fibrosis?
Draw a Punnett square to explain your answer. Use **f** to represent the allele for cystic fibrosis and **F** to represent the healthy allele.

(4 marks)

Learning Objectives:

- Know that variation within a species is the differences in the characteristics of the individuals.
- Know that variation can be a result of genes, the environment, or a combination of both.
- Know that there is usually a lot of genetic variation within a population.
- Know that mutations occur continuously.
- Understand that mutations lead to new genetic variants.
- Know that most genetic variants have no effect on phenotype.
- Know that some genetic variants can influence phenotype, and a few can lead to a new phenotype.
- Know that if a new phenotype makes an individual more suited to the environment, it can become common throughout the species quickly.

Specification Reference
4.6.2.1

1. Variation

These pages are all about the differences between you, me, and well... everyone else really. It's fascinating stuff...

What is variation?

Different species look... well... different — my dog definitely doesn't look like a daisy. But even organisms of the same species will usually look at least slightly different — e.g. in a room full of people you'll see different colour hair, individually shaped noses, a variety of heights, etc.

These differences are called the variation within a species — and there are two types of variation: **genetic variation** and **environmental variation**.

Genetic variation

All plants and animals have characteristics that are in some ways similar to their parents' (e.g. I've got my dad's nose, apparently). This is because an organism's characteristics are determined by the **genes** inherited from their parents.

Genes are the codes inside your cells that control how you're made (there's more about genes on page 204). These genes are passed on in **sex cells** (**gametes**), which the offspring develop from (see page 206).

Most animals (and quite a lot of plants) get some genes from the mother and some from the father. This combining of genes from two parents causes genetic variation — no two of the same species are genetically identical (other than identical twins). This means that there is a lot of genetic variation within a population.

Some characteristics are determined only by genes.

Figure 1: *Identical twins have exactly the same genes, which is why they look so alike.*

> **Examples**
>
> - Violet flower colour.
> - Eye colour.
> - Blood group.
> - Inherited disorders (e.g. haemophilia or cystic fibrosis).

Environmental variation

The environment that organisms live and grow in also causes differences between members of the same species — this is called environmental variation.

Environmental variation covers a wide range of differences — from losing your toes in a piranha attack, to getting a suntan, to having yellow leaves and so on. Basically, any difference that has been caused by the conditions something lives in is an environmental variation.

Tip: Plants are strongly influenced by environmental factors, e.g. sunlight, moisture level, temperature and soil mineral content.

Example

A plant grown on a nice sunny windowsill would grow luscious and green. The same plant grown in darkness would grow tall and spindly and its leaves would turn yellow — these are environmental variations.

Genetic and environmental variation

Most characteristics are determined by a mixture of genetic and environmental factors.

Examples

- Height — the maximum height that an animal or plant could grow to is determined by its genes. But whether it actually grows that tall depends on its environment, e.g. how much food it gets.

- Intelligence — one theory is that although your maximum possible IQ might be determined by your genes, whether or not you get to it depends on your environment, e.g. your upbringing and school life.

- Health — some people are more likely to get certain diseases (such as cancer or heart disease) because of their genes. But lifestyle also affects the risk, e.g. whether you smoke or how much junk food you eat.

Tip: Environmental factors aren't just the physical things around you. They can include things like the way you were brought up too.

Mutations

Occasionally, a gene may mutate. A mutation is a change in an organism's DNA. Mutations occur continuously.

Mutations mean that the gene is altered, which produces a **genetic variant** (a different form of the gene). As the gene codes for the sequence of amino acids that make up a protein, gene mutations sometimes lead to changes in the protein that it codes for.

Tip: A mutation involves a change to the order of smaller molecules that make up the larger DNA molecule. See page 204 for a recap on DNA structure.

Most genetic variants have very little or no effect on the protein the gene codes for. Some will change it to such a small extent that its function is unaffected. This means that most mutations have no effect on an organism's phenotype.

Tip: Mutations in DNA happen at random — it doesn't matter whether or not they'll result in a beneficial change.

Examples

- A mutation to a gene may produce a genetic variant that codes for the same sequence of amino acids, so the same protein is produced.

- The mutation may cause a change one amino acid in a protein, but the change has no effect on the protein's function.

Some variants have a small influence on the organism's phenotype — they alter the individual's characteristics but only slightly.

Example

Some characteristics, e.g. eye colour, are controlled by more than one gene. A mutation in one of the genes may change the eye colour a bit, but the difference might not be huge.

Very occasionally, variants can have such a dramatic effect that they determine phenotype.

Example

The genetic disorder, cystic fibrosis, is caused by a mutation that has a huge effect on phenotype. The gene codes for a protein that controls the movement of salt and water into and out of cells. However, the protein produced by the mutated gene doesn't work properly. This leads to excess mucus production in the lungs and digestive system, which can make it difficult to breathe and to digest food.

Tip: Mutations that result in a new phenotype are very rare.

If the environment changes, and the new phenotype makes an individual more suited to the new environment, it can become common throughout the species relatively quickly by natural selection — see page 235.

Example

A mutation may make a bacterium resistant to an antibiotic (see page 134). If the antibiotic appears in the bacterium's environment (e.g. a person with a bacterial infection starts taking antibiotics), the mutation may give the bacterium a better chance of surviving, reproducing and passing the beneficial mutation on to future generations. Over time, the mutation will accumulate in the bacterial population.

Topic 6c Evolution and Classification

Practice Questions — Fact Recall

Q1 True or False? Only differences in genes can cause variation within a population.

Q2 a) What is a mutation?

b) Explain why most mutations have no effect on an organism's phenotype.

c) Outline how mutations can result in variation.

Practice Questions — Application

Q1 For the animal characteristics below, say whether they are determined by genes only, the environment only, or both.

a) eye colour

b) height

c) sickle cell anaemia, a genetic disorder

Q2 For the plant characteristics below, say whether they are determined by genes only, the environment only, or both.

a) stem height

b) spots caused by a fungus

Q3 Your sporting ability may be affected by your genes and your environment. Suggest one environmental factor that may affect your sporting ability.

Q4 Identical twins have exactly the same genes.
Non-identical twins don't. Studies have shown that:

- identical twins tend to have more similar IQs than non-identical twins (Study 1).

- identical twins who are brought up together tend to have more similar IQs than identical twins who are brought up separately (Study 2).

What do the results of Studies 1 and 2 suggest about the influence of genes and the environment on IQ? Explain your answer.

- Know that, according to the theory of evolution, all of today's species have evolved from simple life forms that first started to develop over three billion years ago.
- Understand and be able to explain how evolution by natural selection happens.
- Know that evolution is the changing of the inherited characteristics of a population over time.
- Know that the theory of evolution by natural selection has largely been accepted.
- Be able to describe examples of evidence that support Darwin's theory.
- Know that if the phenotypes of two populations of the same species change so much that they can no longer interbreed to produce fertile offspring, they have become two new species.
- Know that extinction has occurred when no individuals of a species remain.
- Be able to describe possible causes of extinction.

Specification References
4.6.2.2, 4.6.3.1,
4.6.3.3

2. Evolution and Extinction

This is it. The 'Big One' — how life on Earth began, and, um, kept on going...

The theory of evolution

The theory of evolution is this:

> All of today's species have evolved from simple life forms that first started to develop over three billion years ago.

It means that rather than just popping into existence, complex organisms like animals and plants 'developed' over billions of years from simpler single-celled organisms, such as bacteria.

Charles Darwin

Charles Darwin came up with a really important theory about evolution. He used the observations he made on a huge round-the-world trip, along with new knowledge of fossils and geology, to suggest the theory of evolution by natural selection. It works like this:

1. All of the individuals within a species show a wide range of variation for a particular characteristic. For example, they might have a wide range of fur lengths.

2. Because of this range of variation, some of these individuals will be more suited to the environment than others — e.g. in a warm environment, those with a short fur length may be more suited to the conditions.

3. The individuals who are most suited to the environment will be more likely to survive, and therefore more likely to breed successfully.

4. The useful characteristic will be passed on to the offspring.

New discoveries

Darwin's theory wasn't perfect. Because the relevant scientific knowledge wasn't available at the time, he couldn't give a good explanation for why new characteristics appeared or exactly how individual organisms passed on beneficial adaptations to their offspring.

We now know that phenotype is controlled by genes. New genetic variants (see page 231) arise because of mutations (changes in DNA), and these genetic variants can give rise to phenotypes that are suited to the environment. Beneficial genetic variants are passed on to future generations in the DNA that parents contribute to their offspring.

These new discoveries have meant that scientists have been able to develop Darwin's original ideas into the theory of evolution by natural selection that is accepted today.

Today's theory of evolution by natural selection

Scientists have developed Darwin's theory using what we now know about genetics. It works like this:

1. Individuals within a species show wide variation in their characteristics (phenotypic variation) because of the mix of genetic variants present in the population.

   > **Example**
   >
   > Some rabbits have big ears and some have small ones.

2. Some genetic variants give rise to characteristics that are better suited to the environment. Organisms with these characteristics have a better chance of survival and so are more likely to breed successfully.

   > **Example**
   >
   > Big-eared rabbits are more likely to hear a fox approaching them, and so are more likely to survive and have lots of offspring. Small-eared rabbits are more likely to get eaten.
   >
   >

3. So, the genetic variants that are responsible for the useful characteristics are more likely to be passed on to the next generation.

   > **Example**
   >
   > All the baby rabbits are born with big ears.

Over time, the genetic variant for a useful characteristic will become more common (accumulate) in a population. This will lead to a change in the species. The changing of the inherited characteristics of a population over time is evolution.

An accepted hypothesis

(WORKING SCIENTIFICALLY)

There's so much evidence for Darwin's idea that it's now an accepted hypothesis (a theory). As well as the discovery of genetics, other evidence was also found by looking at fossils of different ages (the fossil record) — this allows you to see how changes in organisms developed slowly over time. The relatively recent discovery of how bacteria are able to evolve to become resistant to antibiotics also further supports evolution by natural selection.

Tip: Remember, genetic variants are different forms of genes. They arise when DNA mutates (see page 231).

Tip: Genetic differences between individuals of a species are also caused by sexual reproduction (see page 206).

Tip: Remember, it's the <u>genes</u> that get passed on to the next generation (not the characteristics themselves).

Exam Tip
Don't get natural selection and evolution mixed up. Natural selection is when a useful characteristic (i.e. one that gives a better chance of survival) becomes more common in a population. Evolution is the changing of the characteristics of a population over time (which happens as a result of natural selection).

Tip: There's more about fossils on p. 243-244.

Tip: You can read more about antibiotic resistance on p. 246.

Speciation

Over a long period of time, the phenotype of organisms can change so much because of natural selection that a completely new species is formed. This is called speciation.

Speciation happens when populations of the same species change enough to become reproductively isolated — this means that they can't interbreed to produce fertile offspring.

Extinction

Tip: If an environment changes too rapidly, a species may not be able to evolve quickly enough to survive. If so, the species will eventually die out.

Extinction is when no living individuals of a species remain. The fossil record contains many species that don't exist any more — these species are said to be **extinct**. Dinosaurs and mammoths are extinct animals, with only fossils to tell us they existed at all.

Species become extinct for these reasons:

Tip: If lots of species die out at the same time (e.g. due to a catastrophic event), it's known as a mass extinction.

- The environment changes too quickly (e.g. destruction of habitat).

- A new predator kills them all (e.g. humans hunting them).

- A new disease kills them all.

- They can't compete with another (new) species for food.

- A catastrophic event happens that kills them all (e.g. a volcanic eruption or a collision with an asteroid).

Figure 1: An artist's impression of the dodo.

> **Example**
>
> Dodos (a type of large, flightless bird) are now extinct. Humans not only hunted them, but introduced other animals which ate all their eggs, and also destroyed the forest where they lived — they really didn't stand a chance.

Practice Questions — Fact Recall

Q1 According to the theory of evolution, how long ago did life on Earth begin?

Q2 According to the theory of evolution, how did complex organisms come to exist on Earth?

Q3 a) Who came up with the idea of natural selection?

b) What is natural selection?

Q4 How can you tell that speciation (the formation of a new species) has taken place?

Q5 What does it mean if a species has become extinct?

Practice Questions — Application

Q1 Warfarin™ is a chemical that was commonly used to kill rats. It is now used less often as many rats have become resistant to it.

Use the theory of evolution by natural selection to explain how most rats have become warfarin-resistant.

Q2 In 1810, a herd of reindeer were taken from the Arctic to an area with a warmer climate. The herd were then left to live and reproduce in the area and were revisited in 1960.
Some information about the herd is shown in the graph.

Tip: To help you answer Q2 b), think about how the change in fur length might affect the reindeer in their new environment.

a) By roughly how much did the average fur length of the herd change between 1810 and 1960?

b) Explain this change in terms of natural selection.

3. Selective Breeding

Learning Objectives:

- Know what selective breeding is.
- Know some characteristics that might be selectively bred for.
- Understand the process of selective breeding.
- Know that humans have been selectively breeding plants and animals for thousands of years.
- Be able to explain how selective breeding has affected crops and domesticated animals.
- Understand that selective breeding can lead to inbreeding, which can mean that some breeds are more susceptible to certain defects or diseases.

Specification Reference 4.6.2.3

Selective breeding is all about getting the characteristics you want.

What is selective breeding?

Selective breeding is when humans artificially select the plants or animals that are going to breed so that the genes for particular characteristics remain in the population. Organisms are selectively bred to develop features that are useful or attractive:

> **Examples**
>
> - Animals that produce more meat or milk.
> - Crops with disease resistance.
> - Dogs with a good, gentle temperament.
> - Decorative plants with big or unusual flowers.

The process of selective breeding

This is the basic process involved in selective breeding:

1. From your existing stock, select the ones which have the characteristics you're after.

2. Breed them with each other.

3. Select the best of the offspring, and breed them together.

4. Continue this process over several generations, and the desirable trait gets stronger and stronger. Eventually, all the offspring will have the characteristic.

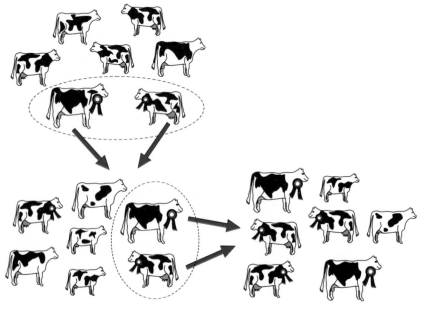

Figure 1: *Diagram showing the best offspring being selectively bred together over many generations — the desirable trait becomes more common.*

Tip: Selective breeding is also known as 'artificial selection'.

In agriculture (farming), selective breeding can be used to improve yields.

Example

To improve meat yields, a farmer could breed together the cows and bulls with the best characteristics for producing meat, e.g. large size. After doing this for several generations the farmer would get cows with a very high meat yield.

Selective breeding is nothing new — people have been doing it for thousands of years. It's how we ended up with edible crops from wild plants and how we got domesticated animals like cows and dogs.

Exam Tip
You could be asked how an organism would be selectively bred for a different characteristic than this. Don't worry — the general process would still be exactly the same.

Reducing the gene pool

The main problem with selective breeding is that it reduces the gene pool — the number of different alleles (forms of a gene) in a population. This is because the farmer keeps breeding from the "best" animals or plants — which are all closely related. This is known as **inbreeding**.

Inbreeding can cause health problems because there's more chance of the organisms inheriting harmful genetic defects when the gene pool is limited. Some dog breeds are particularly susceptible to certain defects because of inbreeding — e.g. pugs often have breathing problems.

There can also be serious problems if a new disease appears, because there's not much variation in the population. All the stock are closely related to each other, so if one of them is going to be killed by a new disease, the others are also likely to succumb to it.

Figure 2: *Flow diagram showing a problem associated with reducing a gene pool.*

Practice Questions — Fact Recall

Q1 Give an example of a feature that an organism might be selectively bred for.

Q2 Outline the process of selective breeding.

Q3 Explain one problem associated with selective breeding.

4. Genetic Engineering

Humans are able to change an organism's genes through a process called genetic engineering. It's really quite clever...

Learning Objectives:

- Know that genetic engineering involves 'cutting out' and transferring a gene for a desired characteristic from one organism's genome to another organism's genome so that it also has the desired characteristic.

- **H** Understand that in genetic engineering, enzymes are used to cut out the desired gene, which is transferred to the target organism using a vector.

- **H** Know that 'new' genes are often inserted at an early stage of an organism's development.

- Know that genetic engineering can be used to produce human insulin, and also to produce crops with better fruit or resistance to disease, insects or herbicides.

- Know that genetically modified (GM) crops are ones that have had their genes modified.

- Understand why GM crops usually have an increased yield.

- Know that scientists are investigating genetic modification as a treatment for some inherited disorders.

- Be able to explain the benefits and concerns surrounding genetic engineering in medicine and GM crops.

Specification Reference
4.6.2.4

What is genetic engineering?

The basic idea of genetic engineering is to transfer a gene responsible for a desirable characteristic from one organism's genome into another organism, so that it also has the desired characteristic. This is done by 'cutting out' the desired gene and transferring it into the cells of another organism.

How genetic engineering works   Higher

1.   A useful gene is isolated (cut) from one organism's genome using enzymes and is inserted into a **vector**.

2.   The vector is usually a virus or a bacterial plasmid (a small ring of DNA), depending on the type of organism that the gene is being transferred to.

3.   When the vector is introduced to the target organism, the useful gene is inserted into its cell(s).

 Example — Higher

The human insulin gene can be inserted into bacteria to produce human insulin:

1.   The insulin gene is first cut out of human DNA using enzymes.

2.   The same enzymes are then used to cut the bacterial DNA and different enzymes are used to insert the human insulin gene.

3.   The bacteria are then allowed to multiply. The insulin they produce while they grow is purified and used by people with diabetes.

This is summarised in Figure 1.

Figure 1: *Diagram showing how bacteria can be genetically engineered to produce insulin.*

In some cases, the transfer of the gene is carried out when the organism receiving the gene is at an early stage of development (e.g. egg or embryo). This means that the organism develops with the characteristic coded for by the gene.

Uses of genetic engineering

Scientists use genetic engineering to do all sorts of things:

Examples

- Bacteria have been genetically modified to produce human insulin that can be used to treat diabetes.

- Genetically modified (GM) crops have had their genes modified, e.g. to improve the size and quality of their fruit, or make them resistant to disease, insects and herbicides (chemicals used to kill weeds).

- Sheep have been genetically engineered to produce substances, like drugs, in their milk that can be used to treat human diseases.

- Scientists are researching genetic modification treatments for inherited disorders caused by faulty genes, e.g. by inserting working genes into people with the disorder. This is called gene therapy.

Tip: Herbicides kill weeds, but they can also end up killing crops. 'Selective herbicides' are usually used to stop this from happening, but they don't always kill all the weeds. If a crop is herbicide-resistant, more effective herbicides can be used to get rid of weeds — without risk to the crop.

The issues surrounding genetic engineering

Genetic engineering is an exciting new area in science which has the potential for solving many of our problems (e.g. treating diseases, more efficient food production, etc.) but not everyone thinks it's a great idea.

There are worries about the long-term effects of genetic engineering — that changing a person's genes might accidentally create unplanned problems, which could then get passed on to future generations.

It's the same with GM crops...

The issues surrounding GM crops

Benefits

- On the plus side, the characteristics chosen for GM crops can increase the yield, making more food.

- People living in developing nations often lack nutrients in their diets. GM crops could be engineered to contain the nutrient that's missing. For example, 'golden rice' is a GM rice crop that contains beta-carotene — lack of this substance causes blindness.

Tip: 'Yield' just means the amount of product made. So the yield of a wheat field would be the amount of wheat produced. Insects eating the crop, disease, and competition with weeds all reduce crop yield.

Concerns

- Some people say that growing GM crops will affect the number of wild flowers (and so the population of insects) that live in and around the crops — reducing farmland biodiversity.

- Not everyone is convinced that GM crops are safe and some people are concerned that we might not fully understand the effects of eating them on human health. E.g. people are worried they may develop allergies to the food — although there's probably no more risk for this than for eating usual foods.

- A big concern is that transplanted genes may get out into the natural environment. For example, the herbicide resistance gene may be picked up by weeds, creating a new 'superweed' variety.

Tip: GM crops are already being grown elsewhere in the world (not the UK) often without any problems.

Practice Questions — Fact Recall

Q1 What does genetic engineering involve?

Q2 In genetic engineering, useful genes are sometimes transferred into animals and plants in the early stages of their development. Explain why.

Q3 Give an example of a characteristic that bacterial cells have been genetically engineered to have.

Q4 a) What does the 'GM' stand for in 'GM crop'?

b) Some GM crops are resistant to viruses.
What else can they be made resistant to? Give two examples.

Figure 2: A B. thuringiensis bacterium (top). GM cotton which produces the Bt crystal protein (bottom).

Practice Questions — Application

B. thuringiensis is a species of bacteria. It produces a crystal protein, which is poisonous to insects when eaten. Some crop plants, including cotton and potatoes, have been genetically engineered to produce the *Bt* crystal protein.

Q1 Explain how enzymes would be used to make a cotton plant that can produce the *Bt* crystal protein.

Q2 Suggest a benefit of genetically engineering crop plants to produce the *Bt* crystal protein. Explain your answer.

Q3 Suggest a possible risk of growing crop plants that have been genetically engineered to produce the *Bt* crystal protein.

5. Fossils

Fossils might sound a bit dull, but they're actually dead interesting. Without them, we wouldn't know that dinosaurs ever existed.

What are fossils?

Fossils are the remains of organisms from many years ago, which are found in rocks. They provide the evidence that organisms lived ages ago. Fossils can tell us a lot about how much or how little organisms have changed (evolved) over time. By comparing fossils with species that are alive today, we can see that many of today's species have developed from much simpler organisms over millions of years.

How do fossils form?

Fossils form in rocks in one of three ways:

1. From gradual replacement by minerals

Things like teeth, shells, bones, etc., which don't **decay** easily, can last a long time when buried. They're eventually replaced by minerals as they decay, forming a rock-like substance shaped like the original hard part (see Figures 1 and 2).

The surrounding sediments also turn to rock, but the fossil stays distinct inside the rock and eventually someone digs it up. Most fossils are made this way.

Figure 1: *Fossil of a reptile skeleton, dug out of the rock in China.*

Figure 2: *Fossils of ammonite shells. Ammonites were ancient marine organisms.*

2. From casts and impressions

Sometimes, fossils are formed when an organism is buried in a soft material like clay. The clay later hardens around it and the organism decays, leaving a **cast** of itself. An animal's **burrow** (see Figure 3, next page) or a plant's **rootlet traces** can be preserved as casts. Things like **footprints** can also be pressed into soft materials, leaving an impression when the material hardens (see Figure 4, next page).

Learning Objectives:
- Know what fossils are.
- Know that fossils show how much organisms have evolved as life on Earth developed.
- Understand the main ways in which fossils form, including by gradual replacement by minerals, from casts and impressions, and from parts of organisms that haven't decayed.
- Understand why scientists have different views on how life on Earth began.

Specification Reference 4.6.3.2

Tip: When organisms die, they usually get broken down (digested) by microorganisms such as bacteria and fungi. This process is known as decay. Decay can take place at different rates. Very occasionally, it doesn't happen at all (see next page).

Tip: The soft tissue of this reptile (Figure 1) and the soft bodies of the ammonites (Figure 2) decayed away quickly, so they haven't formed part of the fossils.

Tip: Rootlet traces are the impressions made by plant roots.

Figure 3: *Fossilised burrows made in the sea bed by small organisms millions of years ago.*

Figure 4: *The footprint of an early human-like primate, preserved in hardened volcanic ash.*

3. From preservation in places where no decay happens

The microbes involved in decay need the right conditions in order to break down material — that means plenty of oxygen (for aerobic respiration, see p. 159), enough moisture, and the right temperature and pH for their enzymes to work properly (see pages 110-111). If the conditions aren't right, decay won't take place and the dead organism's remains will be preserved.

Tip: As it happens, the conditions needed for decay are usually right — so it's very rare for dead organisms to be preserved in this way.

> ### Examples
>
> - In amber (a clear yellow 'stone' made from fossilised tree sap) and tar pits there's no oxygen or moisture so decay microbes can't survive (see Figure 5).
>
> - In glaciers it's too cold for the decay microbes to work.
>
> - Peat bogs are too acidic for decay microbes. Whole human bodies have been preserved as fossils in peat bogs (see Figure 6).

Tip: The 'Tollund Man' lived over 2000 years ago. He was so well preserved in the bog that scientists were able to tell what he ate for his last meal from the contents of his stomach (barley gruel, yum).

Figure 5: *Fossil of a midge, preserved in amber.*

Figure 6: *Photo of the 'Tollund Man'. This well preserved fossil of a man was discovered in a bog.*

Tip: 'Primordial' means 'original' or 'first'. So primordial swamps were the first swamps.

Tip: Organic molecules are molecules containing carbon, e.g. amino acids.

The origins of life on Earth

There are various **hypotheses** suggesting how life first came into being, but no one really knows the answer.

Maybe the first life forms came into existence in a primordial swamp (or under the sea) here on Earth. Maybe simple organic molecules were brought to Earth on comets — these could have then become more complex organic molecules, and eventually very simple life forms.

These hypotheses can't be supported or disproved because there's a lack of good, **valid evidence**. There's a lack of evidence because:

Tip: Validity is explained on page 9.

- Scientists believe many early organisms were soft-bodied, and soft tissue tends to decay away completely, without forming fossils.

- Fossils that did form millions of years ago may have been destroyed by **geological activity**, e.g. the movement of tectonic plates may have crushed fossils already formed in the rock.

This means that the **fossil record** is incomplete — in other words, we don't have fossils of every organism or even every type of organism that has ever lived.

Tip: Tectonic plates are the large 'pieces' of rock that make up the Earth's crust.

Practice Questions — Fact Recall

Q1 What is a fossil?

Q2 What do fossils provide evidence of?

Q3 Explain why there is a lack of valid evidence to support any hypothesis about how life on Earth began.

Practice Question — Application

Q1 Suggest how each of the following fossils was formed:

A

Fossilised animal burrows preserved in rock.

B

A fossilised snail shell.

C

A fossilised leaf imprint in rock.

D

A fossilised baby mammoth, found in frozen ground in Siberia.

- Know that bacteria are able to evolve quickly because they reproduce rapidly.
- Understand how antibiotic-resistant strains of bacteria develop.
- Know that antibiotic-resistant strains spread because people don't have immunity to it and there's no effective treatment.
- Know that MRSA is an antibiotic-resistant bacteria.
- Know ways to reduce the rate that antibiotic-resistant strains develop.
- Understand why the development of new antibiotics is not likely to keep up with the rate that new resistant strains emerge.

Specification Reference
4.6.3.4

Tip: The gene for antibiotic resistance becomes more common in the population because of natural selection — there's more about how this happens on page 235.

Tip: TB is a very serious lung disease caused by a bacterial infection.

6. Antibiotic-Resistant Bacteria

The use of antibiotics is not always straightforward. Because bacteria can mutate, antibiotic resistance can be a problem...

Antibiotic resistance

Like all organisms, bacteria sometimes develop random mutations (changes) in their DNA. These can lead to changes in the bacteria's characteristics, e.g. being less affected by a particular antibiotic. This can lead to antibiotic-resistant strains forming as the gene for antibiotic resistance becomes more common in the population.

To make matters worse, because bacteria are so rapid at reproducing, they can evolve quite quickly.

For the bacterium, the ability to resist antibiotics is a big advantage. Non-resistant bacteria will be killed by antibiotics, but a resistant bacterium is better able to survive, even in a host who's being treated to get rid of the infection. This means it lives for longer and reproduces many more times. This increases the population size of the antibiotic-resistant strain.

Antibiotic-resistant strains are a problem for people who become infected with these bacteria because they aren't immune to the new strain and there is no effective treatment. This means that the infection easily spreads between people. Sometimes drug companies can come up with a new antibiotic that's effective, but 'superbugs' that are resistant to most known antibiotics are becoming more common.

Examples

- MRSA (methicillin-resistant *Staphylococcus aureus*) is a relatively common 'superbug' that's really hard to get rid of. It often affects people in hospitals and can be fatal if it enters their bloodstream.

- Multi-drug-resistant TB (also known as MDR-TB) is a form of TB that has developed resistance to multiple antibiotics, making it hard to treat. Scientists in China have reported an MDR-TB epidemic there — about 63 000 Chinese people develop MDR-TB each year.

The spread of antibiotic resistance

For the last few decades, we've been able to deal with bacterial infections pretty easily using antibiotics. The death rate from infectious bacterial diseases (e.g. pneumonia) has fallen dramatically.

But the problem of antibiotic resistance is getting worse — partly because of the overuse and inappropriate use of antibiotics.

Examples

- Doctors prescribing antibiotics for non-serious conditions.

- Doctors prescribing antibiotics for infections caused by viruses.

Tip: Antibiotics don't kill viruses.

The more often antibiotics are used, the bigger the problem of antibiotic resistance becomes, so it's important that doctors only prescribe antibiotics when they really need to.

It's not that antibiotics actually cause resistance — they create a situation where naturally resistant bacteria have an advantage and so increase in numbers. If they're not doing you any good, it's pointless to take antibiotics — and it could be harmful for everyone else.

It's also important that you take all the antibiotics a doctor prescribes for you. Lots of people stop taking their antibiotics as soon as they feel better, but this can increase the risk of antibiotic-resistant bacteria emerging. Taking the full course makes sure that all the bacteria are destroyed, which means that there are none left to mutate and develop into antibiotic-resistant strains.

In farming, antibiotics can be given to animals to prevent them becoming ill and to make them grow faster. This can lead to the development of antibiotic-resistant bacteria in the animals which can then spread to humans, e.g. during meat preparation and consumption. Increasing concern about the overuse of antibiotics in agriculture has led to some countries restricting their use.

The increase in antibiotic resistance has encouraged drug companies to work on developing new antibiotics that are effective against the resistant strains. Unfortunately, the rate of development is slow, which means we're unlikely to be able to keep up with the demand for new drugs as more antibiotic-resistant strains develop and spread. It's also a very costly process.

Practice Questions — Fact Recall

Q1 Why can bacteria evolve rapidly?

Q2 Name one type of antibiotic-resistant bacteria.

Q3 Why is the development of new antibiotics unlikely to keep up with the appearance of new antibiotic-resistant strains of bacteria?

Practice Questions — Application

Q1 James has a mild bacterial infection. James' doctor tells him it will clear up on its own and does not prescribe him antibiotics. Suggest why James' doctor did this.

Q2 Many strains of the bacteria *Streptococcus pneumoniae* are now resistant to the antibiotic penicillin. Describe how populations of penicillin-resistant *Streptococcus pneumoniae* may have increased.

Learning Objectives:

- Know that the system of classification proposed by Carl Linnaeus grouped organisms depending on their characteristics and structure.
- Know that the Linnaean system divided organisms into kingdom, phylum, class, order, family, genus and species.
- Be able to use given information to demonstrate understanding of the Linnaean system.
- Know that as microscopes improved and scientists understood more about biochemical processes, new classification models were proposed.
- Know that Carl Woese proposed the three-domain system, where organisms are divided into Archaea, Bacteria and Eukaryota, and know what these domains contain.
- Know that in the binomial system, organisms are named using their genus and species.
- Understand what evolutionary trees are and how they are worked out.
- Be able to read from and interpret evolutionary trees.

Specification References
4.6.3.2, 4.6.4

Tip: Biochemical processes are all the chemical reactions that go on within the body.

7. Classification

Classification means sorting things into groups. Like organisms, for example...

The Linnaean system

Traditionally, organisms have been classified according to a system first proposed in the 1700s by Carl Linnaeus, which groups living things according to their characteristics and the structures that make them up.

In this system (known as the Linnaean system), living things are first divided into kingdoms (e.g. the plant kingdom). The kingdoms are then subdivided into smaller and smaller groups — phylum, class, order, family, genus, species.

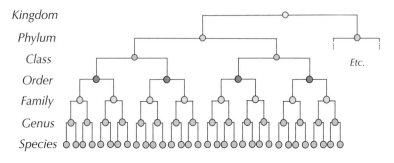

Kingdom
Phylum
Class
Order
Family
Genus
Species

Etc.

Figure 1: *Diagram to show the Linnaean system of classification.*

Example

Using the Linnaean system, humans are classified as follows:

Kingdom = *Animalia*, Phylum = *Chordata*, Class = *Mammalia*, Order = *Primates*, Family = *Hominidae*, Genus = *Homo*, Species = *sapiens*.

The three-domain system

As knowledge of the biochemical processes taking place inside organisms developed and microscopes improved (which allowed us to find out more about the internal structures of organisms), scientists put forward new models of classification.

In 1990, Carl Woese proposed the three-domain system. Using evidence gathered from new chemical analysis techniques such as RNA sequence analysis, he found that in some cases, species thought to be closely related in traditional classification systems are in fact not as closely related as first thought.

In the three-domain system, organisms are first of all split into three large groups called domains:

1. Archaea

Organisms in this domain are primitive bacteria. They're often found in extreme places such as hot springs and salt lakes.

2. Bacteria

This domain contains true bacteria like *E. coli* and *Staphylococcus*. Although they often look similar to Archaea, there are lots of biochemical differences between them.

3. Eukaryota

This domain includes a broad range of organisms including fungi, plants, animals and protists (page 124).

These are then subdivided into smaller groups — kingdom, phylum, class, order, family, genus, species.

Exam Tip
Make sure you know what each of the domains includes in the three-domain system, as you may be asked to describe their features in the exam.

The binomial system

In the binomial system, every organism is given its own two-part Latin name.

The first part refers to the genus that the organism belongs to. This gives you information on the organism's ancestry. The second part refers to the species.

Example

Humans are known as *Homo sapiens*.
'*Homo*' is the genus and '*sapiens*' is the species.

The binomial system is used worldwide and means that scientists in different countries or who speak different languages all refer to a particular species by the same name — avoiding potential confusion.

Tip: Genus and species are the final two groups in the Linnaean and three-domain systems of classification.

Exam Tip
You might have to apply your knowledge of how the Linnaean system works to information given to you in the exam — don't worry, just make sure you understand what's going on on the previous page.

Evolutionary trees

Evolutionary trees show how scientists think different species are related to each other.

They show common ancestors and relationships between species. The more recent the common ancestor, the more closely related the two species — and the more characteristics they're likely to share.

Scientists analyse lots of different types of data to work out evolutionary relationships. For living organisms, they use the current classification data (e.g. DNA analysis and structural similarities). For extinct species, they use information from the fossil record (see page 236).

Tip: An evolutionary tree is a bit like a family tree — but instead of showing a mum, dad, grandparents, etc., it shows ancestors that existed many thousands or even millions of years ago.

Examples

- This evolutionary tree shows that whales and dolphins have a recent common ancestor so are closely related. They're both more distantly related to sharks:

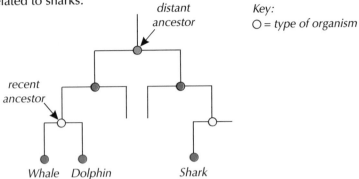

distant ancestor

Key:
○ = type of organism

recent ancestor

Whale Dolphin   Shark

Exam Tip
You may need to interpret other graphs, tables or charts relating to evolutionary data in the exam.

- This evolutionary tree shows the relationships between humans and some of the great apes. Each point at which the lines meet is a common ancestor.

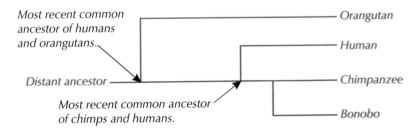

Most recent common ancestor of humans and orangutans.

Distant ancestor

Most recent common ancestor of chimps and humans.

Orangutan

Human

Chimpanzee

Bonobo

Tip: The distant ancestor is the 'oldest' organism on this evolutionary tree (i.e. it evolved first).

You can see that humans are more closely related to chimpanzees than to orangutans because they share a more recent common ancestor.

Practice Question — Application

Q1 The tree below shows the evolutionary relationships between some of the big cats.

Lion

Leopard

Jaguar

Tiger

Snow Leopard

a) Which animal is most closely related to:

   i) the leopard?   ii) the tiger?

b) Which animal evolved first, the jaguar or the lion?

c) Do the lion and the snow leopard share a common ancestor?

Topic 6c Checklist — Make sure you know...

Variation

☐ That variation within a species is the differences in characteristics between individuals, and that these differences are caused by genetic variation, environmental variation, or a combination of both.

☐ That there is usually a lot of genetic variation within a population of a species.

☐ That mutations are changes to an organism's DNA that happen continuously, and that they give rise to genetic variants.

☐ That although most genetic variants have no effect phenotype, some can influence phenotype and a few can lead to a new phenotype. This new phenotype can become more common if it makes the organism more suited to its environment.

Evolution

☐ The theory of evolution — all of today's species have evolved from simple life forms that first started to develop over three billion years ago.

☐ How evolution by natural selection happens.

☐ That evolution is the changing of a species' inherited characteristics over time.

☐ That Darwin's theory has largely been accepted, and the reasons why.

☐ That if two populations of one species change so much that they can no longer interbreed to produce fertile offspring, they have become two new species.

☐ That a species is extinct when there are no living individuals of that species left, and the reasons why species become extinct.

Selective Breeding

☐ What selective breeding is, including examples of its uses, and how it is done.

☐ That humans have been selectively breeding plants and animals for thousands of years, and how this has affected food plants and domesticated animals.

☐ The problems linked to selective breeding.

Genetic Engineering

☐ That genetic engineering involves 'cutting out' and transferring a gene for a desired characteristic from one organism's genome to another organism's genome, so that it also has that characteristic.

☐ H The processes used in genetic engineering.

☐ Some uses of genetic engineering, including the possibility of treating inherited disorders, and that GM is short for genetically modified (e.g. GM crops).

☐ That GM crops usually have an increased yield because they've been engineered to improve the size and quality of their fruit, or to make them resistant to disease, insects and herbicides.

☐ The benefits and concerns of using genetic engineering in medical treatments and GM crop production.

cont...

Fossils

☐ That fossils are the remains of organisms from many years ago, which are found in rocks.

☐ That fossils provide evidence of how species evolved.

☐ That fossils can be made when hard body parts (that don't decay easily) are gradually replaced by minerals, from casts and impressions, and from preservation in places where no decay happens.

☐ That there are various hypotheses as to how life on Earth began, but there's a lack of valid evidence because there are so few fossils of early organisms — their soft bodies decayed easily and didn't form fossils, and geological activity has destroyed many fossils that did form.

Antibiotic-Resistant Bacteria

☐ That bacteria can evolve quickly because they reproduce rapidly.

☐ How antibiotic-resistant strains of bacteria (e.g. MRSA) develop, and why they spread.

☐ Ways to reduce the rate that antibiotic-resistant strains develop.

☐ Why antibiotic development is unlikely to keep up with the rate that new resistant strains emerge.

Classification

☐ About the classification system proposed by Carl Linnaeus and that as microscopes and scientific knowledge improved, new classification models were proposed — such as that of Carl Woese.

☐ That in the binomial system, organisms are named using their genus and their species.

☐ What evolutionary trees are and how they are worked out.

☐ How to read and interpret data from an evolutionary tree.

1 The girls shown below are identical twins.
They have exactly the same genes.

1.1 Both twins have blue eyes. What determines the twins' eye colour?

(1 mark)

1.2 The twin on the left is taller than the twin on the right.
Suggest **one** possible explanation for this difference in height.

(1 mark)

2 The evolutionary tree shows how some groups of animals, including snakes, are related.

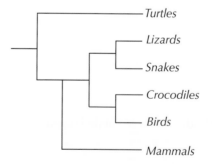

2.1 Which of the following groups of animals are most closely related?

A turtles and lizards
B snakes and crocodiles
C crocodiles and birds
D birds and mammals

(1 mark)

2.2 According to the tree, which group of animals evolved first?

(1 mark)

The picture shows a type of snake called a Sinaloan milk snake.

The milk snake is relatively harmless, but it has evolved to have a very similar pattern and colouring to the deadly poisonous coral snake, which lives in the same environment. The coral snake's colouring warns predators that it is dangerous to eat.

2.3 Using the idea of natural selection, explain how the milk snake may have evolved to have a similar colouring to the coral snake.

(3 marks)

2.4 The theory of evolution by natural selection was proposed by Charles Darwin. Darwin's ideas about natural selection were only gradually accepted.

What evidence is now available to support Darwin's theory?

(3 marks)

3 Fossils of shelled organisms are often found in the Grand Canyon.

3.1 Suggest how these fossils may have formed.

(2 marks)

3.2 Why didn't the soft bodies of these shelled organisms form part of the fossils?

(1 mark)

3.3 Give **one** way in which some fossils may have been destroyed over time.

(1 mark)

Fossils can be found for organisms that are now extinct.

3.4 Give three reasons why a species might become extinct.

(3 marks)

1. Competition

There is only a limited amount of resources to go around, so organisms have to compete with each other to get what they need from their environment.

Important definitions

Topic 7 will make a lot more sense if you become familiar with these terms:

Habitat	The place where an organism lives.
Population	All the organisms of one species living in a habitat.
Community	The populations of different species living in a habitat.
Abiotic factors	Non-living factors of the environment, e.g. temperature.
Biotic factors	Living factors of the environment, e.g. food.
Ecosystem	The interaction of a community of living organisms (biotic) with the non-living (abiotic) parts of their environment.

Competition for resources

Organisms need things from their environment and from other organisms in order to survive and reproduce. Plants need light and space, as well as water and mineral ions (nutrients) from the soil. Animals need space (territory), food, water and mates. Organisms compete with other species (and members of their own species) for the same resources.

> **Examples**
>
> - Weeds compete with crop plants for light and nutrients. Farmers use weedkillers to kill weeds so there is less competition and the crops get all the light and nutrients, which enables them to grow better.
>
> - Lions and hyenas share the same habitat in Africa. They compete with each other for food, water and territory, which results in frequent aggression between the two species.
>
> - Male peacocks compete with each other for mates by displaying their eye-catching tail feathers to females during mating season.

Identifying competition

In the exam you might be given information about several different organisms and the habitat that they share and be asked to analyse the information and work out what resources they are in competition for. Take a look at the example on the next page.

Learning Objectives:

- Know what an ecosystem is.
- Know the levels of organisation that make up an ecosystem.
- Know that organisms need resources from both their surroundings and other organisms in their environment to survive and reproduce.
- Know that organisms compete with each other for the resources they need, and know what animals and plants compete for.
- Be able to identify the resources being competed for in a habitat when given relevant information.
- Be able to read from graphs, charts and tables relating to how organisms in a community interact with each other and interpret the information presented.
- Know that species in a community are interdependent — they rely on each other for the resources they need.
- Know that the removal of one species can have wide-reaching effects on the whole community.
- Know what a stable community is.

Specification Reference 4.7.1.1

Exam Tip
You need to be able to
read from graphs, charts
and tables relating to
how organisms in a
community interact with
each other, and make
sense of the data.

Example

**In 2007, an invasive species
of bush was introduced
to a riverbank and was in
competition with a similar,
native species. The river
usually floods the riverbank
each January, covering it in
nutrient-rich silt. This didn't
occur in 2012. The graph on
the right shows how the
populations of the two species
changed in an area of the
riverbank over an 8 year period.
The table below gives some
information about the bushes.**

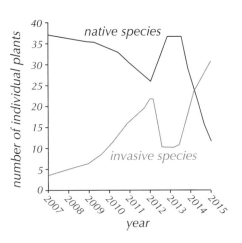

Feature	Invasive species	Native species
Average growth rate of main stem	0.8 cm/day	0.4 cm/day
Average surface area of leaves	11.5 cm^2	6.2 cm^2
Average volume of soil where roots have spread	729 cm^3	5832 cm^3

Exam Tip
Questions like these can
be quite tricky because
the answer isn't always
obvious straight away.
If you think logically
and work through the
information, you should
be able to work out the
right answer.

**Between 2007 and 2012, the invasive species outcompeted the native
species. Use the information above and your own knowledge of plants
to suggest the resource that the invasive species was more successful
at competing for during this time. Explain your answer.**

You need to take a close look at the information and identify any
differences in it. You'll notice that the invasive species was able
to grow much faster on average than the native species and has
leaves with a much bigger surface area. Leaves with a bigger
surface area can absorb more light for photosynthesis and, coupled
with the extra height, block the light from getting to shorter plants
like the native bush. So the resource that the invasive species
was much better at competing for is likely to have been light.

Exam Tip
The introduction
to a question can
sometimes contain vital
information. Make sure
you read everything
you're given carefully or
you might throw away
easy marks.

**Between January 2012 and mid-2013, the pattern in the population
sizes changed. This was due to competition between the species for a
particular resource. Suggest which resource may have been responsible for
the changes in population sizes during this period. Explain your answer.**

During this time period, the population of the native species increased,
while the population of the invasive species decreased. During the
same time period, the nutrient content of the soil is likely to have been
lower than normal because the river didn't flood in January 2012 (so
the riverbank didn't receive any nutrient-rich silt). As the roots of the
native species spread much further than those of the invasive species,
the native species is likely to have been able to absorb more nutrients
from the soil, enabling it to outcompete the invasive species while the
soil nutrient content was low. So the short supply of nutrients was
likely to have been responsible for the changes in population sizes.

Tip: Organisms that
are better adapted to
their environment are
better at competing for
resources and will be
more likely to survive.
See page 261 for more
on adaptations.

Interdependence of species

In a community, each species depends on other species for things such as food, shelter, pollination and seed dispersal — this is called **interdependence**.

The interdependence of all the living things in an ecosystem means that any major change in the ecosystem (such as one species being removed) can have far-reaching effects.

Example

The diagram below shows part of a food web (a diagram of what eats what) from a stream.

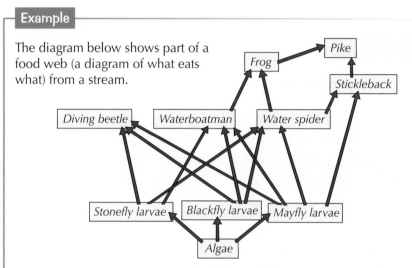

Stonefly larvae are particularly sensitive to pollution. Suppose pollution killed them in this stream. The table below shows some of the effects this might have on some of the other organisms in the food web.

Organism	Effect of loss of stonefly larvae	Effect on population
Blackfly larvae	Less competition for algae	Increase
	More likely to be eaten by predators	Decrease
Water spider	Less food	Decrease
Stickleback	Less food (if water spider or mayfly larvae numbers decrease)	Decrease

---

> **Tip:** Remember that food webs are very complex and that these effects are difficult to predict accurately.

In some communities, all the species and environmental factors are in balance so that the population sizes are roughly constant (they may go up and down in cycles — see pages 263-264). These are called **stable communities**. Stable communities include tropical rainforests and ancient oak woodlands.

Figure 1: *Tropical rainforests (top) and ancient oak woodlands (bottom) are both examples of stable communities.*

Practice Questions — Fact Recall

Q1 What is a community?

Q2 What is an ecosystem?

Q3 Give four resources that animals compete for.

Q4 What is meant by a stable community?

- Be able to recall the following examples of abiotic (non-living) factors:
  - moisture level,
  - light intensity,
  - temperature,
  - carbon dioxide level,
  - direction and intensity of the wind,
  - oxygen level,
  - pH and mineral content of the soil.
- Understand how a community can be affected by changes in the abiotic factors of an ecosystem.
- Be able to recall the following examples of biotic (living) factors:
  - the arrival of new predators,
  - competition from other species,
  - the arrival of new pathogens,
  - availability of food.
- Understand how a community can be affected by changes in the biotic factors of an ecosystem.
- Be able to read and make sense of data about abiotic and biotic factors presented in graphs, charts and tables.

Specification References
4.7.1.2, 4.7.1.3

2. Abiotic and Biotic Factors

Habitats are really fluid environments — they change all the time. It's the abiotic (non-living) and biotic (living) factors that change.

Abiotic factors

Abiotic factors are the non-living factors in an ecosystem.

> **Examples**
>
> - Moisture level
> - Light intensity
> - Temperature
> - Carbon dioxide level (for plants)
> - Wind intensity and direction
> - Oxygen level (for aquatic animals)
> - Soil pH and mineral content

Abiotic factors can vary in an ecosystem. A change in the environment could be an increase or decrease in an abiotic factor. These changes can affect the size of populations in a community. This means they can also affect the population sizes of other organisms that depend on them (see previous page).

> **Examples**
>
> - A decrease in light intensity, temperature or level of carbon dioxide could decrease the rate of photosynthesis in a plant species (see pages 148-150). This could affect plant growth and cause a decrease in the population size.
>
> - A decrease in the mineral content of the soil (e.g. a lack of nitrates) could cause nutrient deficiencies. This could also affect plant growth and cause a decrease in the population size.

Biotic factors

Biotic factors are the living factors in an ecosystem.

> **Examples**
>
> - New predators arriving
> - Competition — one species may outcompete another so that numbers are too low to breed
> - New pathogens
> - Availability of food

Tip: Animals depend on plants for food, so a decrease in a plant population could affect the animal species in a community.

Biotic factors can also vary in an ecosystem. A change in the environment could be the introduction of a new biotic factor, e.g. a new predator or pathogen. These changes can also affect the size of populations in a community, which can have knock-on effects because of interdependence (see page 257).

(see page 257).

Figure 1: *The population size of red squirrels in Britain is decreasing due to increased competition from grey squirrels.*

Examples

- A new predator could cause a decrease in the prey population. There's more about predator-prey populations on p. 263-264.

- Red squirrels are native to the UK. Grey squirrels were introduced in the Victorian times. Grey squirrels quickly took to their new environment and are now found in large numbers in most parts of the UK. Red and grey squirrels live in the same habitat and eat the same food. The greys are able to outcompete the reds for the same resources — there's not enough food for the reds, so the population is decreasing.

Interpreting data on abiotic and biotic factors

In the exam, you might be given a graph, chart or table containing information relating to abiotic or biotic factors and be asked to make sense of it. Take a look at this example:

Example

In an investigation into the effects of fertiliser on the environment, fertiliser was added to a field which contained a pond. The plants and wildlife in and around the pond were then studied for 40 days. The table below shows the size of the fish population in the pond. The graph below shows the percentage cover of the pond by algae over time. A higher percentage cover means that less light is able to reach the plants below the surface of the water.

Number of fish	Days after fertiliser applied				
	0	10	20	30	40
Species A	78	77	56	16	3
Species B	19	19	16	4	1
Species C	58	58	42	12	5
Total	155	154	114	32	9

The amount of algae increased because the fertiliser increased the amount of nutrients in the water. Explain whether the increase in algae was caused by a biotic or abiotic factor.

An abiotic factor because the amount of nutrients in the water is a non-living factor.

Describe the relationship between the percentage cover of algae and the size of the fish population.

Between days 0 and 10, the percentage cover of algae increases, but the fish population barely changes. Between days 10 and 40, as percentage cover continues to increase, the size of the fish population decreases rapidly.

Tip: You need to identify the pattern in both the graph and the table to answer the second question.

Suggest an abiotic factor that could be responsible for the change in the size of the fish population. Explain your answer.

A reduced oxygen level. The algae cover reduces the amount of light reaching the plants below the surface of the water, so the plants can't carry out photosynthesis and die off. One of the products of photosynthesis is oxygen, so if there are fewer plants carrying out photosynthesis, less oxygen is released into the water. This lack of oxygen means that the fish can't survive, so the population decreases.

Tip: Head back to page 144 for a recap on photosynthesis.

The graph below shows how the size of the fish population and a population of fish-eating birds changed over the 40 days of observation.

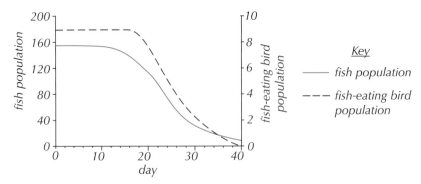

Suggest a biotic factor that could be responsible for the trend in the size of the fish-eating bird population between day 10 and day 40.

A shortage of food for the birds. The size of the bird population starts to decrease shortly after the size of the fish population starts to decrease. Because the size of the fish population decreases, there is less food available to the birds, so the birds either die or move elsewhere to find food.

Practice Questions — Fact Recall

Q1 Give three examples of abiotic factors.

Q2 Give three examples of biotic factors.

Practice Question — Application

Q1 An environmental study was done on a lake over a number of years. Over the course of the study, the concentration of oxygen in the lake gradually decreased due to the effect of pollution. A certain species of fish found in the lake cannot survive in water with a low oxygen concentration. Herons feed on these fish.

a) The population size of the fish changed during the study.

   i) Suggest how the population size changed.

   ii) Was this change due to a biotic or abiotic factor?

b) The population size of the herons also changed during the study. Suggest how and why the population size changed.

3. Adaptations

Different organisms can survive in different environments because they are adapted to them and can compete for resources.

What are adaptations?

Organisms, including microorganisms, are adapted to live in the conditions of their natural environment. The features or characteristics that allow them to do this are called **adaptations**. Adaptations can be structural, behavioural or functional.

Structural adaptations

These are features of an organism's body structure — such as shape or colour.

> **Examples**
>
> - Arctic animals like the arctic fox have white fur so they're camouflaged against the snow. This helps them avoid predators and sneak up on prey.
>
> - Animals that live in cold places (like whales) have a thick layer of blubber (fat) and a low surface area to volume ratio (see page 54) to help them retain heat.
>
> - Animals that live in hot places (like camels) have a thin layer of fat and a large surface area to volume ratio to help them lose heat.
>
> - Plants that live in deserts have a small surface area compared to volume (e.g. cacti have spines instead of leaves). Plants lose water vapour from the surface of their leaves, so this reduces water loss.

Behavioural adaptations

These are ways that organisms behave.

> **Examples**
>
> Many species (e.g. swallows) migrate to warmer climates during the winter to avoid the problems of living in cold conditions.

Functional adaptations

These are things that go on inside an organism's body that can be related to processes like reproduction and metabolism (all the chemical reactions happening in the body).

> **Examples**
>
> - Desert animals conserve water by producing very little sweat and small amounts of concentrated urine.
>
> - Brown bears hibernate over winter. They lower their metabolism which conserves energy, so they don't have to hunt when there's not much food about.

Learning Objectives:

- Know that organisms have adaptations that make them suited for survival in their natural living environment.

- Know that adaptations can be structural, behavioural or functional.

- Know that organisms that live in very extreme environments (e.g. at high temperatures or pressures, or with a high salt concentration) are known as extremophiles (e.g. species of bacteria that live in deep sea vents).

- Be able to identify adaptations in an organism and understand how they help the organism to survive in its environment.

Specification References
4.7.1.1, 4.7.1.4

Figure 1: *An arctic fox camouflaged in the snow.*

Tip: Not all extremophiles are microorganisms. Some other kinds of organism can be extremophiles too, e.g. some plants are able to grow in really salty soil near the sea.

Tip: A hydrothermal vent is an opening in the sea bed which sends out extremely hot water.

Adaptations in microorganisms

Microorganisms have a huge variety of adaptations so that they can live in a wide range of environments. For example, some microorganisms (e.g. bacteria) are known as **extremophiles** — they're adapted to live in seriously extreme conditions like super hot volcanic vents, in very salty lakes or at high pressure on the sea bed.

Example

Thermococcus litoralis is an extremophile. It's a bacterium that's found in deep sea hydrothermal vents. It's adapted to survive and reproduce at temperatures between 85 and 88 °C, which is much higher than most bacteria can tolerate.

Identifying and explaining adaptations

In the exam you might be given information about any organism and its environment and be asked to identify or explain its adaptations. Here's an example to show you how to do it...

Example

The Weddell seal lives in cold Antarctic conditions and hunts fish in water covered by ice. Use this information and the diagram to explain how the seal is adapted to live in the Antarctic.

whiskers
layer of blubber
streamlined body

You need to look at the adaptations labelled on the diagram and think about how they allow the seal to keep warm and hunt fish, for example:

- Its whiskers help it to detect fish in the dark conditions under water.

- Its layer of blubber helps insulate it in the cold water.

- Its streamlined body helps reduce resistance from the water, so it can swim fast to catch fish.

Exam Tip
In the exam you could be asked to identify an animal's adaptations from explanations given. Therefore you need to think about what body features it needs. For example, if you're told that an adaptation helps an animal keep its balance when hopping then it will probably need to have a tail.

Practice Questions — Fact Recall

Q1 What are structural adaptations?

Q2 What are functional adaptations?

Q3 Give two examples of the type of conditions in which you might find an extremophile.

4. Food Chains

It's a fact of life that organisms eat other organisms in a community. To show exactly who eats who, you can produce a food chain.

What are food chains?

Food chains show what's eaten by what in an ecosystem. Food chains always start with a **producer**. Producers make (produce) their own food using energy from the Sun.

Producers are usually green plants or algae — they make glucose (a sugar) by photosynthesis (see page 144). When a green plant produces glucose, some of it is used to make other biological molecules in the plant. These biological molecules are the plant's **biomass** — the mass of living material. Biomass can be thought of as energy stored in a plant.

Energy is transferred through living organisms in an ecosystem when organisms eat other organisms. Producers are eaten by **primary consumers**. Primary consumers are then eaten by **secondary consumers** and secondary consumers are eaten by **tertiary consumers**.

Example

Here's an example of a food chain:

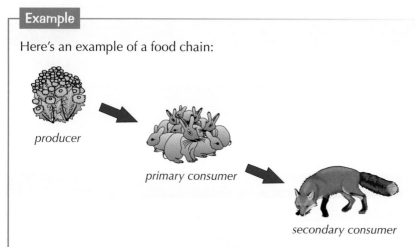

producer

primary consumer

secondary consumer

5000 dandelions feed 100 rabbits, which feed 1 fox.

Predator-prey cycles

Consumers that hunt and kill other animals are called **predators**, and their **prey** are what they eat. In a stable community containing prey and predators (as most of them do of course), the population of any species is usually limited by the amount of food available. If the population of the prey increases, then so will the population of the predators. However as the population of predators increases, the number of prey will decrease.

Learning Objectives:

- Know that food chains show the feeding relationships between different species in an ecosystem.
- Know that all food chains begin with a producer, which is a photosynthetic organism (often a green plant or algae) that makes molecules (such as glucose) and is responsible for producing all of the biomass on Earth.
- Know what primary, secondary and tertiary consumers are.
- Know that a predator is a consumer that kills and eats other animals (its prey).
- Know that the population sizes of predators and prey increase and decrease in predator-prey cycles.
- Be able to interpret graphs showing predator-prey relationships.

Specification Reference 4.7.2.1

Tip: Consumers are organisms that eat other organisms. 'Primary' means first, so primary consumers are the first consumers in a food chain. Secondary consumers are second and tertiary consumers are third.

Exam Tip
You might be asked to interpret a graph like this in the exam — so make sure you really understand what's going on and why.

Example

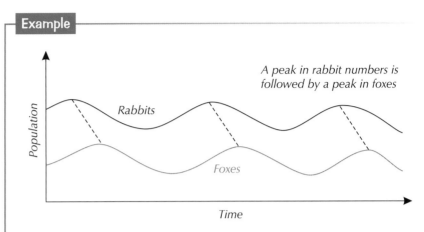

A peak in rabbit numbers is followed by a peak in foxes

More grass means more rabbits. More rabbits means more foxes. But more foxes means fewer rabbits. Eventually fewer rabbits will mean fewer foxes again. This up and down pattern continues...

Tip: Predator-prey cycles are an example of how species in a community can be interdependent. In this case, the predator relies on the prey for food.

Predator-prey cycles are always out of phase with each other. This is because it takes a while for one population to respond to changes in the other population. E.g. when the number of rabbits goes up, the number of foxes doesn't increase immediately because it takes time for them to reproduce.

Practice Questions — Fact Recall

Q1 What type of organism is always found at the start of a food chain?

Q2 Name the group of organisms that eat the secondary consumers.

Q3 What are predators?

Practice Question — Application

Q1 The following food chain is observed in an African savanna.

grass → zebra → cheetah

a) Name the prey organism in this food chain.

This food chain forms part of a stable community.

b) Suggest the effect that an increase in grass growth would have on the population of cheetahs. Explain your answer.

c) After a certain amount of time, the population of cheetahs would return to its previous level. Explain why this would happen.

5. Using Quadrats and Transects

Quadrats are really useful tools for investigating the population size and distribution of organisms in a particular place. You can also use them alongside transects to investigate the distribution of organisms across an area.

Distribution of organisms

As you know from page 255, a habitat is the place where an organism lives, e.g. a playing field. The distribution of an organism is where an organism is found, e.g. in a part of the playing field.

Where an organism is found is affected by environmental factors (see pages 258-259). An organism might be more common in one area than another due to differences in environmental factors between the two areas.

> ### Examples
>
> ▪ In a playing field, you might find that daisies are more common in the open than under trees, because there's more light available in the open and daisies need light to survive (they use it for photosynthesis — see page 144).
>
> ▪ Some types of mayfly are more common in colder parts of a stream, as they can't tolerate the warmer temperatures in other parts of the stream.

There are a couple of ways to study the distribution of an organism:

1. You can measure how common an organism is in two or more sample areas (e.g. using **quadrats** — see below) and compare them.

2. You can study how the distribution changes across an area, e.g. by placing quadrats along a **transect** (see page 267).

Both of these methods give quantitative data (numbers) about the distribution.

The data you collect can be used to provide evidence for environmental change. For instance, if the distribution of organisms across an area changes over time, this could be due to changes in the environment.

Quadrats

A quadrat is a square frame enclosing a known area, e.g. 1 m² (see Figure 2).

Figure 1:
A diagram of a 1 m² quadrat.

1 m

1 m

REQUIRED PRACTICAL **7**

Investigating distribution

You can use quadrats to study the distribution of small organisms that are slow moving or that don't move around. You can investigate the effect of a factor on the distribution of a species by comparing how common an organism is in two sample areas (e.g. shady and sunny spots in a playing field). Just follow these simple steps:

Learning Objectives:

▪ Know that ecologists use quadrats to investigate the population size and distribution of organisms.

▪ Understand how to use sampling to investigate how a factor affects the distribution of species (Required Practical 7).

▪ Understand and be able to work out the mean, mode and median of data on the abundance of organisms.

▪ Understand how to investigate the size of a population of a certain species in a habitat (Required Practical 7).

▪ Know that transects can also be used to investigate the distribution of organisms across an area.

▪ Be able to produce graphs of abundance data with appropriate axes scales.

Specification Reference 4.7.2.1

Tip: Quadrats are a tool used by ecologists. Ecologists are scientists who specialise in studying the interaction between organisms and their environment.

Tip: Before you start this experiment, check the area you're investigating for hazards (e.g. broken glass) and make sure you wash your hands after touching the soil.

Tip: It's really important that the quadrats are placed <u>randomly</u> within the sample area. Taking random samples improves the validity of the study.

Tip: If you're counting flowering plants in your quadrat, make sure you count the number of actual plants, not the number of flowers. Some plants will have more than one flower, and some might not currently have any flowers on them.

Figure 2: *A student using a quadrat to gather data on the distribution of organisms.*

Tip: There's more on means, modes and medians on page 14 of the Working Scientifically section.

1. Place a 1 m² quadrat on the ground at a random point within the first sample area. E.g. divide the area into a grid and use a random number generator to pick coordinates (see page 293).

2. Count all the organisms within the quadrat.

3. Repeat steps 1 and 2 as many times as you can.

4. Work out the mean number of organisms per quadrat within the first sample area.

Example

Anna counted the number of daisies in 7 quadrats within her first sample area and recorded the following results:

Quadrat	1	2	3	4	5	6	7
Number of Daisies	18	22	20	23	23	25	23

Here the mean is: $\dfrac{\text{total number of organisms}}{\text{number of quadrats}}$

$= \dfrac{154}{7} =$ **22 daisies per quadrat**

---

5. Repeat steps 1 to 4 in the second sample area.

6. Finally compare the two means. E.g. you might find 2 daisies per m² in the shade, and 22 daisies per m² (lots more) in the open field.

You might want to find and compare the mode and median of your data too.

Example

1. The mode is the number that appears most often in the data. For Anna's data above, the mode is **23 daisies per quadrat**.

2. To find the median, you first need to put your data in numerical order. The median is the middle value in your data.

18, 20, 22, (23), 23, 23, 25

The median of Anna's data is **23 daisies per quadrat**.

Estimating population size

You can also use quadrats to work out the population size of an organism in one area.

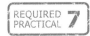 REQUIRED PRACTICAL **7**

Example

Students used 0.25 m² quadrats to randomly sample daisies on an open field. The students found a mean of 10.5 daisies per quadrat. The field had an area of 800 m². Estimate the population of daisies on the field.

1. Work out the mean number of organisms per m².

$1 ÷ 0.25 = 4$ ←

Because the quadrat is only 0.25 m², you first need to work out how many quadrats make up 1 m².

$4 × 10.5 = 42$ daisies per m²

2. Then multiply the mean by the total area (in m²) of the habitat.

$800 × 42 =$ **33 600 daisies in the open field**

Tip: The population size of an organism is sometimes called its abundance.

Tip: If your quadrat has an area of 1 m², the mean number of organisms per m² is just the same as the mean number per quadrat.

Transects

You can use lines called transects (see Figure 4) to help find out how organisms (like plants) are distributed across an area — e.g. if an organism becomes more or less common as you move from a hedge towards the middle of a field.

Tip: Transects can be used in any type of habitat, not just fields. For example, along a beach or in a stream.

tape measure

quadrat

Figure 4: *A diagram showing two transects.*

Here's what to do:

1. Mark out a line in the area you want to study using a tape measure.

2. Then collect data along the line. You can do this by just counting all the organisms you're interested in that touch the line. Or, you can collect data by using quadrats. These can be placed next to each other along the line or at intervals, for example, every 2 m.

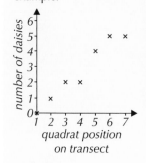

Figure 5: *Students using a quadrat along a transect.*

Percentage cover

If it's difficult to count all the individual organisms in the quadrat (e.g. if they're grass) you can calculate the percentage cover. This means estimating the percentage area of the quadrat covered by a particular type of organism, e.g. by counting the number of little squares covered by the organisms.

Exam Tip
You need to be able to draw your own graphs to show data about the abundance of different organisms. Here's an example:

Make sure you use axes with appropriate scales. See page 18 for more on drawing graphs.

Example

Some students were measuring the distribution of organisms from one corner of a school playing field to another, using quadrats placed at regular intervals along a transect. Below is a picture of one of the quadrats. Calculate the percentage cover of each organism, A and B.

(MATHS SKILLS)

☐ *Organism Type A*

☐ *Organism Type B*

Tip: You count a square if it's more than half covered.

1. Count the number of squares covered by organism A.

    Type A = 42 squares

2. Make this into a percentage — divide the number of squares covered by the organism by the total number of squares in the quadrat (100), then multiply the result by 100.

$$\frac{42}{100} \times 100 = 0.42 \times 100 = \mathbf{42\%}$$

3. Do the same for organism B.

    Type B = 47 squares

$$\frac{47}{100} \times 100 = 0.47 \times 100 = \mathbf{47\%}$$

Practice Questions — Fact Recall

Q1 Describe how you would use random sampling with a quadrat to compare the distribution of organisms in two sample areas.

Q2 Describe one way in which a transect can be used to measure the distribution of organisms across an area.

Practice Questions — Application

Q1 Joanne read that bulrushes grow best in moist soil or in shallow water. She wanted to find out whether this is true, so she investigated the distribution of bulrushes in her garden. She used a transect (as shown in the diagram) and recorded the number of bulrushes in each 1 m² quadrat as shown in the table.

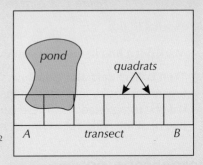

Quadrat	1	2	3	4	5	6
Number of Bulrushes	1	5	5	20	43	37

a) Calculate the mean number of bulrushes per quadrat.

b) Joanne started counting at quadrat 1 and moved along the transect in order, to quadrat 6. Assuming that the information Joanne read was correct, do you think quadrat 1 is at end A or end B of the transect? Explain your answer.

Q2 An area of the Lake District was sampled for the presence of a species of slug. Conservationists used 0.25 m² quadrats placed randomly in the landscape. The mean number of the slugs found in a quadrat was 2.5 and the area under investigation was 2000 m².

Estimate the total population of the slugs in the area.

6. The Cycling of Materials

Materials such as water and carbon are being constantly recycled on Earth. It's really important that this happens. For example, it means that there's always enough material to make new organisms when old organisms die.

The water cycle

The water here on planet Earth is constantly recycled. Energy from the Sun makes water **evaporate** from the land and sea, turning it into water vapour. Water also evaporates from plants — this is known as **transpiration** (see p. 86). The warm water vapour is carried upwards (as warm air rises). When it gets higher up it cools and condenses to form clouds. Water falls from the clouds as **precipitation** (usually rain, but sometimes snow or hail) onto land, where it provides fresh water for plants and animals. It then drains into the sea, before the whole process starts again.

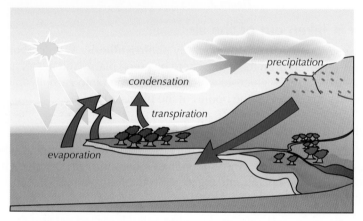

Figure 1: *Diagram showing the steps in the water cycle.*

Recycling of elements

Living things are made of materials they take from the world around them. For example, plants turn elements like carbon, oxygen, hydrogen and nitrogen from the soil and the air into the complex compounds (carbohydrates, proteins and fats) that make up living organisms. These get passed up the food chain.

These materials are returned to the environment in waste products, or when the organisms die and decay. Materials decay because they're broken down (digested) by microorganisms. This happens faster in warm, moist, aerobic (oxygen rich) conditions because microorganisms are more active in these conditions.

Decay puts the stuff that plants need to grow (e.g. mineral ions) back into the soil. In a **stable community**, the materials that are taken out of the soil and used by plants, etc. are balanced by those that are put back in. There's a constant cycle of lots of different materials happening through both the biotic and abiotic parts of an ecosystem.

Learning Objectives:

- Know that the water on Earth is constantly recycled in a process called the water cycle, in which water follows a continuous chain of being evaporated and precipitated, and that this provides the plants and animals on land with fresh water.

- Understand that all materials in our environment are recycled to produce the building blocks required to make new organisms, and that lots of different materials are constantly cycling through both the biotic and abiotic parts of an ecosystem.

- Know that microorganisms decay dead animal and plant material, returning mineral ions to the soil for use by plants.

- Know that the carbon on Earth is constantly cycled between organisms and the atmosphere.

- Know that carbon is removed from the atmosphere by plants as CO_2 to be used in photosynthesis.

- Know that the decay of dead plant and animal material by microorganisms returns carbon to the atmosphere in the form of CO_2, which is produced when the microorganisms respire.

Specification Reference
4.7.2.2

The carbon cycle

Carbon is constantly being cycled — from the air, through food chains and eventually back out into the air again. The carbon cycle shows how carbon is recycled — see Figure 2.

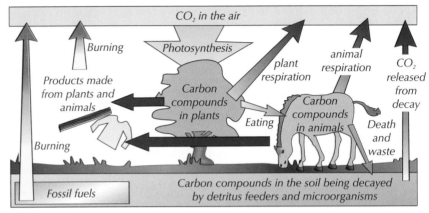

Figure 2: The carbon cycle.

Tip: Fossil fuels are made of decayed animal and plant matter.

Carbon is taken out of the air

The whole carbon cycle is "powered" by **photosynthesis**. CO_2 (carbon dioxide) is removed from the atmosphere by green plants and algae, and the carbon is used to make glucose, which can be turned into carbohydrates, fats and proteins that make up the bodies of the plants and algae.

Carbon moves through food chains

Some of the carbon becomes part of the fats and proteins in animals when the plants and algae are eaten. The carbon then moves through the food chain. The energy that green plants and algae get from photosynthesis is transferred up the food chain.

When plants, algae and animals die, other animals (called **detritus feeders**) and microorganisms feed on their remains. Animals also produce waste, and this too is broken down by detritus feeders and microorganisms.

Figure 3: Woodlice are detritus feeders.

Carbon is returned to the air

Some carbon is returned to the atmosphere as CO_2 when the plants, algae, animals (including detritus feeders) and microorganisms **respire**. Also CO_2 is released back into the air when some useful plant and animal products, e.g. wood and fossil fuels, are burnt (**combustion**).

Practice Questions — Fact Recall

Q1   How does CO_2 from the atmosphere first enter the food chain?

Q2   How is carbon returned to the atmosphere from dead leaves?

Practice Question — Application

Q1   A student said, "Some of the water in trees eventually ends up in the sea." Do you agree with this statement? Explain your answer.

Topic 7a Checklist — Make sure you know...

Competition

- ❑ That an ecosystem is the interaction of a community of living organisms (biotic) with the non-living (abiotic) parts of their environment.

- ❑ The levels of organisation that make up an ecosystem, e.g. population, community.

- ❑ That organisms rely on resources from their environment and other organisms for survival, and that organisms have to compete with each other for the limited resources.

- ❑ That plants compete for light and space, as well as water and mineral ions from the soil, and that animals compete for space, food, water and mates.

- ❑ How to identify the resources being competed for using relevent information given to you.

- ❑ How to read and interpret information about the interaction of organisms in communities from graphs, charts and tables.

- ❑ That species in a community are interdependent — they rely on each other for the resources they need, so changes in an environment can have knock-on effects for lots of different organisms.

- ❑ That a stable community is a community where all the species and environmental factors are in balance so that the population sizes remain roughly constant.

Abiotic and Biotic Factors

- ❑ These examples of abiotic (non-living) factors — moisture level, light intensity, temperature, carbon dioxide level, wind intensity and direction, oxygen level, soil pH and mineral content.

- ❑ How changes in the abiotic factors of an ecosystem can affect a community.

- ❑ These examples of biotic (living) factors — the arrival of new predators, competition from other species, the arrival of new pathogens and the availability of food.

- ❑ How changes in the biotic factors of an ecosystem can affect a community.

- ❑ How to read and interpret data about biotic and abiotic factors from graphs, charts and tables.

Adaptations

- ❑ That adaptations are features or characteristics that allow organisms to survive in the environmental conditions of their habitat.

- ❑ That adaptations can be structural (features of an organism's body structure), behavioural, or functional (the way that things work inside an organism's body).

- ❑ That extremophiles are organisms that live in extreme environments, such as where temperature, pressure or salt concentration are high (e.g. some species of bacteria live in deep sea vents).

- ❑ How to identify an animal's adaptations and understand how they help the organism to survive.

cont...

Food Chains

- [ ] That food chains show the feeding relationships between different species in an ecosystem.
- [ ] That a food chain always starts with a photosynthetic organism such as a green plant or algae, known as a producer, which makes molecules like glucose.
- [ ] That producers make all of the biomass on Earth.
- [ ] That producers are eaten by primary consumers, and primary consumers are eaten by secondary consumers, which are eaten by tertiary consumers.
- [ ] That a predator is a consumer that kills and eats another animal, which is known as its prey, and that the population sizes of predators and prey go up and down in predator-prey cycles.

Using Quadrats and Transects

- [ ] That quadrats (square frames that enclose a known area) can be used by ecologists to investigate the population size and distribution of organisms in an area.
- [ ] How to investigate the effect of a factor on the distribution of a species using a quadrat and sampling techniques (Required Practical 7).
- [ ] How to calculate the mean, mode and median of data on the abundance of organisms.
- [ ] How to investigate the size of a population of a certain species in a habitat using a quadrat (Required Practical 7).
- [ ] How transects can be used to investigate the distribution of organisms across an area (e.g. how the distribution of a certain species varies across an entire field).
- [ ] How to draw graphs, using appropriate axes, to show data relating to the abundance of species.

The Cycling of Materials

- [ ] That the water cycle is a continually occurring chain of evaporation and precipitation that allows the water on Earth to be constantly recycled and provides water to the plants and animals living on land.
- [ ] That there is a constant cycle of lots of different materials through both the biotic and abiotic components of an ecosystem.
- [ ] That the materials used to make the building blocks of organisms are recycled into new organisms.
- [ ] That mineral ions are returned to the soil from dead animal and plant material when microorganisms break the dead material down.
- [ ] That the carbon cycle shows how the carbon on Earth is recycled between organisms and the atmosphere.
- [ ] That carbon is returned to the atmosphere in the form of carbon dioxide when microorganisms that decay dead plant and animal material respire, and that this carbon dioxide is then used by plants in photosynthesis.

Exam-style Questions

1   A biology class were studying the distribution of organisms on a rocky shore line. Three students each set up a transect which ran from the water's edge up the shore, as shown in the diagram. All three students counted the number of limpets in each of the 50 cm × 50 cm quadrats. The number of limpets counted by each student are shown in the table.

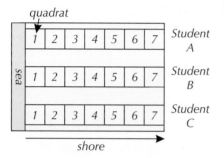

Quadrat number	1	2	3	4	5	6	7
Student A No. of Limpets	18	65	70	55	30	10	0
Student B No. of Limpets	6	72	76	41	21	18	3
Student C No. of Limpets	14	83	84	57	26	16	1

1.1   Calculate the mean number of limpets found in quadrat 4.

(2 marks)

1.2   Limpets need to stay moist in order to survive, but they are able to survive for a period of time without water by clamping down onto the surface of rocks — this helps to prevent them from drying out. Close to the water's edge, limpets have lots of competition from other species for space.

Use this information and the data above to describe the distribution of limpets along the shore line and suggest reasons for it.

(3 marks)

1.3   During the class study, another group of students investigated the distribution of a type of starfish. They placed 20 quadrats at random in each sample area of shoreline that they were interested in studying.

Why did the students place their quadrats randomly?

(1 mark)

2*   The diagram below shows how a particular food chain is part of the carbon cycle.

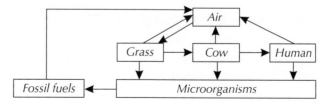

Use the information in the diagram and your own knowledge to describe the processes in which carbon is cycled between this food chain, other living organisms and the air.

(6 marks)

3   Scientists have been studying a species of wolf. The wolf lives in rocky mountains where the temperature at night can drop as low as –15 °C. Its main source of prey is rodents that live in burrows beneath the ground. The wolf has adaptations to help it survive in the rocky mountains as shown on the diagram below.

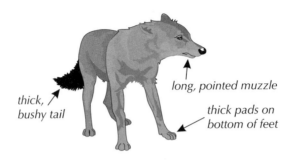

thick, bushy tail

long, pointed muzzle

thick pads on bottom of feet

3.1   What is an adaptation?

(1 mark)

3.2   Use the information and the diagram above to suggest how the wolf is adapted to survive in the rocky mountains.

(3 marks)

Scientists have been recording the total population size of the wolf over a number of years. Their findings and some other data are shown in the table below.

Year	Total population size of wolf	Total population size of one type of prey (million)	Rabies outbreak in this year
2007	401	1.96	No
2008	327	2.01	Yes
2009	330	2.09	No
2010	341	2.06	No
2011	265	2.01	Yes
2012	269	1.99	No

3.3   Describe the overall trend in the total population size of the wolf species studied.

(1 mark)

3.4   Suggest the biotic factor that's responsible for this trend.
Use data from the table to support your answer.

(3 marks)

3.5   The trend in the total population size of the wolf species led to lots of changes in the community that weren't obviously linked to the wolves. Explain why a change in the population of one species can have far reaching effects in a community.

(2 marks)

1. Biodiversity and Waste

How humans impact the environment makes it onto the news a lot nowadays — everything we do has an effect, and it's not usually good...

What is biodiversity?

> Biodiversity is the variety of different species of organisms on Earth, or within an ecosystem.

High biodiversity is important. It makes sure that ecosystems (see page 255) are stable. Different species are interdependent — they depend on each other for things like shelter and food. Different species can also help to maintain the right physical environment for each other (e.g. the acidity of the soil). A high biodiversity means that one species is less likely to have to rely on a single different species for the resources and physical environment that it needs. This is because there's a higher chance that more than one species in the ecosystem can help provide the same resources and conditions.

For the human species to survive, it's important that a good level of biodiversity is maintained. Lots of human actions, including waste production (see next page) and deforestation (see p. 281), as well as global warming (see page 278) are reducing biodiversity. However, it's only recently that we've started taking measures to stop this from continuing.

The increasing human population

There are currently over seven billion people in the world — the population is rising very quickly, and it's not slowing down (see Figure 1).

This is mostly due to modern medicine and farming methods, which have reduced the number of people dying from disease and hunger. This is great for all of us humans, but it means we're having a bigger effect on the environment we live in.

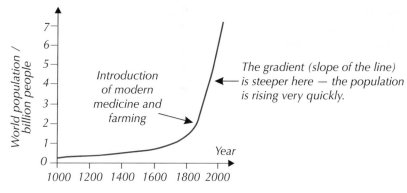

Figure 1: Graph showing the increasing population of the world.

Learning Objectives:

- Know that biodiversity is the variety of different species of organisms on Earth, or within an ecosystem.
- Know that high biodiversity is important because it results in stable ecosystems, where one species is less dependent on another single species for the resources it needs.
- Know that maintaining biodiversity is vital for the survival of the human species.
- Know that lots of things that humans do reduce biodiversity and it's only relatively recently that we've started to put measures in place to stop this from continuing.
- Understand that the human population is growing very quickly and the standard of living is getting higher, which means that more resources are being used and more waste is being produced.
- Know that, unless dealt with properly, the increasing amounts of waste and chemicals being produced can lead to increasing amounts of pollution.
- Know how pollution can occur in water, land and air, and how this can reduce biodiversity.

Specification References
4.7.3.1, 4.7.3.2

Demands on the environment

When the Earth's population was much smaller, the effects of human activity were usually small and local. Nowadays though, our actions can have a far more widespread effect. Our increasing population puts pressure on the environment, as we take the resources we need to survive.

People around the world are also demanding a higher **standard of living** (and so demand luxuries to make life more comfortable — cars, computers, etc.). So we use more raw materials (e.g. oil to make plastics), but we also use more energy for the manufacturing processes. This all means we're taking more and more resources from the environment more and more quickly.

Unfortunately, many raw materials are being used up quicker than they're being replaced. So if we carry on like we are, one day we're going to run out.

Waste

Tip: Fertilisers are chemicals added to soil to provide nutrients for crop growth. Pesticides are chemicals that kill pests (like insects) that eat and damage the crops. Herbicides kill weeds that compete with the crops for nutrients, water, etc.

As we make more and more things we produce more and more waste, including waste chemicals. And unless this waste is properly handled, more harmful pollution will be caused. Pollution affects water, land and air and kills plants and animals, reducing biodiversity.

Water

Sewage and toxic chemicals from industry can pollute lakes, rivers and oceans, affecting the plants and animals that rely on them for survival (including humans). And the chemicals used on land to help grow crops (e.g. fertilisers, pesticides and herbicides) can be washed into water.

Example

If too much fertiliser is added to a field and it rains, then the excess fertiliser can get washed into nearby rivers and lakes. The nutrients in the fertiliser allow lots of algae to grow, causing an algal bloom (see Figure 2). The bloom blocks out the light, so plants in the water can't photosynthesise and die. Microorganisms feeding on the dead plants use up the oxygen in the water, which can eventually lead to the death of fish and other animals.

Figure 2: *Algal bloom in a pond. The algae is the thick yellow-green material that you can see covering the surface of the water.*

Land

We use toxic chemicals for farming (e.g. pesticides and herbicides). We also bury nuclear waste underground, and we dump a lot of household waste in landfill sites, where it doesn't break down so easily (and some doesn't break down at all).

Tip: Finding land to dump and bury waste (landfill sites) will become more of a problem as the population grows and we produce more waste.

Air

Smoke and acidic gases released into the atmosphere can pollute the air.

Examples

- Burning some fossil fuels releases sulfur dioxide. When sulfur dioxide mixes with clouds it forms dilute sulfuric acid, which falls as acid rain. Acid rain can damage buildings and kill plants.

- Carbon dioxide (CO_2) is also released when fossil fuels are burnt. The increasing level of CO_2 is contributing to global warming and climate change (see page 278).

(see page 278)

Tip: Fossil fuels are fuels formed from the remains of organisms that died a very, very long time ago. The three main types of fossil fuel are oil, gas and coal.

Practice Questions — Fact Recall

Q1   Explain why it's important to have high biodiversity.

Q2   True or false? The population of the world is decreasing, but people's standard of living is increasing.

Q3   How can the chemicals used to grow crops cause water pollution?

Q4   How do humans cause land pollution?

Practice Question — Application

Q1   The graph below shows the amount of waste recycled and the amount sent to landfill in one city for three separate years.

Figure 3: *Landfill sites take up room, pollute the land around them and are ugly (they cause visual pollution).*

a) Describe the trends shown by the graph.

b) What percentage of the total waste shown in the graph for 2010 was recycled?

c) Suggest why the amount of space taken up by landfill sites around the world is increasing.

d) Suggest one reason why it is important to recycle products such as metal cans.

Tip: Metal is a raw material.

2. Global Warming

Learning Objectives:

- Know that the increasing levels of carbon dioxide and methane in the atmosphere are leading to global warming.

- Be able to recall some of the biological consequences that global warming can lead to.

Specification Reference 4.7.3.5

You've probably heard the term 'global warming' thrown about. Now it's time to get down to the details of what it really means and what causes it.

Global warming

The temperature of the Earth is a balance between the energy it gets from the Sun and the energy it radiates back out into space. Gases in the atmosphere naturally act like an insulating layer. They absorb most of the energy that would normally be radiated out into space, and re-radiate it in all directions (including back towards the Earth). This increases the temperature of the planet. It's called the greenhouse effect — see Figure 1.

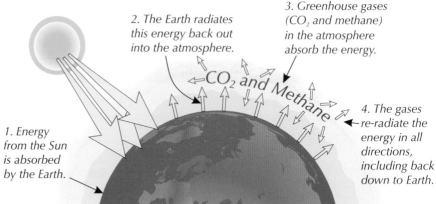

2. The Earth radiates this energy back out into the atmosphere.

3. Greenhouse gases (CO$_2$ and methane) in the atmosphere absorb the energy.

CO$_2$ and Methane

1. Energy from the Sun is absorbed by the Earth.

4. The gases re-radiate the energy in all directions, including back down to Earth.

Figure 1: *Diagram illustrating the greenhouse effect.*

Tip: Scientists now agree that human activities are causing global warming — our activities are causing more greenhouse gases to be released. E.g. deforestation is causing more CO$_2$ to be released (see page 281). Burning fossil fuels is also causing more CO$_2$ to be released.

If this didn't happen, then at night there'd be nothing to keep any energy in, and we'd quickly get very cold indeed. But recently we've started to worry that this effect is getting a bit out of hand...

There are several different gases in the atmosphere which help keep the energy in. They're called "greenhouse gases", and the main ones whose levels we worry about are carbon dioxide (CO$_2$) and methane — because the levels of these two gases are rising quite sharply.

The Earth is gradually heating up because of the increasing levels of greenhouse gases — this is global warming. Global warming is a type of **climate change** and causes other types of climate change, e.g. changing rainfall patterns.

Increasing levels of CO$_2$ and methane. ➡ *Increasing greenhouse effect.* ➡ *Global warming.* ➡ *Other types of climate change.*

Figure 2: *A flow chart summarising the causes and effects of an increasing greenhouse effect.*

The consequences of global warming

Global warming could be a big problem for us. An increase of even a few degrees could have serious consequences for our planet, for example:

Rising sea level leading to habitat loss

As the sea gets warmer, it expands, causing sea level to rise. Sea level has risen a little bit over the last 100 years. If it keeps rising it'll be bad news for people and animals living in low-lying places like the Netherlands, East Anglia and the Maldives. It will lead to flooding, resulting in the loss of habitats (where organisms live).

Higher temperatures also make ice melt. Water that's currently 'trapped' on land (as ice in glaciers and at the poles) runs into the sea, causing sea level to rise even more.

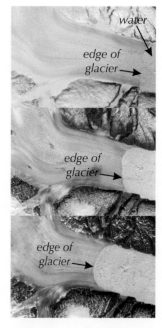

Figure 3: Satellite images of the Helheim glacier in 2001 (top), 2003 (middle) and 2005 (bottom).

> **Examples**
>
> - The coastline of Louisiana (a southern state of the USA) has seen a sea level rise of at least 8 inches in the last 50 years.
>
> - The Helheim glacier (a thick mass of ice in Greenland) has retreated (melted) by 4 km in four years. We know this because of satellite images like the ones in Figure 3. The glacier had stayed in roughly the same position up until 2001.

Changes in the distribution of organisms

The distribution of organisms is just where they're usually found within a certain area. E.g. in the UK, red squirrels are found in the north of England and in Scotland. Wild plants and animals are found in places where they can survive — where it's the right temperature and they have access to the right resources like water, food and shelter. As the average global temperature goes up and other changes to the weather occur (e.g. more or less rainfall), the distribution of many wild animal and plant species may change.

> **Tip:** A decrease in rainfall could lead to drought.

Some species may become more widely distributed, e.g. species that need warmer temperatures may spread further as the conditions they thrive in exist over a wider area. Other species may become less widely distributed, e.g. species that need cooler temperatures may have smaller ranges as the conditions they thrive in exist over a smaller area.

> **Examples**
>
> - The Comma is a species of butterfly that was until recently only found in England and Wales. Its distribution is extending further north though, into Scotland, and this is thought to be due to global warming.
>
> - An increasing number of warm-water striped dolphins are being spotted in the waters around England. At the same time there's been a decline in spottings of the cold-water white-beaked dolphins. This could be because the sea around England is getting warmer.

Figure 4: A Comma butterfly.

Changes to migration patterns

Tip: Global warming is also affecting when animals and plants do other things, e.g. they might breed or flower at different times of the year.

Lots of birds and other animals migrate — they move to different areas at different times of the year. For example, swallows come to the UK in summer but they spend their winters in hotter countries. Global warming could lead to changes in migration patterns. This includes changes to where organisms migrate (e.g. some birds may migrate further north, as more northern areas are getting warmer), when they migrate, and possibly if they migrate at all.

┌─ **Example** ───

Studies have shown that some birds living in Africa over winter have started to migrate back to their European summer breeding grounds earlier than ever before. This could be directly due to temperature change, or because the temperature is causing the birds' food sources to appear at earlier times.

Less biodiversity

Biodiversity (see page 275) could be reduced — if some species are unable to adapt to a change in the climate, then they won't survive and the species will become extinct. For example, if it's too hot for them where they usually live but they can't survive in other habitats because there isn't the right food source, then they might die out.

Practice Questions — Fact Recall

Q1 True or False? Decreasing levels of greenhouse gases are contributing to an increase in the average global temperature.

Q2 Name the two main greenhouse gases we are worried about.

Practice Questions — Application

Q1 Since the 1950s, a species of bird has started to become more common in a small island country. The population of the species on the island started increasing as the average global temperature rose due to global warming. Scientists have suggested that it is the effect of global warming that has changed the distribution of the species.

   a) Explain how global warming can lead to changes in the distribution of organisms.

   b) Besides causing distribution changes, suggest one other way in which global warming might affect birds found in the country.

3. Deforestation and Land Use

The expanding human population means that we need more development. More development means that we need to use more land. Sometimes, that can lead to problems. Another page of bad news, I'm afraid...

Using land

Humans reduce the amount of land available to other animals and plants. The four main human activities that do this are:

- Building
- Quarrying
- Farming
- Dumping waste

Sometimes, the way we use land has a bad effect on the environment — for example, if it requires deforestation or the destruction of habitats like peat bogs and other areas of peat.

Deforestation

Deforestation is the cutting down of forests. This causes big problems when it's done on a large-scale, such as cutting down rainforests in tropical areas. It's done for various reasons, including:

- To clear land for farming (e.g. cattle or rice crops) to provide more food.

- To grow crops from which biofuels (such as those based on ethanol) can be produced.

Problems caused by deforestation

Deforestation leads to a variety of issues:

Less biodiversity

The more species, the greater the biodiversity. Habitats like tropical rainforests can contain a huge number of different species, so when they are destroyed there is a danger of many species becoming extinct — reducing biodiversity.

More carbon dioxide released into the atmosphere

As you saw on page 278, an increasing level of carbon dioxide in the atmosphere is contributing to global warming. Deforestation increases the amount of carbon dioxide released into the atmosphere, as carbon dioxide is released when trees are burnt to clear land — see Figure 1 on the next page. (Carbon in wood doesn't contribute to atmospheric pollution until it's released by burning.) Microorganisms feeding on bits of dead wood also release carbon dioxide as a waste product of respiration.

Learning Objectives:

- Know that humans use land for things like building, quarrying, farming and waste disposal, which means that there's less land for other animals and plants.

- Know that humans cut down large areas of tropical forest to clear the land for livestock, rice crops and crops to make biofuels from.

- Know that humans sometimes destroy peat bogs and other areas of peat to use the peat in compost for gardeners.

- Know that the destruction of areas of peat results in more CO_2 being released into the atmosphere (when the peat is burnt or broken down by microorganisms).

- Know why the destruction of areas of peat reduces biodiversity.

Specification References 4.7.3.3, 4.7.3.4

Tip: Head back to page 275 for more on biodiversity.

Tip: Remember, carbon dioxide (CO_2) is a greenhouse gas.

Less carbon dioxide taken in

Cutting down loads of trees means that the amount of carbon dioxide removed from the atmosphere during photosynthesis is reduced — see Figure 1. Trees 'lock up' some of the carbon that they absorb during photosynthesis in their wood, which can remove it from the atmosphere for hundreds of years. Removing trees means that less is locked up.

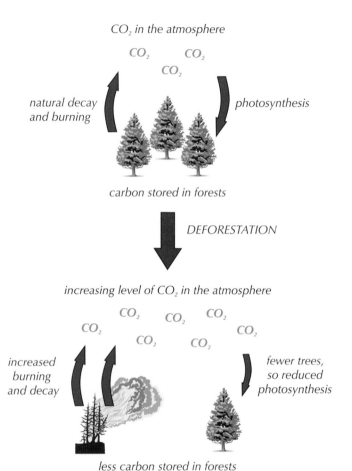

Tip: The destruction of peat bogs also leads to the release of more CO_2 (see next page).

Figure 1: The amount of carbon dioxide in the atmosphere should stay fairly constant (top cycle). But deforestation leads to an increase in the atmospheric carbon dioxide level (bottom cycle).

The destruction of peat bogs

Bogs are areas of land that are acidic and waterlogged. Plants that live in bogs don't fully decay when they die, because there's not enough oxygen. The partly-rotted plants gradually build up to form **peat** (a brown, soil-like material — see Figure 2). So the carbon in the plants is stored in the peat instead of being released into the atmosphere.

However, peat bogs are often drained so that the area can be used as farmland, or the peat is cut up and dried to use as fuel. It's also sold to gardeners as compost. Peat is being used faster than it forms.

Figure 2: Some peat.

When peat is drained, it comes into more contact with air and some microorganisms start to decompose it. These microorganisms use oxygen and substances found in the peat as reactants for respiration. They release carbon dioxide as a product of respiration, contributing to global warming (see page 278). Carbon dioxide is also released when peat is burned as a fuel.

Destroying the bogs also destroys (or reduces the area of) the habitats of some of the animals, plants and microorganisms that live there, so reduces biodiversity.

Figure 3: *A peat bog that's had some peat harvested from it. The brown trench is where peat blocks have been dug up and taken away.*

Practice Questions — Fact Recall

Q1 Give three things that humans use land for that reduces the amount of land available to other animals and plants.

Q2 What is deforestation?

Practice Questions — Application

Q1 The graph shows how much forest was cleared each year in one region of a rainforest and the use of the area after clearance.

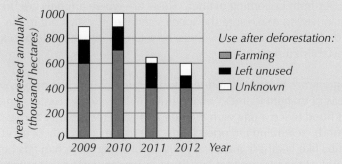

Use after deforestation:
- ▨ Farming
- ▪ Left unused
- ☐ Unknown

a) How much forest was cleared in this region in 2009?

b) i) How much land was used for farming after clearance in 2012?

   ii) What kind of farming might be taking place on the cleared land?

Q2 Dave needs some compost for his vegetable plot. A peat-free variety is being advertised as an environmentally-friendly option. Explain why the manufacturers are making this claim.

Tip: The bar chart in Q1 is a composite bar chart — it's just like a normal one except the bars are placed on top of each other instead of side by side. Here's the information for 2011 shown in composite form (left) and normal form (right):

- Know that programmes have been set up to reduce the effects of human activities on ecosystems and biodiversity.

- Know the following examples of programmes designed to maintain ecosystems and biodiversity:

  - Breeding programmes,

  - Programmes to protect and regenerate rare habitats,

  - Programmes to reintroduce field margins and hedgerows to single-crop fields,

  - Programmes to reduce deforestation and carbon dioxide emissions,

  - Recycling programmes.

- Know examples of the positive and negative effects of human interaction with ecosystems, and be able to evaluate their effect on biodiversity.

Specification Reference 4.7.3.6

4. Maintaining Ecosystems and Biodiversity

You learned about biodiversity back on p. 275 and ecosystems on p. 255. It's important that we protect and maintain them. These pages tell you about some of the methods being used, as well as some of the issues involved.

Protection programmes

It's important that biodiversity is maintained at a high enough level to make sure that ecosystems are stable.

In some areas, programmes have been set up by concerned citizens and scientists to minimise damage by human activities to ecosystems and biodiversity.

You need to know some examples of these programmes:

Example

- Breeding programmes have been set up to help prevent endangered species from becoming extinct. These are where animals are bred in captivity to make sure the species survives if it dies out in the wild. Individuals can sometimes be released into the wild to boost or re-establish a population.

- Programmes to protect and regenerate rare habitats like mangroves (areas of mangrove trees, which grow in the mud in coastal regions that flood twice a day with the tide and have roots partly above ground), heathland (an open landscape made up mainly of short shrubs like heather) and coral reefs. Protecting these habitats helps to protect the species that live there — preserving the ecosystem and biodiversity in the area.

- There are programmes to reintroduce hedgerows and field margins around fields on farms where only a single type of crop is grown. Field margins are areas of land around the edges of fields where wild flowers and grasses are left to grow. Hedgerows and field margins provide a habitat for a wider variety of organisms than could survive in a single crop habitat.

- Some governments have introduced regulations and programmes to reduce the level of deforestation taking place and the amount of carbon dioxide being released into the atmosphere by businesses. This could reduce the increase of global warming (see page 278).

- People are encouraged to recycle to reduce the amount of waste that gets dumped in landfill sites. This could reduce the amount of land taken over for landfill, leaving ecosystems in place.

Figure 1: *There are breeding programmes in place to protect various endangered animals, such as the Mauritius Olive White-eye shown in this photo.*

Conflicting pressures of maintaining biodiversity

Maintaining biodiversity isn't as simple as you would hope. There are lots of conflicting pressures that have to be taken into account:

Tip: You need to be able to describe some of the positive and negative ways in which humans interact with ecosystems and understand how they impact biodiversity. You can read about some of the negatives on pages 276-283. Page 284 covers some of the positives.

Examples

- Protecting biodiversity costs money. For example, governments sometimes pay farmers a subsidy to reintroduce hedgerows and field margins to their land. It can also cost money to keep a watch on whether the programmes and regulations designed to maintain biodiversity are being followed. There can be conflict between protecting biodiversity and saving money — money may be prioritised for other things.

- Protecting biodiversity may come at a cost to local people's livelihood. For example, reducing the amount of deforestation is great for biodiversity, but the people who were previously employed in the tree-felling industry could be left unemployed. This could affect the local economy if people move away with their family to find work.

- There can be conflict between protecting biodiversity and protecting our food security. Sometimes certain organisms are seen as pests by farmers (e.g. locusts and foxes) and are killed to protect crops and livestock so that more food can be produced. As a result, however, the food chain and biodiversity can be affected.

- Development is important, but it can affect the environment. Many people want to protect biodiversity in the face of development, but sometimes land is in such high demand that previously untouched land with high biodiversity has to be used for development, e.g. for housing developments on the edge of towns, or for new agricultural land in developing countries.

Figure 2: *This photo shows a large area of rainforest being cleared for use as agricultural land.*

Practice Questions — Fact Recall

Q1 What is the purpose of a breeding programme?

Q2 Outline and explain what a farmer who only grows one crop might do to protect biodiversity.

Q3 Give one reason why people are encouraged to recycle as much waste as possible.

Topic 7b Checklist — Make sure you know...

Biodiversity and Waste

☐ The meaning of 'biodiversity' — the variety of species of organisms on Earth, or within an ecosystem.

☐ The importance of biodiversity in maintaining stable ecosystems, which often involve lots of interdependent species — species relying on each other for things like food, shelter and keeping the physical environment right.

☐ That high biodiversity means that one species is less dependent on another single species, because there is more likely to be multiple species in the ecosystem that can help provide the resources and physical environment that it needs.

☐ That for the survival of the human species, it's important that biodiversity is maintained at a good level.

☐ That many human activities lead to a reduction in biodiversity, and that actions to combat this have only been put into place relatively recently.

☐ That the rapidly growing human population and the increase in the standard of living is putting a strain on resources and producing increasing amounts of waste.

☐ How the increasing amounts of waste cause pollution of water, land and air, and that this can kill plants and animals, which can result in a reduction in biodiversity.

Global Warming

☐ That increasing levels of carbon dioxide and methane, which trap energy inside the Earth's atmosphere, are contributing to global warming, causing the average global temperature to rise.

☐ Examples of how global warming can have biological consequences for the planet.

Deforestation and Land Use

☐ That humans use lots of land for activities like building, quarrying, farming and dumping waste, and that this reduces the amount of land available to other species.

☐ That deforestation of large areas of tropical forest is sometimes carried out by humans to make the land available for things like farming cattle and growing crops for food, or for growing crops for biofuel production.

☐ That humans often destroy peat bogs and other areas of peat, e.g. to use the peat in garden compost.

☐ That when areas of peat are destroyed, there is an increase in the amount of carbon dioxide released into the atmosphere due to the burning and decomposition of peat, and biodiversity is also reduced.

Maintaining Ecosystems and Biodiversity

☐ That there are programmes to help reduce the effects of human activities on ecosystems, such as breeding programmes for endangered species, protection and regeneration of rare habitats, programmes to introduce margins and hedgerows around fields, schemes to reduce deforestation and carbon dioxide emissions, and recycling programmes.

☐ Examples of both positive and negative ways that humans interact with ecosystems, and how these can affect the level of biodiversity in an ecosystem.

Exam-style Questions

1. **Figure 1** shows the edge of a mangrove forest where it meets the water. Mangrove forests are ecosystems found in tropical and subtropical coastal areas. The trees in mangrove forests form branching root systems that are partly exposed above the ground. Mangrove forests frequently flood with sea water as the tide comes in. They're important habitats for a huge variety of organisms, including fish, crabs, birds and even Bengal tigers.

   Enormous areas of mangrove forest have been destroyed to make way for large-scale shrimp farming. This has badly affected biodiversity in the areas involved.

   Figure 1

1.1 Explain what is meant by biodiversity.

(1 mark)

1.2 Some projects now aim to protect the biodiversity of mangrove forests by protecting the remaining areas of mangrove forest from being used for shrimp farming.

Suggest **two** pressures that could affect the success of these projects.

(2 marks)

1.3 The reason that shrimp farming has increased is not due to the increasing requirement for food to feed the growing human population.

Suggest a reason for why the size of the shrimp farming industry has increased.

(2 marks)

Global warming is a major issue facing modern scientists and society as a whole. It is caused by increasing levels of certain gases.

1.4 Suggest why clearing areas of mangrove forest could contribute to global warming.

(4 marks)

Tip: The Required
Practical Activities in
this book are marked
with a big stamp like
this...

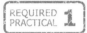

REQUIRED
PRACTICAL **1**

The practicals that you
do in class might be
slightly different to the
ones in this book (as
it's up to your teacher
exactly what method you
use), but they'll cover
the same principles and
techniques.

Tip: When you're
reading off a scale,
write down the value of
the graduation that the
amount is closest to.

1. Measuring Substances

*For the biology part of GCSE Combined Science, you'll have to do at least
seven practicals, called Required Practical Activities. You'll need to know how
to use various pieces of apparatus and carry out different scientific techniques.
And not only do you need to carry out the practicals, you could also be asked
about them in the exams. Luckily, all the biology Required Practical Activities
are covered in this book, and the next few pages cover some of the techniques
that you'll need to know about.*

Measuring the mass of a solid

To weigh a solid, start by putting the container you are weighing your
substance into on a balance. Set the balance to exactly zero and then
weigh out the correct amount of your substance. Easy peasy.

Measuring temperature

You can use a thermometer to measure the temperature of a solution.
Make sure that the bulb of the thermometer is completely submerged in
the solution and that you wait for the temperature to stabilise before you
take your initial reading. Read off the scale on the thermometer at eye
level to make sure it's correct.

Measuring the volume of a liquid

There's more than one way to measure the volume of a liquid.
Whichever method you use, always read the volume from the bottom of
the meniscus (the curved upper surface of the liquid) when it's at eye level.

Figure 1: *The meniscus of a
fluid in a measuring cylinder,
viewed at eye level.*

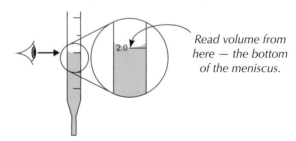

Read volume from
here — the bottom
of the meniscus.

Figure 2: *The technique for correctly measuring the volume of a liquid.*

Tip: You could use a
dropping pipette if you
just wanted to transfer a
couple of drops of liquid
and didn't need it to be
particularly accurate,
for example, if you were
adding an indicator to a
mixture (see next page).

Measuring cylinders

Measuring cylinders come in all different sizes. Make sure you choose one
that's the right size for the measurement you want to make. It's no good using
a huge 1 dm³ cylinder to measure out 2 cm³ of a liquid — the graduations
will be too big, and you'll end up with massive errors. It'd be much better to
use one that measures up to 10 cm³.

Pipettes

Pipettes are used to suck up and transfer volumes of liquid between containers. Dropping pipettes are used to transfer drops of liquid. Graduated pipettes are used to transfer accurate volumes. A pipette filler (see Figure 3) is attached to the end of a graduated pipette, to control the amount of liquid being drawn up.

Measuring the volume of a gas

There are a few different ways of measuring the volume of a gas. However you do it, it's key that you make sure that the equipment is set up so that none of the gas can escape, otherwise your results won't be accurate.

Gas syringes

To accurately measure the volume of gas, you should use a gas syringe (see Figure 4).

delivery tube

conical flask containing sample

bung

gas syringe

Figure 4: A gas syringe attached to a conical flask.

Displacement of water

As an alternative to using a gas syringe, you can use an upturned measuring cylinder filled with water. The gas will displace the water so you can read the volume off the scale.

Other methods

Other methods to measure the amount of gas include counting the bubbles produced or measuring the length of a gas bubble drawn along a tube (see page 153). These methods are less accurate, but will give you relative amounts of gas to compare results.

Measuring the pH of a substance

The method you should use to measure pH depends on your experiment:

Indicator dyes

Indicators are dyes that change colour depending on whether they're in an acid or an alkali. You use them by adding a couple of drops of the indicator to the solution you're interested in. Universal indicator is a mixture of indicators that changes colour gradually as pH changes — see Figure 5. It's useful for estimating the pH of a solution based on its colour.

Indicator paper

Indicator paper is useful if you don't want to colour the entire solution that you're testing. It changes colour depending on the pH of the solution it touches. You can also hold a piece of damp indicator paper in a gas sample to test its pH.

pH meters

pH meters have a digital display that gives an accurate value for the pH of a solution.

Measuring time

You should use a stopwatch to time experiments. These measure to the nearest 0.1 s so are pretty sensitive. Make sure you start and stop the stopwatch at exactly the right time.

Figure 3: Graduated pipettes with two different types of pipette filler attached.

Figure 5: A set of test tubes containing liquids at a range of pH levels with universal indicator added.

Tip: Blue litmus paper turns red in acidic conditions and red litmus paper turns blue in alkaline conditions.

2. Heating Substances and Using Potometers

Lots of scientific experiments involve heating one or more of the substances involved. The method of heating used depends on the substance being heated and what temperature it needs to be heated to. Potometers are handy pieces of apparatus that are used to measure how much water a plant takes up.

Bunsen burners

Bunsen burners are good for heating things quickly. You can easily adjust how strongly they're heating. But you need to be careful not to use them if you're heating flammable substances as the flame means the substance would be at risk of catching fire.

To use a Bunsen burner, you should first connect it to a gas tap, and check that the hole is closed. Place it on a heat-proof mat. Next, light a splint and hold it over the Bunsen burner. Now, turn on the gas. The Bunsen burner should light with a yellow flame. The more open the hole is, the more strongly the Bunsen burner will heat your substance. Open the hole to the amount you want. As you open the hole more, the flame should turn more blue.

Tip: Some things take a long time to cool down, and you can't necessarily tell by looking whether they're hot or cold. So, after heating equipment, you should always handle it with tongs so you don't get burnt.

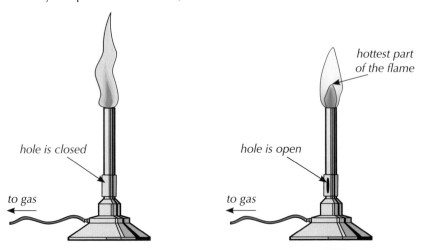

Figure 1: *A Bunsen burner with the hole closed (left) and the hole open (right).*

If your Bunsen burner is alight but not heating anything, make sure you close the hole so that the flame becomes yellow and clearly visible. Use the blue flame to heat things. If you're heating a vessel in the flame, hold it at the top (e.g. with tongs) and point the opening away from yourself (and others). If you're heating something over the flame (e.g. a beaker of water), you should put a tripod and gauze over the Bunsen burner before you light it, and place the vessel on this.

Electric heaters

Electric heaters are often made up of a metal plate that can be heated to a specified temperature. The vessel containing the substance you want to heat is placed on top of the hot plate. The vessel is only heated from below, so you'll usually have to stir the substance inside to make sure it's heated evenly.

Figure 2: *An electric heater.*

Water baths

A water bath is a container filled with water that can be heated to a specific temperature. A simple water bath can be made by heating a beaker of water over a Bunsen burner and monitoring the temperature with a thermometer. However, it is difficult to keep the temperature of the water constant.

An electric water bath will monitor and adjust the temperature for you. To use one, start by setting the temperature on the water bath, and allow the water to heat up. To make sure it has reached the right temperature, use a thermometer. Place the vessel containing your substance in the water bath using a pair of tongs. The level of the water outside the vessel should be just above the level of the substance inside the vessel. The substance will then be warmed to the same temperature as the water.

As the substance in the vessel is surrounded by water, the heating is very even. Water boils at 100 °C though, so you can't use a water bath to heat something to a higher temperature than this — the water won't get hot enough.

Figure 3: A typical water bath.

Measuring water uptake with a potometer

A potometer is a special piece of apparatus used to measure the water uptake by a plant. Here's how to set one up:

Tip: If there are air bubbles in the apparatus or the plant's xylem, it will affect your results. That's why the whole process of setting up a potometer is done underwater.

1. Cut a shoot underwater to prevent air from entering the xylem. Cut it at a slant to increase the surface area available for water uptake.

2. Assemble the potometer in water and insert the shoot under water, so no air can enter.

3. Remove the apparatus from the water but keep the end of the capillary tube submerged in a beaker of water.

4. Check that the apparatus is watertight and airtight.

5. Dry the leaves, allow time for the shoot to acclimatise and then shut the tap.

reservoir of water used to return bubble to start for repeats

as the plant takes up water, the air bubble moves along the scale

tap is shut off during experiment

water moves this way

capillary tube with a scale

bubble moves this way

beaker of water

Figure 4: A potometer set up and ready to use.

Tip: There are different types of potometer available. They won't all look like the one shown in Figure 4.

6. Remove the end of the capillary tube from the beaker of water until one air bubble has formed, then put the end of the tube back into the water.

7. A potometer can be used to estimate the transpiration rate of a plant. There's more about this on page 87.

Figure 5: Students using a potometer with a slightly different design to the one shown in Figure 4.

3. Stage Micrometers and Eyepiece Graticules

Stage micrometers and eyepiece graticules are useful tools in microscopy.

Using stage micrometers and eyepiece graticules

When you're looking at something magnified down a microscope, you can use a **stage micrometer** and **eyepiece graticule** to work out the actual size of whatever you're looking at. An eyepiece graticule is fitted onto the eyepiece of the microscope. It's like a transparent ruler with numbers, but no units. The stage micrometer is placed on the stage of the microscope. It's a microscope slide with an accurate scale (it has units).

The stage micrometer is used to work out the value of the divisions on the eyepiece graticule at a particular magnification. This means that when you take the stage micrometer away and replace it with the slide containing your sample, you'll be able to measure the size of, for example, the cells.

Tip: The stage is the flat surface where you would normally put the slide containing the sample you want to magnify. There's more on using microscopes on pages 25-26.

Example

- Line up the eyepiece graticule and the stage micrometer (see Figure 1).
- Each division on the stage micrometer is 0.1 mm long.
- At this magnification, 1 division on the stage micrometer is the same as 4.5 divisions on the eyepiece graticule.

Figure 1: Lining up the eyepiece graticule and stage micrometer.

0 10 20 30 40 50 ← eyepiece graticule

10   20   30   stage ← micrometer

4.5 eyepiece divisions = 1 stage division

1 division = 0.1 mm

Figure 2: An image taken down the eyepiece of a microscope showing an eyepiece graticule (numbered scale) and a stage micrometer (numberless scale).

- To work out the size of 1 division on the eyepiece graticule, you need to divide the size of the division on the stage micrometer by the number of divisions on the eyepiece graticule:

  $0.1 \div 4.5 = 0.022...$ mm

- So if you look at a cell under the microscope at this magnification and it's 4 eyepiece divisions long (see Figure 3), you know it measures:
  $4 \times 0.022...$
  $= 0.088...$
  $= \textbf{0.09 mm}$ (1 significant figure)

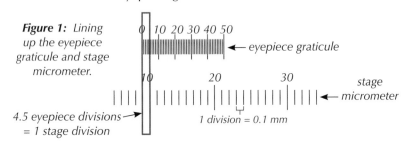

eyepiece graticule

View down the eyepiece

Figure 3: Using the calibrated eyepiece graticule to measure cells.

Tip: Re-calibrating the micrometer and graticule means to work out the value of the eyepiece graticule divisions again using the stage micrometer down the new objective lens.

If you change the objective lens you're using, you need to re-calibrate the micrometer and graticule. This is because using a different objective lens will change the magnification, meaning that one division on the stage micrometer will be equal to a different number of divisions on the eyepiece graticule.

4. Sampling

When you're investigating the population size of a certain organism, or its distribution in an area, using sampling can save you an awful lot of time and effort. Read on for more...

What is sampling?

When you're investigating a population, it's generally not possible to count every single organism in the population. This means that you need to take samples of the population you're interested in. The sample data will be used to draw conclusions about the whole population, so it's important that it accurately represents the whole population. To make sure a sample represents a population, it should be random.

If you're interested in the distribution of an organism in an area, or its population size, you can take population samples in the area you're interested in using quadrats or transects (see pages 265-267).

If you only take samples from one part of the area, your results will be biased — they may not give an accurate representation of the whole area. To make sure that your sampling isn't biased, you need to use a method of choosing sampling sites in which every site has an equal chance of being chosen. For example:

Tip: If a sample doesn't represent the population as a whole, it's said to be biased.

Tip: See pages 266-267 to see how sampling can be used to estimate the total population of a species in an area.

Example

If you're looking at plant species in a field...

1. Divide the field into a grid.

2. Label the grid along the bottom and up the side with numbers or letters.

3. Use a random number generator (on a computer or calculator) to select coordinates, e.g. (2,6).

4. Take your samples at these coordinates.

<u>Non-random sampling</u>

Only looks at a small part of the field.

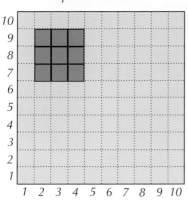

<u>Random sampling</u>

Randomly selects squares from all over the field.

Figure 1: *Many scientific calculators have a handy random number generator built in.*

Collecting health data using sampling

As mentioned on the previous page, it's not practical (or even possible) to study an entire human population. You need to use random sampling to choose members of the population you're interested in.

Example

A health professional is investigating how many people diagnosed with Type 2 diabetes in a particular country also have heart disease.

1. All the people who have been diagnosed with Type 2 diabetes in the country of interest are identified by hospital records. In total, there are 270 196 people.

2. These people are assigned a number between 1 and 270 196.

3. The sample size is decided — e.g. 4250 people.

4. Then a random number generator is used to choose the sample group (e.g. it selects the individuals #72 063, #11 822, #193 123, etc.)

5. The proportion of people in the sample that have heart disease can be used to estimate the total number of people with Type 2 diabetes that also have heart disease:

   - Find the number of people in the sample that have heart disease too — here it's 935 people.

   - Work out what proportion of the sample that number is — you can calculate it as a percentage.

$$\text{proportion (\%)} = \frac{\text{number of people sampled with heart disease}}{\text{total number of people sampled}} \times 100$$

$$= \frac{935}{4250} \times 100$$

$$= \mathbf{22\%}$$

   - Then use your proportion to estimate the total number of people in the population with both Type 2 diabetes and heart disease.

$$= \frac{\text{total population size}}{100} \times \text{proportion (\%)}$$

$$= \frac{270\ 196}{100} \times 22\%$$

$$= \mathbf{59\ 443\ people}$$

Tip: See page 298 for more on percentages.

Tip: Some calculators have a percentage button, which you can use instead of doing this second calculation.

5. Safety and Ethics

Science can be quite dangerous at times, so it's really important that you keep yourself (and others) safe in the lab. Some experiments can also involve ethical issues that you must deal with respectfully and responsibly.

Working safely

Make sure you're working safely in the lab. Before you start any experiment, make sure you know about any safety precautions to do with your method or the chemicals you're using. You need to follow any instructions that your teacher gives you carefully. The chemicals you're using may be hazardous — for example, they might be flammable (catch fire easily), or they might irritate or burn your skin if it comes into contact with them.

Make sure that you're wearing sensible clothing when you're in the lab (e.g. open shoes won't protect your feet from spillages). When you're doing an experiment, you should wear a lab coat to protect your skin and clothing. Depending on the experiment, you may need to also wear safety goggles and gloves.

Figure 1: *You'll often see hazard labels on bottles of chemicals. These tell you in what way a chemical is dangerous.*

Figure 2: *Diagram showing lab safety gear.*

You also need to be aware of general safety in the lab, e.g. keep anything flammable away from lit Bunsen burners, don't directly touch any hot equipment, handle glassware carefully so it doesn't break, etc.

Working ethically

You need to think about ethical issues in your experiments.

Any organisms involved in your investigations need to be treated safely and ethically. Animals need to be treated humanely — they should be handled carefully and any wild animals captured for studying (e.g. during an investigation of the distribution of an organism) should be returned to their original habitat. Any animals kept in the lab should also be cared for in a humane way, e.g. they should not be kept in overcrowded conditions.

If you are carrying out an experiment involving other students (e.g. investigating the effect of caffeine on reaction time), they should not be forced to participate against their will or feel pressured to take part.

Tip: See pages 177-178 for more on investigating the effect of caffeine on reaction time.

Maths Skills

Exam Tip
At least 10% of the marks in your biology exams will test mathematical skills. That's a lot of marks so it's definitely worth making sure you're up to speed.

Maths skills for GCSE Combined Science

Maths crops up quite a lot in GCSE Combined Science, so it's really important that you've mastered all the maths skills you'll need before sitting your exams. Maths skills are covered throughout this book, but here's an extra little section, just on maths, to help you out with the biology exams.

1. Calculations

Calculations are the cornerstone of maths in science. So being able to carry them out carefully is pretty important.

Standard form

You need to be able to work with numbers that are written in **standard form**. Standard form is used for writing very big or very small numbers with lots of zeros in a more convenient way. Standard form must always look like this:

This number must always be between 1 and 10. → $A \times 10^n$ ← *This number is the number of places the decimal point moves.*

Examples

- 1 000 000 can be written as 1×10^6.

- 0.017 can be written as 1.7×10^{-2}.

You can write numbers in standard form by moving the decimal point. Which direction the decimal point moves, and how many places it moves, is described by 'n'. If the decimal point has moved to the left, 'n' is positive. If the decimal point has moved to the right, 'n' is negative.

Tip: When you're writing a measurement in standard form, make sure you keep the same number of significant figures. E.g. 0.00400 cm³ = 4.00×10^{-3} cm³. This'll make sure that you don't lose any accuracy.

Example

Here's how to write out 0.000056 in standard form.

1. Move the decimal point to give the smallest number you can between 1 and 10 — this is 'A'.

$$0.000056 \rightarrow 5.6$$

2. Count the number of places the decimal point has moved. In this example, the decimal point has moved five places to the right.

3. Write that number in the place of 'n'. Remember, if the decimal point has moved to the left, 'n' is positive. If the decimal point has moved to the right (like in this example), 'n' is negative.

4. So 0.000056 is the same as 5.6×10^{-5}.

Tip: Double check you've got it right by doing the multiplication — you should end up with the number you started with. So for this example, you'd check $5.6 \times 10^{-5} = 0.000056$. It's easy to do this on your calculator — see the next page for how to type it in.

The key things to remember with numbers in standard form are...

- When 'n' is positive, the number is big. The bigger 'n' is, the bigger the number is.

- When 'n' is negative, the number is small. The smaller 'n' is (the more negative), the smaller the number is.

- When 'n' is the same for two or more numbers, you need to look at the start of each number to work out which is bigger. For example, 4.5 is bigger than 3.0, so 4.5×10^5 is bigger than 3.0×10^5.

There's a special button on your calculator for using standard form in a calculation — it's the 'Exp' button. So if, for example, you wanted to type in 2×10^7, you'd only need to type in: '2' 'Exp' '7'. Some calculators may have a different button that does the same job, for example it could say 'EE' or '$\times 10^x$' instead of 'Exp' — see Figure 1.

Figure 1: The 'Exp' or '$\times 10^x$' button is used to input standard form on calculators.

Using ratios

Ratios can be used to compare quantities.

> **Example**
>
> An organism with a surface area to volume ratio of 2 : 1 would theoretically have a surface area twice as large as its volume.

Ratios are usually written like this:

A colon separates one quantity from the other.   x and y stand for the quantities that you want to compare.

Ratios are usually most useful in their simplest (smallest) form. To simplify a ratio, divide each side by the same number. It's in its simplest form when there's nothing left you can divide by to give a whole number ratio.

> **Example**
>
> To simplify the ratio 28 : 36, divide both sides by 4.
>
> You get **7 : 9**. ←——— You can't divide 7 and 9 by the same number to get two whole numbers, so this must be the ratio's simplest form.

To compare two ratios, it's best to get the number on the right-hand side of each ratio to be 1. Then you can easily see which ratio is the largest. To get a ratio of X : Y in the form X : 1, divide both sides by Y.

> **Example**
>
> Organism A has a surface area to volume ratio of 6 : 1.
> Organism B has a surface area to volume ratio of 30 : 9.
>
> To compare the two ratios, you need to write the ratio 30 : 9 in the form of X : 1. To do this, just divide both sides by 9:
>
> $$30 \div 9 = 3.3... \qquad 30 : 9 \qquad 9 \div 9 = 1$$
> $$= 3.3 \qquad\qquad 3.3 : 1$$
>
> So the ratio of Organism B is equal to **3.3 : 1**. 3.3 is smaller than 6, so Organism A has the larger surface area to volume ratio.

Tip: When you divide one side of a ratio by an amount, you have to divide the other side by the same number for the ratio to keep the same proportions.

Tip: If you're not sure what number to divide by to simplify a ratio, start by trying to divide both sides by a small number, e.g. 2 or 3, then check to see if you can simplify your answer further. E.g. you could simplify 28 : 36 by dividing each side by 2 to get 14 : 18. But you could simplify it further by dividing by 2 again to get 7 : 9. You can't simplify the ratio any further, so it's in its simplest form.

Calculating percentages

Percentages are another way of comparing quantities. They come in handy when you want to compare amounts from different-sized samples.

To give the amount X as a percentage of total amount Y, you need to divide X by Y, then multiply by 100.

Exam Tip
Rather than having to calculate a percentage, you might be asked to give your answer as a fraction, i.e. X/Y. To simplify a fraction, divide the top and bottom of the fraction by the same number. E.g. 4/40 = (4 ÷ 4)/(40 ÷ 4) = 1/10. To get the fraction as simple as possible, you might have to do this more than once.

Example

The amount of biomass available in the first level of a food chain is 40 kg. 4 kg of this biomass is transferred to the next level of the food chain. What percentage of the original biomass is transferred?

1. You want to give 4 kg as a percentage of 40 kg, so divide 4 by 40:
$$4 \div 40 = 0.1$$

2. Multiply this amount by 100:
$$0.1 \times 100 = \textbf{10\%}$$

Calculating percentage change

When investigating the change in a variable, you may want to compare results that didn't have the same initial value. For example, you may want to compare the change in mass of potato cylinders left in different concentrations of sugar solution that had different initial masses (see p. 49). One way to do this is to calculate the percentage change.

To calculate it you use this equation:

Tip: A positive value for percentage change indicates an increase and a negative value indicates a decrease.

$$\text{percentage (\%) change} = \frac{\text{final value} - \text{original value}}{\text{original value}} \times 100$$

Example

A student is investigating the effect of the concentration of sugar solution on potato cells. She records the mass of potato cylinders before and after placing them in sugar solutions of different concentrations. The table below shows some of her results.

Potato cylinder	Concentration (mol/dm³)	Mass at start (g)	Mass at end (g)
1	0.0	7.5	8.7
2	1.0	8.0	6.8

Which potato cylinder had the largest percentage change?

---

1. Stick each set of results into the equation:

$$\% \text{ change} = \frac{\text{final value} - \text{original value}}{\text{original value}} \times 100$$

potato cylinder 1: $\frac{8.7 - 7.5}{7.5} \times 100 = 16\%$

potato cylinder 2: $\frac{6.8 - 8.0}{8.0} \times 100 = -15\%$

2. Compare the results.

16% is greater than 15%, so potato cylinder 1 (in the 0.0 mol/dm^3 sugar solution) had the largest percentage change.

Tip: The mass at the start is the original value and the mass at the end is the final value.

Tip: A decrease in mass gives a negative value for the percentage change.

Estimating values

Estimating can help you to check your answer is roughly correct. To estimate the answer to a calculation, just round everything off to nice, convenient numbers so that you get a simple calculation that you can do in your head.

Most of the time, you should round the numbers to just one significant figure.

Example

A student calculated the number of stomata per mm^2 on ten different leaves.

The results are shown in the table below.

Leaf	1	2	3	4	5	6	7	8	9	10
Number of stomata/mm^2	245	287	322	185	316	299	178	250	332	420

The student calculates that the mean number of stomata per mm^2 is 283. You could estimate the mean of the data like this:

1. Round the numbers to one significant figure.

200   300   300   200   300   300   200   300   300   400

2. Do the calculation with the rounded numbers.

(200 + 300 + 300 + 200 + 300 + 300 + 200 + 300 + 300 + 400) ÷ 10

$$= 2800 \div 10 = \mathbf{280}$$

From the estimated calculation, 283 is a sensible answer. If your answer was massively different, you would know that your calculation had gone wrong somewhere.

Exam Tip
By working out an estimate in the exam, you can check that you haven't made any silly mistakes while calculating your answer (like missing out a decimal place along the way) and it's a lot quicker than typing the whole thing into your calculator again.

Percentiles

Percentiles are useful if you want to compare the value of one data point to the rest of your data.

To find a percentile, you rank your data from smallest to largest, then divide it into one hundred equal chunks. Each chunk is one percentile. This means that each percentile represents one percent of the data, and so the value of a percentile tells you what percentage of the data has a value lower than the data points in that percentile.

Example

If you were in the 90th percentile for height in your class, this would mean that 90% of the class were shorter than you.

Percentiles can be used to give a more realistic idea of the spread of data than the range (see page 14). By finding the range between the 10th and 90th percentiles in a data set (the middle 80% of the data), you can look at the spread of the data while ignoring any outlying results — see Figure 2.

Tip: The median is the middle value (see page 14). It's also the 50th percentile.

Tip: An outlier is a value that's much larger or smaller than the rest of the values in a data set.

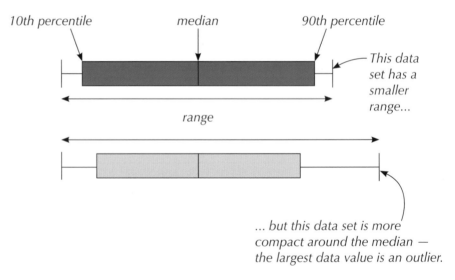

10th percentile   *median*   *90th percentile*

This data set has a smaller range...

range

... but this data set is more compact around the median — the largest data value is an outlier.

Figure 2: *Diagram showing how percentiles can be used to understand the spread of a data set.*

2. Algebra

Every so often, biology can involve a bit of rearranging equations and substituting values into equations. It can be easy to make simple mistakes though, so here are a few things to remember...

Algebra symbols

Here's a reminder of some of the symbols that you will come across:

Symbol	Meaning
=	equal to
<	less than
<<	much less than
>	greater than
>>	much greater than
∝	proportional to
~	roughly equal to

Tip: An example of using 'proportional to' can be found on p.155. There are two types of proportion — direct and inverse. When two values are directly proportional to each other, if one increases, the other increases at the same rate. When two values are inversely proportional to each other, if one increases, the other decreases at the same rate.

Using equations

Equations can show relationships between variables. To rearrange an equation, make sure that whatever you do to one side of the equation you also do to the other side.

Example

You can find the magnification of something using the equation:
magnification = image size ÷ real size

You can rearrange this equation to find the image size by multiplying each side by the real size: image size = magnification × real size.

To use an equation, you need to know the values of all but one of the variables. Substitute the values you do know into the equation, and do the calculation to work out the final variable. Always make sure the values you put into an equation have the right units.

Tip: The word formula is sometimes used instead of the word equation.

Tip: There's more about this equation for magnification on p. 27.

Tip: Converting all the values into the correct units <u>before</u> putting them into the equation stops you making silly mistakes.

Example

Calculating a BMI is one way to find whether a person is a healthy weight. It's calculated by this equation: $BMI = \dfrac{weight\ (kg)}{height^2\ (m)}$

A man weighs 84 kg and is 2.0 m tall. Calculate his BMI.

In this scenario, the weight is 84 kg and the height is 2.0 m. The units for both of these values are the right ones for the equation, so you can just go ahead and substitute them in:

$$BMI = \frac{weight\ (kg)}{height^2\ (m)} = \frac{84}{2.0^2} = \frac{84}{4} = \mathbf{21}$$

To make sure your units are correct, it can help to write down the units on each line of your calculation.

3. Graphs

Results are often presented using graphs. They make it easier to see relationships between variables and can be used to calculate other quantities.

Finding the intercept of a graph

The *y*-intercept of a graph is the point at which the line of best fit crosses the *y*-axis. Meanwhile, the *x*-intercept is the point at which the line of best fit crosses the *x*-axis.

Tip: See pages 49-50 for more on how to carry out this experiment and analyse the results.

Example

A graph can be plotted to show the percentage change in mass of several pieces of potato against the different concentrations of sucrose solution that they were left in overnight.

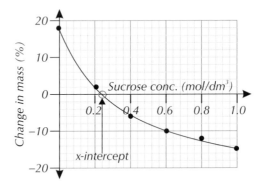

The approximate concentration of the solution in the potato cells, which is equal to the *x*-intercept, is **0.24 mol/dm³**.

Linear graphs

A linear graph is a straight line graph. This means that one of the variables plotted on the axes increases or decreases in relation to the other, which is shown by a straight line. An example of a linear graph is shown in Figure 1.

Tip: If one variable increases in proportion with the other (so if *x* is doubled, *y* is doubled, etc.), the graph shows a directly proportional relationship.

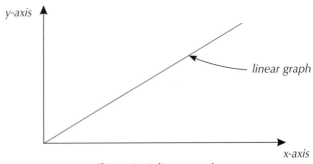

Figure 1: *A linear graph.*

Finding the rate

Rate is a measure of how much something is changing over time. Calculating a rate can be useful when analysing your data, e.g. you might want to the find the rate of a reaction. You can find the rate from a graph that shows a variable changing over time by finding the **gradient** (how steep it is).

For a linear graph, you can calculate the rate by finding the gradient of the line, using the equation:

$$\text{Gradient} = \frac{\text{Change in } y}{\text{Change in } x}$$

Change in y is the change in value on the y-axis and **change in x** is the change in value on the x-axis.

Tip: The gradient of a graph tells you how quickly the dependent variable changes if you change the independent variable.

Tip: When using this equation to find a rate, x should always be the time.

Example

To find the rate at which oxygen is produced in the graph below:

1. Pick two points on the line that are easy to read and a good distance apart.

2. Draw a vertical line down from one point and a horizontal line across from the other to make a triangle.

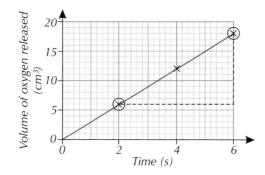

3. Use the scales on the axes to work out the length of each line. The vertical side of the triangle is the change in y and the horizontal side of the triangle is the change in x.

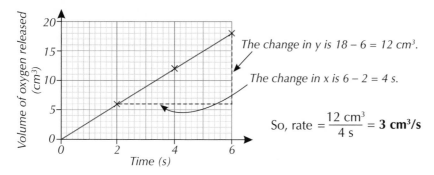

The change in y is $18 - 6 = 12$ cm^3.

The change in x is $6 - 2 = 4$ s.

So, rate $= \dfrac{12 \text{ cm}^3}{4 \text{ s}} = \textbf{3 cm}^3\textbf{/s}$

Tip: The units for the gradient are the units for y divided by the units for x.

$y = mx + c$

The y-intercept and the gradient of a linear graph can be used to work out the equation of the graph line. The equation of a straight line is given by:

Tip: *mx* is just the same as writing '*m* × *x*'.

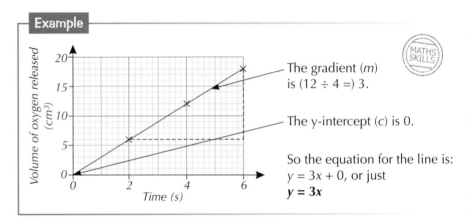

The equation of the line shows the relationship between the two variables. To work out the equation, you just need to plug in the values for *m* and *c*.

Tip: If the straight line passes through the origin of the graph (the point at which the x-axis and y-axis meet), then the y-intercept is just zero.

Tip: You can check your equation is correct using the values of *x* and *y* from a point on the graph. Just pop the value for *x* into the equation and it should give you the value of *y*.

Example

The gradient (*m*) is (12 ÷ 4 =) 3.

The y-intercept (*c*) is 0.

So the equation for the line is:
$y = 3x + 0$, or just
$y = 3x$

Exam Help

1. The Exams

Unfortunately, you'll need to sit some exams for GCSE Combined Science. And that's what this page is about — what to expect in your exams.

Assessment for GCSE Combined Science

To get your GCSE in Combined Science you'll have to do some exams that test your science knowledge, your understanding of the Required Practical Activity experiments and how comfortable you are with Working Scientifically. You'll also be tested on your maths skills.

All the biology content that you need to know is in this book. All the biology Required Practical Activities are also covered in detail and clearly labelled, examples that use maths skills are marked up, and there are even dedicated sections on Working Scientifically (pages 2-22), Maths Skills (pages 296-304) and Practical Skills (pages 288-295). You'll also need to know all the chemistry and physics content, which isn't covered in this book.

The exams

You'll sit six separate exams at the end of Year 11 — two for each of biology, chemistry and physics.

In the biology exams, you'll be tested on maths skills in at least 10% of the marks, and could be asked questions on the Required Practical Activities and Working Scientifically requirements in either exam. You're allowed to use a calculator in all of your GCSE Combined Science exams, so make sure you've got one.

The structure of the biology exams is shown below:

> **Exam Tip**
> Make sure you have a good read through these pages. It might not seem all that important now but you don't want to get any surprises just before an exam.

> **Exam Tip**
> As well as a calculator, you should make sure you've got a ruler for both exams. And don't forget the basics — a couple of black pens and sharp pencils.

> **Exam Tip**
> Use these topic lists as a guide, but be aware that you may be expected to use basic biology knowledge from different parts of the course in either exam.

2. Exam Technique

Knowing the science is vitally important when it comes to passing your exams. But having good exam technique will also help. So here are some handy hints on how to squeeze every mark you possibly can out of those examiners.

Time management

Good time management is one of the most important exam skills to have — you need to think about how much time to spend on each question. Check out the length of your exams (you'll find them on the previous page and on the front of your exam papers). These timings give you about 1 minute per mark. Try to stick to this to give yourself the best chance to get as many marks as possible.

Don't spend ages struggling with a question if you're finding it hard to answer — move on. You can come back to it later when you've bagged loads of other marks elsewhere. Also, you might find that some questions need a lot of work for only a few marks, while others are much quicker — so if you're short of time, answer the quick and easy questions first.

Exam Tip
You shouldn't really be spending more time on a 1 mark question than on a 4 mark question. Use the marks available as a rough guide for how long each question should take to answer.

> ### Example
>
> The questions below are both worth the same number of marks but require different amounts of work.
>
> **1.1**   What name is given to the tissue that covers the leaf?
>
> *(1 mark)*
>
> **2.1**   By reading the information above and looking at the diagram, suggest **one** way in which the structure of a motor neurone cell helps it to carry out its function.
>
> *(1 mark)*
>
> Question 1.1 only asks you to write down the name of a tissue — if you can remember it this shouldn't take you too long.
>
> Question 2.1 asks you to make a suggestion about something you don't already know the answer to. Since you need to interpret some information and a diagram, and then apply your existing scientific knowledge to work out your answer, it may take you a bit longer than just writing down a name.
>
> So, if you're running out of time it makes sense to do questions like 1.1 first and come back to questions like 2.1 if you've got time at the end.

Exam Tip
Don't forget to go back and do any questions that you left the first time round — you don't want to miss out on marks because you forgot to do the question.

Reading the question

Make sure you always read the whole question carefully. It can be easy to look at a question and read what you're expecting to see, rather than what it's actually asking you. Read it through before you start answering, and read it once again when you've finished, to make sure your answer is sensible and matches up to what the question is asking.

Remember to pay attention to the marks available too. They can often give you a sense of how much work is needed to answer the question. If it's just a one or two mark question, it'll often only need a single word or phrase as an answer, or a very simple calculation. Questions worth more marks are likely to be longer questions, which need to be clearly structured and will involve writing a short paragraph or a more complicated calculation.

Exam Tip
The amount of space given for your answer should also give you an idea about how much you need to write.

Making educated guesses

Make sure you answer all the questions that you can — don't leave any blank if you can avoid it. If a question asks you to tick a box, circle something or draw lines between boxes, you should never, ever leave it blank, even if you're short on time. It only takes a second or two to answer these questions, and even if you're not absolutely sure what the answer is you can have a good guess.

> **Example**
>
> Look at the question below.
>
> **1.1**   Which of the following are hormones involved in the menstrual cycle? Tick **two** boxes.
>
> Insulin ☐   Oestrogen ☐
>
> Testosterone ☐   Luteinising hormone ☐
>
> *(2 marks)*
>
> Say you knew that oestrogen is involved in the menstrual cycle, and that insulin helps to regulate blood sugar level, but weren't sure about the other two hormones.
>
> You can tick oestrogen — you know it's involved in the menstrual cycle. You can leave the insulin box blank because you know it's involved in regulating blood sugar level. That leaves you with testosterone and luteinising hormone. If you're not absolutely sure which is involved in the menstrual cycle and which isn't, just have a guess. You won't lose any marks if you get it wrong and there's a 50% chance that you'll get it right.

Exam Tip
If you're asked, for example, to tick two boxes, make sure you only tick two. If you tick more than two, you won't get the marks even if some of your answers are correct.

3. Question Types

If all questions were the same, exams would be mightily boring. So really, it's quite handy that there are lots of different question types. Here are just a few...

Command words

Command words are just the bits of a question that tell you what to do. You'll find answering exam questions much easier if you understand exactly what they mean, so here's a brief summary of the most common ones:

Exam Tip
When you're reading an exam question, you might find it helpful to underline the command words. It can help you work out what type of answer to give.

Exam Tip
It's easy to get <u>describe</u> and <u>explain</u> mixed up, but they're quite different. For example, if you're asked to describe some data, just state the overall pattern or trend. If you're asked to explain data, you'll need to <u>give reasons</u> for the trend.

Exam Tip
Some questions might ask you to both describe <u>and</u> explain something — so make sure you do both things.

Command word:	What to do:
Give / Name / Write down	Give a brief one or two word answer, or a short sentence.
Complete	Write your answer in the space given. This could be a gap in an equation or table, or you might have to finish a diagram.
Describe	Write about what something's like, e.g. describe the trend in a set of results.
Explain	Make something clear, or give the reasons why something happens. The points in your answer need to be linked together, so you should include words like because, so, therefore, due to, etc.
Calculate	Use the numbers in the question to work out an answer.
Suggest	Use your scientific knowledge to work out what the answer might be.
Compare	Give the similarities and differences between two things.
Determine	Use data or information you're given in the question to work something out, e.g. you might be asked to determine the rate of a reaction from a graph.
Estimate	Use rounded numbers to work out an approximate answer.

Some questions will also ask you to answer 'using the information provided' (e.g. a graph, table or passage of text) — if so, you must refer to the information you've been given or you won't get the marks.

Required Practical Activities

The Required Practical Activities are seven specific experiments that you need to cover during your lessons. At least 15% of the total marks in your exams will be for questions that test your understanding of these experiments and the techniques involved in them. There are a lot of different types of question you could be asked on these experiments. Here are some basic areas you might be asked about:

Tip: There are Required Practical Activities in physics and chemistry too, but they're not covered in this book.

- Carrying out the experiment — e.g. planning or describing a method, describing how to take measurements or use apparatus.

- Risk assessment — e.g. describing or explaining dangers which can arise from the experiment, or safety precautions which should be taken.

- Understanding variables — e.g. identifying control, dependent and independent variables.

- Data handling — e.g. plotting graphs or doing calculations using some sample results provided.

- Analysing results — e.g. making conclusions based on sample results.

- Evaluating the experiment — e.g. making judgements on the quality of results, identifying where mistakes have been made in the method, suggesting improvements to the experiment.

Required Practical Activity questions won't be pointed out to you in the exam, so you'll need to make sure you know the practicals inside out, and can recognise them easily. For an example of a question testing your understanding of a practical, see page 123.

Exam Tip
The Required Practical Activity questions are likely to have some overlap with Working Scientifically, so make sure you've brushed up on pages 2-22.

Levels of response questions

Some questions are designed to assess your ability to present and explain scientific ideas in a logical and coherent way, as well as your scientific knowledge. These questions often link together different topics and are worth more marks than most other question types. You'll be told which questions these are on the front of your exam paper.

This type of question is marked using a 'levels of response' mark scheme. Your answer is given a level depending on the number of marks available and its overall quality and scientific content. Here's an idea of how the levels may work out for a 6 mark question:

Exam Tip
You're likely to get level of response questions with command words like 'Explain', 'Compare' or 'Describe'.

Example

- An answer that has no relevant information and makes no attempt to answer the question receives no marks.

- A Level 1 answer usually makes one or two correct statements, but does not fully answer the question. For instance, when asked to explain how the features of an organism make it adapted to its environment, it might state one or two correct facts about the organism's features, but not attempt to link them to the environment. These answers receive 1 or 2 marks.

- A Level 2 answer usually makes a number of correct statements, with explanation, but falls short of fully answering the question. It may miss a step, omit an important fact, or not be organised as logically as it should be. These answers receive 3 or 4 marks.

- A Level 3 answer will answer the question fully, in a logical fashion. It will make a number of points that are explained and related back to the question. Any conclusions it makes will be supported by evidence in the answer. These answers receive 5 or 6 marks.

Exam Tip
It might be useful to write a quick plan of your answer in the spare space of your paper. This can help you get your thoughts in order, so you can write a logical, coherent answer. But remember to cross your plan out after you've written your answer so it doesn't get marked.

Exam Tip
Make sure your writing is legible — you don't want to lose marks just because the examiner couldn't read your handwriting.

Exam Tip
Make sure your writing style is appropriate for an exam. You need to write in full sentences and use fairly formal language.

Make sure you answer the question fully, and cover all points indicated in the question. You also need to organise your answer clearly — the points you make need to be in a logical order. Use specialist scientific vocabulary whenever you can. For example, if you're describing cell division, you'd need to use scientific terms like mitosis and chromosomes. Obviously you need to use these terms correctly — it's no good knowing the words if you don't know what they actually mean.

There are some exam-style questions that use this type of mark scheme in this book (marked up with an asterisk, *). You can use them to practise writing logical and coherent answers. Use the worked answers given at the back of this book to mark what you've written. The answers will tell you the relevant points you could've included, but it'll be down to you to put everything together into a full, well-structured answer.

Comparing and evaluating information

In the exam, you may be given some information to read and then be asked to make some comparisons.

> **Example**
>
> Drug X and drug Y are both weight-loss drugs. You may be given some information on how drug X and drug Y work, how effective they are and what side effects they have. You could then be asked to compare the drugs directly, or give the advantages of one compared to the other.

To compare the two types of drug, you need to do more than just pick out relevant information from the question and repeat it in your answer — you need to make clear comparisons between the two.

> **Example**
>
> If the information tells you that people taking drug X lose 1 kilogram per week on average and that people taking drug Y lose 1.5 kilograms per week on average, you need to say in your answer that "people taking drug Y lose **more** weight per week on average than people taking drug X". It's even better to say that "people taking drug Y lose **0.5 kilograms more** weight per week on average than people taking drug X".

Evaluating information

If you are asked to evaluate two things, you need to weigh up their advantages and disadvantages.

The question may ask you to write a conclusion too, e.g. make an overall judgement about which drug is best. If so, you must include a conclusion in your answer and you must back it up with evidence from the question.

Calculations

In the biology exams for GCSE Combined Science, around 10% of the total marks will come from questions that test your maths skills. Questions that involve a calculation can seem a bit scary. But they're really not that bad. Here are some tips to help you out...

- Show your working — this is the most important thing to remember. It only takes a few seconds more to write down what's in your head and it might stop you from making silly errors and losing out on easy marks. You won't get a mark for a wrong answer, but you could get marks for the method you used to work out the answer.

- Check your answer — a good way to do this is to work backwards through your calculation. You should also think about whether your answer seems sensible — if it's a much bigger or smaller number than you were expecting, you might have gone wrong somewhere.

Figure 1: A calculator. Under the pressure of an exam it's easy to make mistakes in calculations, even if they're really simple ones. So don't be afraid to put every calculation into the calculator.

Example

A potato chip weighs 10.2 g at the start of the experiment. At the end of the experiment it weighs 11.6 g. To calculate the change in mass, you'd subtract 10.2 g from 11.6 g — which works out as 1.4 g. You'd expect the answer to be around 1 g, so this seems sensible. To check it though, just add 1.4 to 10.2 — you should end up with 11.6.

- Sometimes you'll be asked to pick some numbers out of a table or read values off a graph to use in your calculation. If so, always read the question carefully so you know exactly what figures you need to use. Make sure you read the headings in the table carefully too (or the axes on the graph) to make sure you understand what's being shown.

In the exam, you should be prepared to do things like estimate a value, calculate a percentage or a mean, put numbers into equations that you've been given, and also be able to rearrange these equations.

Exam Tip
These aren't the only calculations you could be asked to do in an exam — they're just examples of the sort of thing that's likely to come up.

Answers

Topic 1 — Cell Biology

Topic 1a — Cell Structure and Cell Division

1. Cell Structure

Page 24 — Fact Recall Questions

Q1   the genetic material / the nucleus
Q2   In the cytoplasm.
Q3   aerobic respiration
Q4   A cell wall, a permanent vacuole and chloroplasts.
Q5   A small ring of DNA.

2. Microscopy

Page 29 — Application Questions

Q1   magnification = image size ÷ real size
= 18 ÷ 0.002 = **× 9000**
Q2   image size = magnification × real size
= 400 × 0.08 = **32 mm**
Q3   real size = image size ÷ magnification
= 10.5 ÷ 1500 = 0.007 mm
0.007 mm × 1000 = **7 µm**
The question asks for the answer to be in µm, so to convert mm to µm you need to multiply by 1000.

3. Cell Differentiation and Specialisation

Page 32 — Fact Recall Questions

Q1   The process by which a cell changes to become specialised for its job.
Q2   In most animal cells, the ability to differentiate is lost at an early stage, whereas lots of plant cells don't ever lose this ability.
Q3   a) To carry electrical signals from one part of the body to another.
b) It is long in order to cover more distance and it has branched connections at each end to connect to other nerve cells (to form a network throughout the body).
Q4   They contain lots of mitochondria.

Page 32 — Application Questions

Q1   E.g. you'd expect to find a lot of ribosomes because they make proteins.
The function of a gastric chief cell is to secrete proteins — and ribosomes are where proteins are made in the cell. So it makes sense that you'd find a lot of ribosomes in a gastric chief cell.
Q2   E.g. the folds in the cell membrane give the cells a large surface area for absorbing food molecules efficiently. Lots of mitochondria provide the energy from respiration needed to absorb food molecules.
This question is pretty tricky — you need to think about the unusual shape of the cell and look at the things it contains. Cells that need to absorb things tend to have a large surface area (e.g. like red blood cells and palisade leaf cells), so look for anything about the cell that increases its surface area. You also know that the cell needs energy — so look for mitochondria, which are the site of respiration (a process which transfers energy).

4. Chromosomes

Page 34 — Fact Recall Questions

Q1   in the nucleus
Q2   DNA
Q3   a) short sections of DNA/a chromosome (that control our characteristics)
b) controlling the development of different characteristics

Page 34 — Application Questions

Q1   a) X
b) Z
c) Y
Q2   Because genes are too small.

5. Mitosis

Page 37 — Fact Recall Questions

Q1   Any two from: e.g. growth / development / replacing damaged cells.
Q2   once

Page 37 — Application Questions

Q1   a) genetically identical
Mitosis produces cells that are genetically identical to the parent cells.
b) two
If a cell has two sets of chromosomes it means that it will have two copies of each chromosome.
Q2   (6 ÷ 198) × 1500 = 45.45...
45.45... ÷ 60 = **0.76 hours**
6 out of 198 cells are in the last stage of mitosis. This suggests that the proportion of time the cells spend in this stage must be 6/198th of the cell cycle. Once you've worked out the time taken in minutes, don't forget to convert your answer into hours as the question asks.

6. Stem Cells

Page 40 — Fact Recall Questions

Q1   An undifferentiated cell that has the potential to differentiate into different types of cell.
Q2   any type of cell
Q3   E.g. in the bone marrow.
Q4   They would be genetically identical to the patient, so they won't be rejected by the patient's body.
Q5   meristem

Page 40 — Application Questions

Q1   a) Stem cells could be made to differentiate into neurones, which could replace the damaged/dead neurones.
b) E.g. producing nerve cells to replace damaged tissue in people with paralysis. / Producing insulin-producing cells for people with diabetes.
Q2   Because the embryos leftover from fertility clinics will be destroyed anyway.
Q3   E.g. because the embryo still has the potential to develop into a human life before this point.

Pages 43-44 — Cell Structure and Cell Division Exam-style Questions

1.1 the nucleus *(1 mark)*

1.2 two *(1 mark)*

1.3 mitosis *(1 mark)*

2.1 D *(1 mark)*

2.2 A eukaryotic cell, e.g. because it has a nucleus/ mitochondria/chloroplasts / it doesn't have plasmids/ circular strand of DNA in the cytoplasm *(1 mark)*.

2.3 A cell that performs a specific function *(1 mark)*.

2.4 stem cells *(1 mark)*

2.5 E.g. it has lots of chloroplasts / its chloroplasts are mainly at the top of the cell (nearer the light) / it's thin so lots of them can be packed in at the top of the leaf *(1 mark)*.

3.1 To highlight objects of interest in the cell. / To make parts of the cell visible. *(1 mark)*

3.2 E.g. wear gloves to protect his skin / wear goggles to protect his eyes *(1 mark)*.

3.3 He would have stood the cover slip upright on the slide, next to the liquid droplet *(1 mark)*. Then he would have carefully tilted and lowered it to cover the specimen *(1 mark)*.

3.4 magnification = image size ÷ real size
width of image = 66 mm
55 μm ÷ 1000 = 0.055 mm
66 ÷ 0.055 = **× 1200** *(3 marks for correct answer, otherwise 1 mark for correctly measuring the image and 1 mark for converting units.)*

3.5 magnification = image size ÷ real size
image size = real size × magnification
real size = 5 μm
5 μm × 500 = 2500 μm
2500 ÷ 1000 = **2.5 mm** *(3 marks for correct answer, otherwise 1 mark for rearranging equation and 1 mark for converting units.)*

3.6 An electron microscope *(1 mark)* e.g. because it has a greater magnification/resolution than a light microscope, so allows smaller things (like the structure of the nucleus) to be seen in more detail *(1 mark)*.

3.7 They do not need to make any proteins *(1 mark)*.

3.8 E.g. it has a long tail / a streamlined head *(1 mark)* to help it swim to the egg *(1 mark)*. It has lots of mitochondria *(1 mark)* to provide the energy it needs to swim *(1 mark)*. It also carries enzymes in its head *(1 mark)* to digest through the egg cell membrane *(1 mark)*.

Topic 1b — Transport in Cells

1. Diffusion

Page 47 — Fact Recall Questions

Q1 Diffusion is the spreading out of particles from an area of higher concentration to an area of lower concentration.

Q2 E.g. oxygen, glucose, amino acids, water

Q3 The rate of diffusion is increased because the particles have more energy, so they move faster.

Page 47 — Application Questions

Q1 B

Q2 Inside respiring cells. The carbon dioxide molecules must be diffusing from an area of higher concentration (inside respiring cells) to an area of lower concentration (the bloodstream).

Q3 a) The smoke particles diffuse from where there is a higher concentration (near the stage), to where there is a lower concentration (at the opposite end of the hall).

b) There are already some smoke particles in the air the second time the smoke machine is set off, whereas there weren't the first time. This means there is a smaller difference in the concentration of the smoke particles at each end of the hall, so the rate of diffusion is slower the second time.

2. Osmosis

Page 51 — Fact Recall Questions

Q1 The movement of water molecules across a partially permeable membrane from a region of higher water concentration to a region of lower water concentration.

Q2 If a cell is short of water, the surrounding solution will usually have a higher concentration of water molecules/be more dilute than the solution inside the cell. This means water molecules will move by osmosis from the surrounding solution into the cell.

Page 51 — Application Question

Q1 a) i) They got longer/increased in length (by an average of 3.1 mm in the 0.00 M solution and an average of 2.1 mm in the 0.25 M solution).

ii) The solutions contained a higher concentration of water molecules/were more dilute than the fluid inside the potato cells. So water molecules moved into the potato cells by osmosis and the potato cylinders increased in size.

Cells that take on water by osmosis will also increase in mass. So you could vary this experiment slightly by measuring the change in mass of the potato cylinders.

b) Accept any answer between –3 mm and –4 mm.

c) i) the length of the potato cylinders

The dependent variable is the variable you measure — in this case potato cylinder length.

ii) the concentration of the sugar solution

The independent variable is the variable you change.

d) Any two from: e.g. the volume of each solution / the temperature each solution was kept at / the time the cylinders were left for / the type of sugar used.

3. Active Transport

Page 53 — Fact Recall Questions

Q1 The movement of particles against a concentration gradient (i.e. from an area of lower concentration to an area of higher concentration) using energy transferred during respiration.

Q2 false

Cells can absorb ions from very dilute solutions using active transport.

Q3 They are essential for healthy growth.

Q4 The concentration of mineral ions inside the root hair cells is greater than in the soil / they are taking up mineral ions against the concentration gradient.

Q5 E.g. glucose/sugar

4. Exchange Surfaces
Page 56 — Fact Recall Questions
Q1 a) diffusion, active transport and osmosis
   b) diffusion and active transport

Q2 Any three from: e.g. they may be thin. / They may have a large surface area. / They may have lots of blood vessels. / They may be ventilated.

Page 57 — Application Questions
Q1 a) Any two from: e.g. it may be thin, so oxygen and carbon dioxide have a short distance to diffuse/a short diffusion pathway. / It may have a large surface area so lots of oxygen/carbon dioxide can diffuse at once. / It may have lots of blood vessels to get gases into and out of the blood quickly.
   b) Because elephants have a much smaller surface area to volume ratio than earthworms. This means that not enough oxygen can diffuse from their outside surface to supply their entire volume, so they need a specialised gas exchange surface for the oxygen to diffuse across efficiently.

Q2 a) A — $6 \times (1 \times 1) = $ **6 μm²**
   B — $2 \times (0.5 \times 0.5) + 4 \times (2 \times 0.5) = 0.5 + 4$ $= $ **4.5 μm²**
   C — $2 \times (0.2 \times 0.4) + 2 \times (1 \times 0.4) + 2 \times (1 \times 0.2)$ $= 0.16 + 0.8 + 0.4 = $ **1.36 μm²**
   b) A — volume: $1 \times 1 \times 1 = $ **1 μm³**
   B — volume: $2 \times 0.5 \times 0.5 = $ **0.5 μm³**
   C — volume: $1 \times 0.4 \times 0.2 = $ **0.08 μm³**
   c) A — **6 : 1**
   B — 4.5 : 0.5
      $4.5 \div 0.5 = 9$, $0.5 \div 0.5 = 1$
      so ratio is **9 : 1**
   C — 1.36 : 0.08
      $1.36 \div 0.08 = 17$, $0.08 \div 0.08 = 1$
      so ratio is **17 : 1**
   d) C, because it has the largest surface area to volume ratio.

5. Exchanging Substances
Page 59 — Fact Recall Questions
Q1 E.g. they have a large surface area. / They have a moist lining for dissolving gases. / They have thin walls. / They have a good blood supply.

Q2 They increase the surface area of the small intestine so that nutrients can be absorbed more quickly.

Page 61 — Fact Recall Questions
Q1 By diffusion through the stomata.

Q2 E.g. oxygen

Q3 It has a flattened shape and there are air spaces inside the leaf.

Q4 They increase the surface area of the gills available for diffusion of gases (and so increase the rate of diffusion).

Q5 It maintains a large concentration gradient of oxygen between the water and the blood because it flows in the opposite direction to water. The concentration of oxygen in the water is always higher than in the blood, so as much oxygen as possible diffuses from the water into the blood.

Pages 64-65 — Transport in Cells
Exam-style Questions
1.1 surface area:
   $0.6 \times 0.6 = 0.36$
   $3.0 \times 0.6 = 1.8$
   $(2 \times 0.36) + (4 \times 1.8) = 7.92$ μm²
   volume:
   $0.6 \times 0.6 \times 3.0 = 1.08$ μm³
   ratio:
   $7.92 \div 1.08 = 7.3333... = 7$
   so the ratio is **7 : 1** *(3 marks for correct answer, otherwise 1 mark for correct surface area and 1 mark for correct volume.)*

1.2 Because it is a single-celled organism *(1 mark)*, so it has a large surface area to volume ratio *(1 mark)*. This means it can exchange enough substances across its cell membrane/outer surface to meet its needs *(1 mark)*.

1.3 small holes in the surface of a leaf *(1 mark)*

1.4 It is a lower concentration than inside the leaf *(1 mark)*.

1.5 E.g. the flattened shape of the leaf increases its surface area for diffusion into and out of the leaf *(1 mark)*. / There are air spaces inside the leaf to increase the surface area available for diffusion into and out of the cells *(1 mark)*.

1.6 gills *(1 mark)*

1.7 It would decrease the rate of diffusion of oxygen *(1 mark)* because it would reduce the difference in concentration of oxygen between the water and the blood in the gills / reduce the concentration gradient *(1 mark)*.

2.1 Glucose may be absorbed by active transport when the concentration of glucose molecules in the small intestine is lower than the concentration of glucose molecules in the blood *(1 mark)*. Respiration is needed to provide energy for this process *(1 mark)*.

2.2 The damage to the villi would decrease the surface area of the small intestine *(1 mark)*, meaning less glucose and other nutrients would be absorbed *(1 mark)*.

2.3 Osmosis *(1 mark)*. The water moves from an area of higher concentration (in the large intestine) to an area of lower concentration (in the bloodstream) *(1 mark)*.

3.1 Water moves by osmosis from a region of higher water concentration to region of a lower water concentration *(1 mark)*. The potato has a lower water concentration than the water in the dish, so water moves from the dish into the potato cells *(1 mark)*. The potato has a higher water concentration than the sugar/well, so water moves from the potato into the well and dissolves the sugar/creates a sugar solution *(1 mark)*.

3.2 There's no sugar in the well in the potato in experiment B, so no water is drawn out of the potato into the well at the top *(1 mark)*. This means the difference in the concentration of the solution in the potato cells and in the dish is smaller *(1 mark)*, so the movement of water molecules by osmosis is reduced *(1 mark)*.

Topic 2 — Organisation

Topic 2a — Tissues, Organs and Organ Systems

1. Cell Organisation

Pages 68-69 — Fact Recall Questions
Q1 cells
Q2 A group of similar cells that work together to carry out a particular function.
Q3 A group of different tissues that work together to perform a certain function.
Q4 organ system
Q5 A is the salivary glands, which produce digestive juices. B is the liver, which produces bile. C is the stomach, where food is digested. D is the pancreas, which produces digestive juices. E is the small intestine, where food is digested and soluble food molecules are absorbed. F is the large intestine, which absorbs water from undigested food, leaving faeces.

Page 69 — Application Questions
Q1 A tissue, because it consists of a group of similar cells that work together to perform a particular function.
Q2 a) It contracts, to move the fertilised egg cell along the fallopian tube to the uterus.
   b) An organ, because it consists of a group of different tissues that work together to perform a certain function.
   c) egg cell, muscular tissue, uterus, reproductive system

2. The Lungs

Page 72 — Fact Recall Question
Q1 a) trachea
   b) bronchi
   c) i) alveolus
      ii) Because this is where gas exchange occurs. Oxygen diffuses out of part C/the alveoli into the blood being carried by the capillaries. At the same time, carbon dioxide diffuses out of the blood in the capillaries into part C/the alveoli.

Page 72 — Application Question
Q1 breaths per minute = 366 ÷ 9
                        = 40.666...
                        = **41 breaths per minute**
If your answer doesn't come out as a whole number, you'll need to round it up because you can't take part of a breath.

3. Circulatory System — The Heart

Page 76 — Fact Recall Questions
Q1 To transport food and oxygen to every cell in the body and to carry waste products such as carbon dioxide and urea to where they can be removed from the body.
Q2 One circuit pumps deoxygenated blood from the heart to the lungs, and then oxygenated blood from the lungs back to the heart. The other circuit pumps oxygenated blood from the heart to the rest of the body, and then deoxygenated blood from the rest of the body back to the heart.
Q3 right atrium, right ventricle, left atrium, left ventricle
Q4 a) vena cava and pulmonary vein
   b) pulmonary artery and aorta
Q5 Blood flows through the pulmonary vein and the vena cava into the atria. The atria contract, pushing blood into the ventricles. The ventricles then contract, forcing the blood into the pulmonary artery and aorta, and out of the heart.

Page 76 — Application Questions
Q1 Because the coronary arteries supply the heart with its own supply of oxygenated blood. When this supply is blocked, the heart might not get all the oxygen it needs to function.
Q2 a) It is controlled by a group of cells in the right atrium wall that act as a pacemaker. These cells produce a small electric impulse which spreads to the surrounding muscle cells, causing them to contract.
   b) A pacemaker is a little device that's implanted under the skin and has a wire going to the heart. It produces an electric current to keep the heart beating regularly.
Q3 Similarity:
   E.g. both circulatory systems involve the blood going to an organ to pick up oxygen. / Both systems involve a heart pumping blood around the body.
   Difference:
   E.g. the circulatory system of a fish is just one circuit, whereas that of a human is two separate circuits. / The circulatory system of a fish picks up oxygen at the gills, whereas that of a human picks up oxygen at the lungs.

4. Circulatory System — The Blood Vessels

Page 79 — Fact Recall Questions
Q1 An artery has thick walls compared to its lumen. The walls have thick layers of muscle and elastic fibres.
Q2 a capillary
Q3 Capillaries carry blood very close to the body cells. The substances needed by the body cells diffuse out of the blood, through the walls of capillaries, and into the body cells.
Q4 Any two from: e.g. a vein has thinner walls than an artery. / A vein has a bigger lumen than an artery. / A vein has valves whereas an artery doesn't.

Page 79 — Application Questions

Q1   A vein, because veins carry blood into the heart.

Q2   A. Arteries carry blood at a higher pressure than veins and their walls are more muscular as a result. Blood vessel A carries blood at a higher pressure than blood vessel B, and so is more likely to be an artery and have more muscle in its walls.

Q3   rate of blood flow = 1075 ÷ 5
                         = 215 ml/min
  Yes, the patient may have a blockage in this artery because the rate of blood flow is much less than the average for this artery.

5. Circulatory System — The Blood

Page 81 — Fact Recall Questions

Q1   a) haemoglobin
    b) It carries oxygen.

Q2   To defend against microorganisms that cause disease.

Q3   False
    White blood cells do have a nucleus. Red blood cells don't (so they have more room for haemoglobin).

Q4   Small fragments/pieces of cells.

Page 82 — Application Questions

Q1   Platelets, because platelets help the blood to clot at the site of a wound.

Q2   Haemoglobin is needed to carry oxygen around the body in red blood cells, so without enough haemoglobin, organs won't get enough oxygen.

Q3   Fay, because the number of white blood cells in her blood is below the normal range / lower than the number of white blood cells in Imogen's blood. White blood cells help to defend the body against microorganisms, so with fewer white blood cells in her blood, Fay is more likely to get an infection.

6. Plant Cell Organisation

Page 84 — Fact Recall Questions

Q1   false

Q2   palisade mesophyll tissue

Q3   They allow gases to diffuse in and out of cells.

Q4   In the growing tips of shoots and roots.

Q5   So that light can pass through to the palisade layer, which contains lots of chloroplasts for photosynthesis.

7. Transpiration and Translocation

Page 86 — Fact Recall Questions

Q1   a) food substances / dissolved sugars
    b) the leaves

Q2   water and mineral ions

Q3   Water is transported up a plant in the transpiration stream. Water escapes from the leaves by evaporation and diffusion. This creates a slight shortage of water in the leaves, which causes more water to be drawn up the xylem and into the leaves. This in turn causes more water to be drawn up the xylem from the roots.
  Remember, the transpiration stream only goes on in the xylem — it doesn't involve the phloem.

8. Transpiration and Stomata

Page 89 — Fact Recall Questions

Q1   The transpiration rate increases.

Q2   The uptake of water by a plant.

Q3   a) guard cells
    b) When the plant is short of water, the guard cells lose water and become flaccid, making the stomata close.

Page 90 — Application Questions

Q1   a) They have lost water by evaporation and diffusion (through their stomata).
    b) The plant next to the fan. Diffusion is quicker when air flow is greater. The movement of the fan will increase air flow.
    c) E.g. instead of using a fan he could leave one plant in a warmer/colder place than the other plant, e.g. in an airing cupboard/refrigerator.

Q2   a) As temperature increases, the distance moved by the bubble in 20 minutes/the transpiration rate also increases. This is because at higher temperatures, water evaporates from the leaves more quickly. This means that water is drawn into the xylem from the glass tube more quickly, so the bubble moves further along the tube in a given time.
    b) rate of transpiration = 26 ÷ 20
                          = 1.3 mm/min
    c) E.g. they could have tested the transpiration rate at more temperatures/a wider range of temperatures.
    One feature of a valid experiment is that it answers the original question, in this case: how does temperature affect transpiration rate? Testing the transpiration rate at more temperatures gives them a better idea of this.
    d) You would expect the bubble to have moved less than 26 mm in 20 minutes. Coating the underside of some of the leaves with nail varnish would have blocked some of the plant's stomata and reduced the amount of water that was able to escape from the leaves. Therefore the rate of transpiration would have been slower, so the bubble would have moved a shorter distance in 20 minutes.

Pages 93-94 — Tissues, Organs and Organ Systems Exam-style Questions

1.1   C *(1 mark)*

1.2   C *(1 mark)*

2.1   A — vena cava *(1 mark)*, B — right ventricle *(1 mark)*, C — left atrium *(1 mark)*.

2.2   X, because veins have thinner walls than arteries *(1 mark)*.

3   Red blood cells *(1 mark)*. They have a biconcave shape to give them a large surface area for absorbing oxygen *(1 mark)*. They contain a red pigment called haemoglobin, which carries the oxygen *(1 mark)*. They don't have a nucleus, allowing for more room for haemoglobin, meaning that they can carry more oxygen *(1 mark)*.

4.1   epidermal tissue *(1 mark)*

4.2 Palisade mesophyll tissue *(1 mark)*. Having lots of chloroplasts suggests that the cells are adapted for photosynthesis *(1 mark)* and it is in the palisade mesophyll tissue that most photosynthesis takes place *(1 mark)*.

4.3 A decrease in the concentration of carbon dioxide in the air spaces outside the leaf cells would reduce the rate of diffusion of carbon dioxide into the cells *(1 mark)*. This is because the difference between the concentration of carbon dioxide inside the cells and outside the cells would be smaller *(1 mark)*.

5.1 A plant loses water through its stomata *(1 mark)*. Evaporation/water loss is quickest in hot, dry conditions *(1 mark)*. So closing the stomata when it is hot and dry and only opening them when it is cooler, will reduce water loss from the plant *(1 mark)*.

5.2 Trapping water vapour close to the surface of the leaf will reduce the difference in the concentration of water molecules between the inside and outside of the leaf *(1 mark)*. This will slow down evaporation/water loss from the plant *(1 mark)*.

Plants in dry conditions want to conserve as much water as possible because there's so little available in the environment.

Topic 2b — Health and Disease

1. Introduction to Health and Disease
Page 96 — Fact Recall Questions
Q1 Health is the state of physical and mental wellbeing.
Q2 Communicable diseases can be spread between people or between people and animals, whereas non-communicable diseases cannot.
Q3 Whether or not you have a good, balanced diet, the amount of stress that you're under and your life situation.

Page 96 — Application Question
Q1 People with high-stress jobs had on average 3 more colds per year than people with low-stress jobs. This could be due to the fact that being under stress can have an effect on physical health, which may increase the likelihood of catching a cold.

2. Cardiovascular Disease
Page 100 — Fact Recall Questions
Q1 Disease of the heart or blood vessels.
Q2 The arteries that supply blood to the heart muscle get blocked by fatty deposits, causing them to become narrow and restrict blood flow.
Q3 a) A tube inserted inside arteries to widen them and keep them open.
   b) They can be inserted into the coronary arteries to make sure blood can pass through to the heart muscles. This keeps the person's heart beating and keeps the person alive.

Page 100 — Application Question
Q1 a) E.g. they are less likely to be rejected by the body's immune system than donor hearts.
   b) Any two from: e.g. surgery to fit an artificial heart can lead to bleeding and infection. / Artificial hearts don't work as well as healthy natural ones — parts of the heart could wear out or the electrical motor could fail. / Blood doesn't flow through artificial hearts as smoothly as through natural hearts, which can cause blood clots and lead to strokes. / A patient receiving an artificial heart has to take drugs to thin their blood and make sure clots don't occur, which can cause problems with bleeding if they're hurt in an accident. / Having an artificial heart in the body may be uncomfortable for the patient.
   c) E.g. artificial heart two may be more convenient for the patient, as they will be able to move around more freely than if they had to carry a battery pack around with them. Also, artificial heart two doesn't need to have wires coming out of the patient's body, unlike artificial heart one. This may reduce the risk of infection compared to artificial heart one, as there are no openings in the skin where microorganisms could enter the body. However, artificial heart two has only been implanted into 14 patients, whereas artificial heart one has been implanted into 1100 patients. So there's a greater chance that there may be problems with the use of artificial heart two, which have not yet been identified due to the small number of patients it has been used for. Overall, artificial heart two may be more convenient for the patient and have a lower risk of infection than artificial heart one, but there's a greater risk of unexpected problems occurring.

Remember, if you're asked to evaluate the use of something in the exam, you should give arguments for and against its use and use any relevant facts you're given to support the points you make. It's a good idea to sum up your evaluation at the end too.

3. Risk Factors for Non-Communicable Diseases
Page 102 — Fact Recall Questions
Q1 Something linked to an increase in the likelihood that a person will develop a certain disease during their lifetime.
Q2 The presence of substances in the environment and aspects of a person's lifestyle.
Q3 E.g. nationally, people from deprived areas are more likely to smoke, have a poor diet and not exercise. This means the incidence of cardiovascular disease, obesity and Type 2 diabetes is higher in those areas.
Q4 Any two from: e.g. cardiovascular disease / lung disease / lung cancer
Q5 E.g. obesity
Q6 Something that causes cancer.

4. Cancer

Page 104 — Fact Recall Questions

Q1 No

Benign tumours aren't cancerous but malignant ones are.

Q2 Malignant tumours grow and spread to neighbouring healthy tissues. Cells can break off and spread to other parts of the body by travelling in the bloodstream. The malignant cells then invade healthy tissues elsewhere in the body and form secondary tumours. Malignant tumours are dangerous and can be fatal — they are cancers.

Page 104 — Application Question

Q1 a) Robyn's BMI = 77 ÷ (1.78 × 1.78) = **24.3**
    Lauren's BMI = 75 ÷ (1.55 × 1.55) = **31.2**

    b) Lauren, because she is obese, and obesity is a risk factor for cancer.

Pages 107-108 — Health and Disease Exam-style Questions

1.1 D *(1 mark)*

1.2 malignant tumour *(1 mark)*

1.3 Because there was more than one similar tumour, it suggests that cells from the original tumour had spread to another part of the body in the bloodstream *(1 mark)* to form a secondary tumour *(1 mark)*. Only malignant/cancerous tumours can do this *(1 mark)*.

1.4 C *(1 mark)*

1.5 Statins reduce the amount of 'bad' cholesterol present in the bloodstream *(1 mark)*. This slows down the rate of fatty deposits forming inside arteries *(1 mark)*.

2.1 The damage may cause the valve tissue to stiffen, so it won't open properly *(1 mark)*, or it might cause the valve to become leaky, allowing blood to flow in both directions rather than just forward *(1 mark)*. This means that blood doesn't circulate as effectively as normal *(1 mark)*.

2.2 Mechanical heart valves are man-made *(1 mark)*, whereas biological heart valves are taken from humans or other mammals *(1 mark)*.

2.3 The patient could be fitted with an artificial heart *(1 mark)*.

3.1 (3 ÷ 154) × 100 = **1.9%** *(1 mark)*

3.2 Stents can be inserted into narrowed arteries/arteries with restricted blood flow *(1 mark)* to help keep them open/allow blood to flow more freely *(1 mark)*. People who have had a heart attack are likely to have narrowed coronary arteries, so putting stents in these arteries can prevent another heart attack *(1 mark)*.

3.3 E.g. yes, because the results show that patients are less likely to die after having a drug-eluting stent inserted compared to a bare-metal stent *(1 mark)*. Also renarrowing of the artery is much less likely in patients treated with a drug-eluting stent (9%) compared to those treated with a bare-metal stent (21%) *(1 mark)*. The trial was fairly large (307 patients) which means the results are more likely to be representative of the whole population *(1 mark)*.

Topic 2c — Enzymes and Digestion

1. Enzymes

Page 111 — Fact Recall Questions

Q1 Because they increase the speed of a biological reaction without being changed or used up in the reaction.

Q2 active site

Q3 false

Different enzymes work best at different pHs.

Page 111 — Application Question

Q1 It should slow down the rate of reaction. This is because heating hexokinase up to a high temperature/50 °C will probably cause the bonds in hexokinase to break and the active site to lose its shape. This would mean that glucose will no longer be able to fit into hexokinase and the reaction won't be catalysed.

For questions like this you just need to apply your own knowledge — e.g. that enzymes lose their shape at high temperatures and that enzymes need their unique shape to work — to the specific enzyme named in the question.

2. Investigating Enzymatic Reactions

Page 113 — Application Question

Q1 a) By adding a buffer solution to the boiling tube containing the enzyme and starch mixture.

    b) The iodine solution would remain browny-orange rather than changing to blue-black.

    c) $$\text{Rate} = \frac{1000}{\text{time}} = \frac{1000}{120}$$
    $$= \textbf{8.3 s}^{-1} \text{ (2 s.f.)}$$

3. Enzymes and Digestion

Page 116 — Fact Recall Questions

Q1 false

Digestive enzymes catalyse the breakdown of big molecules into smaller molecules, e.g. protease enzymes catalyse the breakdown of proteins into amino acids.

Q2 amylase

Q3 In the stomach, the pancreas and the small intestine.

Q4 lipases

Q5 Bile neutralises the stomach acid and so creates the ideal alkaline conditions for enzymes in the small intestine to work in.

Page 117 — Application Question

Q1

	Amylase	Proteases	Lipases	Bile
Made where?	B, F, G	D, F, G	F, G	C
Work(s) where?	A, G	D, G	G	G

Make sure you learn where digestive enzymes and bile are produced and where they work — you can pick up easy marks with this information in the exam. However, it's easy to get things mixed up, so watch out. E.g. bile is made in the liver but stored in the gall bladder — make sure you don't get those two organs mixed up.

4. Food Tests

Page 120 — Fact Recall Questions

Q1 Benedict's solution

Q2 The solution would change from browny-orange to black or blue-black.

Q3 blue

Page 120 — Application Question

Q1 A pestle and mortar should be used to grind up the piece of food into little bits. The ground up food should then be transferred into a beaker and mixed with some distilled water. A glass rod should be used to give it a good stir to dissolve some of the food in the water. The mixture should then be poured through a funnel lined with filter paper to remove any solid bits of food. 5 cm^3 of the filtered solution should then be transferred into a test tube and a pipette used to add 3 drops of Sudan III stain solution to the test tube. The test tube should then be gently shaken. If the food sample contains lipids, the mixture will separate out into two layers. The top layer will be bright red. If no lipids are present, no separate red layer will form at the top of the liquid.

Pages 122-123 — Enzymes and Digestion Exam-style Questions

1.1 C *(1 mark)*

1.2 To act as a biological catalyst. / To speed up the rate of a reaction (in a living organism) without being changed or used up itself *(1 mark)*.

1.3 How to grade your answer:

Level 0: There is no relevant information.
[No marks]

Level 1: There is a brief description of the function of at least one type of digestive enzyme, with mention of where it is made or where it functions. *[1 to 2 marks]*

Level 2: There is a description of the function of at least two types of digestive enzyme, with mention of where they are made and where they work. *[3 to 4 marks]*

Level 3: There is a detailed description of the function of several types of digestive enzyme, including where each of them is made and where each of them works in the digestive system. *[5 to 6 marks]*

Here are some points your answer may include:
Carbohydrases are digestive enzymes that convert carbohydrates into simple sugars.
Amylase is a carbohydrase that catalyses the conversion of starch into sugars. Amylase is made in the salivary glands, the pancreas and the small intestine. It works in the mouth and the small intestine.
Protease enzymes are digestive enzymes that catalyse the conversion of proteins into amino acids. Proteases are made in the stomach, the pancreas and the small intestine. They work in the stomach and the small intestine.
Lipase enzymes are digestive enzymes that catalyse the conversion of lipids into glycerol and fatty acids. Lipases are made in the pancreas and the small intestine. They work in the small intestine.

2.1 Because every enzyme has an active site with a unique shape that usually only fits the substrate involved in a single reaction *(1 mark)*. If the substrate doesn't match the enzyme's active site, then the reaction won't be catalysed *(1 mark)*.

2.2 A, because higher temperatures can increase the rate of an enzyme-controlled reaction *(1 mark)*.

2.3 Because the temperature was too high *(1 mark)*, so the enzyme became denatured *(1 mark)* and so could no longer catalyse the reaction *(1 mark)*.

3.1 A *(1 mark)*

3.2 That glucose is not present in the sample *(1 mark)*.

3.3 She should have ground up the food in a pestle and mortar *(1 mark)*. The ground up food should then have been transferred to a beaker and distilled water added *(1 mark)*. The mixture should then have been stirred to dissolve some of the food *(1 mark)*. Finally, the solution should have been filtered through a funnel lined with filter paper *(1 mark)*.

3.4 Iodine solution *(1 mark)*. If the sample contained starch, the solution would have changed from a browny-orange *(1 mark)* to black or blue-black *(1 mark)*.

4 The photograph shows that in the test tubes with hydrochloric acid only and pepsin only (test tubes 1 and 2), the meat hasn't been fully digested *(1 mark)*. However, in the test tube with both pepsin and hydrochloric acid (test tube 3) the meat sample has been completely digested *(1 mark)*. This suggests that pepsin requires acidic conditions/low pH to function at its best *(1 mark)*.

Topic 3 — Infection and Response

1. Communicable Disease

Page 125 — Application Questions

Q1 They produce toxins that damage your cells and tissues.

Q2 The infected student might cough or sneeze, releasing droplets containing the virus into the air. Someone else in the classroom could breathe these in and become infected.

2. Viral Diseases

Page 126 — Fact Recall Questions

Q1 In the air through droplets from an infected person's sneeze or cough.

Q2 E.g. a red skin rash and a fever.

Q3 By sexual contact or by exchanging bodily fluids.

Q4 antiretroviral drugs

Q5 E.g. tomatoes

Q6 In plants with tobacco mosaic virus, parts of the leaves become discoloured. This means that the plant can't carry out photosynthesis as well, so growth is affected.

Photosynthesis produces glucose, which, amongst other things, is used by a plant for growth.

3. Fungal and Protist Diseases
Page 127 — Fact Recall Questions
Q1 Purple or black spots will develop on the leaves, and the leaves may turn yellow and drop off.

Q2 Because this can prevent people from being bitten by mosquitoes when they're asleep, meaning that the protist that causes malaria isn't passed on.

4. Bacterial Diseases and Preventing Disease
Page 129 — Fact Recall Questions
Q1 Any three from: e.g. fever / stomach cramps / vomiting / diarrhoea

Q2 E.g. eating chicken that caught the disease when it was alive / eating food that has been contaminated by being prepared in unhygienic conditions.

Q3 It is treated with antibiotics.

Q4 The vectors spread the disease to humans, and so by destroying the vectors, the disease cannot be passed on.

Page 129 — Application Questions
Q1 It will prevent them from passing the disease on to anyone else.

Q2 The nurse may come into contact with pathogens for many diseases. By washing his hands, this will prevent pathogens being passed on to other people that he comes into contact with.

5. Fighting Disease
Page 131 — Fact Recall Questions
Q1 It acts as a barrier to pathogens. It secretes antimicrobial substances which kill pathogens.

Q2 They consume pathogens using phagocytosis. They produce antitoxins. They produce antibodies.

Page 131 — Application Questions
Q1 E.g. hairs and mucus in your nose trap particles that could contain the SARS-CoV. / The trachea and bronchi secrete mucus to trap the SARS-CoV. / The trachea and bronchi are lined with cilia. These waft mucus containing the SARS-CoV up to the back of the throat where it can be swallowed.

Q2 a) John should now be immune to measles. If he is infected with the measles virus again, his white blood cells should rapidly produce the antibodies against it — meaning he won't get ill.

b) Antibodies are specific to a particular type of antigen. John has never had German measles before, so he won't have made antibodies against the antigens on the German measles virus. This means it will take his white blood cells time to produce antibodies against, the virus, during which he could get ill.

6. Fighting Disease — Vaccination
Page 133 — Application Question
Q1 a) E.g. the vaccination will involve injecting a small amount of the dead or inactive whooping cough pathogen. The pathogen will carry antigens which will trigger the white blood cells to produce antibodies to attack the pathogen. If the vaccinated person is infected with the whooping cough pathogen at a later date, their white blood cells should be able to rapidly mass-produce antibodies to kill off the pathogen.

b) If a large percentage of the population are vaccinated it means that the people who aren't vaccinated (i.e. very young babies) are less likely to catch the disease because there are fewer people to pass it on.

7. Fighting Disease — Drugs
Page 136 — Fact Recall Questions
Q1 false

Q2 Antibiotics are drugs that kill or prevent the growth of bacteria. E.g. penicillin / methicillin.

Q3 Because different antibiotics kill different types of bacteria.

Q4 Viruses reproduce using your own body cells, so it's difficult to develop drugs that destroy the virus without killing the body's cells.

Q5 To slow down the rate of development of resistant strains.

Q6 aspirin

Q7 Alexander Fleming. He noticed that one of his Petri dishes of bacteria also had mould on it and the area around the mould was free of the bacteria. He found that the mould on the Petri dish was producing a substance that killed the bacteria — this substance was penicillin.

Page 136 — Application Question
Q1 a) Because antibiotics don't kill viruses.

b) E.g. because it won't tackle the underlying cause of Chloe's flu (it will only help to relieve her symptoms).

8. Developing Drugs
Page 139 — Fact Recall Questions
Q1 Human cells, human tissues and animals.

Q2 Any two from: e.g. to find out whether the drug works. / To find out about the drug's toxicity. / To find out the optimum/best dose of the drug.

Q3 a) healthy volunteers
b) It is very low.

Q4 A placebo is a substance that's like the drug being tested but doesn't do anything.

Q5 A double-blind trial is a clinical trial where neither the doctor nor the patients know who has been given the drug and who has been given the placebo, until the results of the trial have been gathered.

It's helpful to remember that 'double' means 'two' — so in a double-blind trial, there are two groups of people (doctors and patients) who don't know who receives the drug or who receives the placebo.

Page 139 — Application Questions

Q1 a) E.g. a capsule without paracetamol
   b) E.g. an inhaler without steroids
   c) E.g. an injection without cortisone

Q2 a) i) No, because it was a double-blind trial.
      ii) E.g. a pill without any weight-loss drug.
   b) E.g. Group 2 was included in the trial to make sure that the new drug, Drug X, worked as well as/better than other, similar weight-loss drugs already available on the market (like Drug Y). / To see how Drug X compared to Drug Y.
   c) That, on average, people taking Drug X in this trial lost 4 lbs more than those taking the placebo, but 3 lbs less than those taking Drug Y.

Pages 142-143 — Infection and Response Exam-style Questions

1.1 E.g. repeating episodes of fever *(1 mark)*.
1.2 protist *(1 mark)*
1.3 The vaccination involves being injected with a small amount of dead or inactive typhoid pathogens *(1 mark)*. These carry antigens *(1 mark)* which cause your white blood cells to produce antibodies to attack them *(1 mark)*. If live pathogens of the same type appear after that, the white blood cells can rapidly mass-produce antibodies to kill off the pathogen *(1 mark)*.
2.1 fungus *(1 mark)*
2.2 It may have been carried in water *(1 mark)* or by the wind *(1 mark)*.
2.3 The plant should be treated with a fungicide *(1 mark)* and stripped of its affected leaves *(1 mark)*. The leaves should then be destroyed *(1 mark)*.
3.1 It produces hydrochloric acid which kills pathogens *(1 mark)*.
3.2 The trachea and bronchi secrete mucus to trap pathogens *(1 mark)*. They are also lined with cilia *(1 mark)*. These waft the mucus up to the back of the throat where it can be swallowed *(1 mark)*.
3.3 They can produce toxins that damage your cells and tissues *(1 mark)*.
3.4 E.g. *Salmonella* food poisoning / gonorrhoea *(1 mark)*
3.5 White blood cells *(1 mark)* consume pathogens by phagocytosis *(1 mark)* and also produce antitoxins *(1 mark)* and antibodies *(1 mark)*.
4.1 A microorganism that causes disease *(1 mark)*.
4.2 virus *(1 mark)*
4.3 Accept any answer between 1.2 million/1 200 000 and 1.4 million/1 400 000 *(1 mark)*
4.4 In 1980, there were just over 4 million reported measles cases *(1 mark)*. Between 1980 and 2014 the number of reported measles cases dropped to around 0.3 million (after rising to a peak of 4.5 million in around 1981) *(1 mark)*. The estimated vaccine coverage was around 15% of the population in 1980 *(1 mark)*. Between 1980 and 2014 it increased to around 85% *(1 mark)*.

The question asks you to use data from the graph to support your answer — so you must include some figures to get the marks. The graph has three different axes, which can make things a bit tricky. Take your time and work out what each one shows before answering the question.

4.5 E.g. the data suggests that as the estimated percentage vaccination coverage increased, the number of reported measles cases decreased — this supports the case for vaccinating people against measles *(1 mark)*. However it doesn't prove that the increase in vaccination coverage definitely caused the decrease in measles cases, since other factors may have been at work *(1 mark)*. It also doesn't tell us anything about the side effects of the vaccine *(1 mark)*.
5.1 Drugs were originally extracted from plants and microorganisms *(1 mark)*. They are now synthesised by chemists in labs in the pharmaceutical industry *(1 mark)*.
5.2 Because live animals have an intact small intestine and circulatory system *(1 mark)*. Testing on just cells or tissues wouldn't show whether the drug has the desired effect on the absorption of nutrients from the small intestine to the bloodstream because these body systems would not be intact *(1 mark)*.
5.3 How to grade your answer:
   Level 0: There is no relevant information.
      [No marks]
   Level 1: There is a brief explanation of what happens during a clinical trial, but no information about placebos or double-blind testing.
      [1 to 2 marks]
   Level 2: There is some explanation of what happens during a clinical trial, including some information about placebos or double-blind testing. *[3 to 4 marks]*
   Level 3: There is a clear and detailed explanation of what happens during a clinical trial, including clear and detailed information about placebos and double-blind trials.
      [5 to 6 marks]

Here are some points your answer may include:
The drug is first tested on healthy volunteers.
This is to make sure that it doesn't have any harmful side effects when the body is working normally.
A very low dose of the drug is given at first, and this is gradually increased.
If the results of the tests on healthy volunteers are good, the drug is tested on people suffering from the illness.
The optimum dose is found — this is the dose of drug that is the most effective and has few side effects.
To test how well the drug works, a placebo may be used.
Patients are randomly put into two groups — one is given the new drug, the other is given a placebo. This is so the doctor can see the actual difference the drug makes — it allows for the placebo effect.
Clinical trials are often double-blind — neither the doctor or the patients in the study know who is getting the drug or the placebo.
This is so the doctors monitoring the patients and analysing the results aren't subconsciously influenced by their knowledge.

Topic 4 — Bioenergetics

1. The Basics of Photosynthesis

Page 145 — Fact Recall Questions
Q1 glucose
Q2 carbon dioxide
Q3 oxygen
Q4 a) chloroplasts
   b) It absorbs light.
Q5 carbon dioxide + water $\rightarrow$ glucose + oxygen
Q6 glucose

Page 145 — Application Questions
Q1 Plant C. It received the most hours of sunlight, so it will have photosynthesised for longer. As photosynthesis produces glucose, it will have produced the most glucose.
Q2 3, because this type of plant cell contains the most chloroplasts. Chloroplasts contain chlorophyll, which is needed for plants to photosynthesise.

2. How Plants Use Glucose

Page 147 — Fact Recall Questions
Q1 respiration
Q2 To strengthen the cell walls.
Q3 nitrate ions
Q4 As fats and oils.
Q5 Starch is insoluble, so it doesn't draw in water and cause the cells to swell up.

3. The Rate of Photosynthesis

Page 151 — Fact Recall Questions
Q1 a) A factor which stops photosynthesis from happening any faster.
   b) E.g. light intensity, carbon dioxide level, temperature.
Q2 true

Pages 151-152 — Application Questions
Q1

Environmental conditions	Most likely limiting factor
Outside on a cold winter's day.	temperature
In an unlit garden at 1:30 am, in the UK, in summer.	light
On a windowsill on a warm, bright day.	carbon dioxide concentration

Q2 a) Because before point X, increasing the light intensity increases the rate of photosynthesis.
   b) Because carbon dioxide concentration is limiting the rate of photosynthesis in Flask A. Flask A has a lower carbon dioxide concentration than Flask B but all the other variables that could affect the rate of photosynthesis are the same for both flasks. Therefore the reason why the rate of photosynthesis levels off at a lower level in Flask A, is most likely to be because of the lower carbon dioxide concentration in this flask.

4. Investigating Photosynthesis Rate

Page 154 — Application Question
Q1 $25 \div 10 = 2.5$ cm
   2.5 cm $\div 3$ min $= 0.833... =$ **0.8 cm/min (1 s.f.)**

5. The Inverse Square Law

Page 155 — Application Question
Q1 a) light intensity $= 1 \div d^2$,
      $1 \div 15^2 =$ **0.004 a.u.**
   b) light intensity $= 1 \div d^2$,
      $1 \div 30^2 =$ **0.001 a.u.**

6. Artificially Controlling Plant Growth

Page 158 — Fact Recall Questions
Q1 E.g. so that they can create the ideal conditions for photosynthesis. This means that their plants photosynthesise faster, so the rate of plant growth is also increased.
Q2 e.g. carbon dioxide concentration

Page 158 — Application Question
Q1 a) i) $30 \div 8 =$ **3.75 cm per week**.
      ii) $17.5 \div 8 =$ **2.19 cm per week**.
   Graphs like this with two y-axes can be tricky — just take your time and make sure you're reading the value off the correct axis.
   b) Carbon dioxide concentration. Light, temperature and carbon dioxide concentration can all affect the rate of photosynthesis, which affects growth rate. The graph shows that there was very little difference in the temperature of each greenhouse throughout the experiment, and both greenhouses were exposed to the same amount of light. Therefore it's most likely to be the extra carbon dioxide produced by the paraffin heater in Greenhouse A which caused the higher average growth rate of plants in this greenhouse.
   c) E.g. the cost of running the heaters.

7. Aerobic Respiration

Page 160 — Fact Recall Questions
Q1 Respiration using oxygen. / The process of transferring energy from glucose using oxygen.
Q2 It transfers energy to the environment.
Q3 CO_2 and H_2O
   To answer this question, you first have to identify what the products of aerobic respiration are — water and carbon dioxide. Then you need to write down the correct symbols.
Q4 E.g. mammals use energy to build larger molecules from smaller ones, to contract muscles and to keep warm.

Page 160 — Application Question
Q1 a) oxygen
   b) water

8. Anaerobic Respiration

Page 162 — Fact Recall Questions

Q1 The body uses anaerobic respiration during vigorous exercise when it can't get enough oxygen to the muscles for aerobic respiration.

We're not respiring by anaerobic respiration all the time — just when increased muscle activity means we can't get oxygen to our muscles fast enough for them to respire aerobically.

Q2 An oxygen debt is the amount of extra oxygen the body needs after exercise to react with the build up of lactic acid and remove it from the cells.

Q3 In the liver, lactic acid is converted to glucose.

Q4 glucose → ethanol + carbon dioxide

Q5 a) fermentation
   b) E.g. making bread and making alcoholic drinks.

9. Exercise

Page 164 — Application Question

Q1 E.g. her breathing rate and breath volume will increase.

10. Metabolism

Page 165 — Fact Recall Questions

Q1 One molecule of glycerol and three fatty acids.

Q2 amino acids

Q3 urea

Q4 Metabolism is the sum of all of the reactions that happen in a cell or the body.

Pages 168-169 — Bioenergetics

Exam-style Questions

1.1 in the chloroplasts *(1 mark)*

1.2 carbon dioxide + water ➔ glucose + oxygen *(1 mark)*

1.3 B. It took the shortest time for all of the discs to be floating *(1 mark)* suggesting that photosynthesis was happening the fastest in this condition *(1 mark)*.

1.4 Increasing the light intensity will increase the rate of photosynthesis up to a point *(1 mark)*. However, past this point increasing the light intensity will have no further effect on the rate of photosynthesis *(1 mark)* as other limiting factors may come into play, such as carbon dioxide concentration or temperature *(1 mark)*.

1.5 It should take less than 18 minutes because the rate of photosynthesis should be faster *(1 mark)*, as there is more carbon dioxide available in the solution for photosynthesis *(1 mark)*.

1.6 How to grade your answer:
   Level 0: There is no relevant information.
   [No marks]
   Level 1: There is a brief description of one or two ways that glucose can be used by plants.
   [1 to 2 marks]
   Level 2: There is some description of three or more ways that glucose can be used by plants.
   [3 to 4 marks]
   Level 3: There is a clear and detailed description of four or more ways that glucose can be used by plants. **[5 to 6 marks]**

Here are some points your answer may include:
Some of the glucose is used for respiration.
Some glucose is converted into cellulose, which is used to make strong cell walls.
Some glucose is combined with nitrate ions from the soil to make amino acids, which can be joined together to make proteins.
Some glucose is converted into starch for storage.
Some glucose is converted into lipids (fats and oils) for storage.

2.1 (151 + 163 + 154) / 3 = **156 beats per minute**
   (2 marks for correct answer, otherwise 1 mark for correct working.)
   Make sure that you always include units in your answer — in this case, the units are beats per minute.

2.2 His heart rate increased to increase blood flow to the muscles *(1 mark)* to provide more oxygen for respiration *(1 mark)*.

2.3 E.g. making larger molecules from smaller ones *(1 mark)*. Keeping the body warm/at a steady temperature *(1 mark)*.

3.1 glucose + oxygen → carbon dioxide + water
   (1 mark each for glucose and oxygen on the left-hand side of the equation, 1 mark each for carbon dioxide and water on the right.)

3.2 Anaerobic respiration forms less ATP than aerobic respiration, which shows that it transfers less energy *(1 mark)*. This is because glucose is not completely oxidised in anaerobic respiration *(1 mark)*.

Topic 5 — Homeostasis and Response

Topic 5a — The Nervous System

1. Homeostasis

Page 171 — Fact Recall Questions

Q1 Homeostasis is the regulation of the conditions inside your body (and cells) to maintain a stable internal environment, in response to changes in both internal and external conditions.

Q2 Any two from: e.g. temperature, blood glucose content, water content of the body.

Q3 A change in the environment.

Q4 the coordination centre

Page 171 — Application Question

Q1 Receptors detect that the water content of the body is too low. They send this information to the coordination centre, which processes the information and organises a response from the effectors. The effectors respond to increase the amount of water in the body / bring the water content back to its optimum level.

2. The Nervous System

Page 173 — Fact Recall Questions

Q1 glands

Q2 E.g. motor neurones, relay neurones

Page 173 — Application Question

Q1 a) i) The sound of the cat moving.
   ii) Receptors in the dog's ears (that are sensitive to sound).
   iii) sensory neurone
b) i) motor neurone
   ii) They will contract.

3. Synapses and Reflexes

Page 176 — Fact Recall Questions

Q1 Chemicals diffuse across the gap between the two neurones, which sets off an electrical impulse in the next neurone.
Q2 A reflex is a fast, automatic response to a stimulus.
Q3 No
   Reflexes are automatic — you don't have to think about them, so they don't pass through conscious parts of the brain.
Q4 a relay neurone
Q5 The muscle will contract.

Page 176 — Application Question

Q1 a) pain
b) A muscle in the leg. It contracts, moving the foot away from the source of the pain (the pin).
c) Stimulus → Receptor → Sensory neurone → Relay neurone → Motor neurone → Effector → Response

4. Investigating Reaction Time

Page 178 — Application Questions

Q1 It would increase reaction time. / It would make the reaction time slower.
Q2 a) E.g. the person being tested should sit with their arm resting on the edge of a table. The ruler should be held vertically between their thumb and forefinger, with the zero end of the ruler level with their thumb and finger. The ruler should then be dropped (without any warning). The person being tested should try to catch the ruler as soon as they see it fall. Their reaction time should be measured by the number on the ruler where it's caught. This test should then be repeated and the mean distance (i.e. reaction time) calculated.
b) E.g. amount of caffeine consumed / amount of sleep / age.

Page 180 — The Nervous System
Exam-style Questions

1.1 The muscle in the upper arm *(1 mark)*.
1.2 sensory neurone *(1 mark)*
1.3 It would get faster *(1 mark)*. The presence of the drug increases the amount of chemical released at the synapses, so it would take less time for an impulse to be triggered in the next neurone *(1 mark)*.
1.4 E.g. reflexes are fast *(1 mark)*, so we quickly respond to danger, decreasing our chances of injury *(1 mark)*. Reflexes are automatic *(1 mark)*, so we don't have to waste time thinking about our response, which reduces our chance of injury *(1 mark)*.

Topic 5b — The Endocrine System

1. Hormones

Page 183 — Fact Recall Questions

Q1 By the blood (plasma).
Q2 false
   They only affect particular organs, called target organs.
Q3 (endocrine) glands
Q4 E.g. oestrogen
Q5 nerves

2. Controlling Blood Glucose

Page 188 — Fact Recall Questions

Q1 the pancreas
Q2 Insulin makes body cells take up more glucose from the blood.
Q3 the pancreas
Q4 It causes glycogen to be converted into glucose which then enters the blood.
Q5 A condition where the pancreas produces little or no insulin, which means blood glucose can rise to a dangerous level.
Q6 E.g. eating a carbohydrate-controlled diet and exercising regularly.

Page 188 — Application Question

Q1 a) Glucagon, because the subject's blood glucose level rises following the injection. Glucagon causes glycogen to be converted back into glucose, which enters the blood, causing the blood glucose level to rise.
b) i) insulin
   ii) The blood glucose level would fall following the injection, as insulin causes body cells to take up more glucose from the blood, causing the blood glucose level to fall.

3. Puberty and the Menstrual Cycle

Page 192 — Fact Recall Questions

Q1 oestrogen
Q2 e.g. stimulates sperm production.
Q3 It causes the egg to mature.
Q4 It stimulates the release of an egg at around the middle (day 14) of the menstrual cycle. / It stimulates ovulation.
Q5 oestrogen and progesterone
Q6 The pituitary gland and the ovaries.

Page 192 — Application Question

Q1 a) LH (luteinising hormone). LH is the hormone responsible for stimulating the release of an egg. The concentration of the hormone on the graph increases just before the middle of the cycle (day 14) — the time at which an egg is normally released.
b) the pituitary gland
c) LH is needed to stimulate the release of an egg. This woman's LH level peaks at a much lower level than the other woman's, suggesting that she may not be releasing an egg during her menstrual cycle. This could be the reason why she's struggling to have children.

4. Contraceptives

Page 194 — Fact Recall Questions

Q1 It inhibits FSH production, and so prevents egg maturation and therefore release.

Q2 progesterone

Q3 E.g. condom / diaphragm.

5. Increasing Fertility

Page 196 — Fact Recall Questions

Q1 To stimulate the maturation of multiple eggs.

Q2 The eggs are fertilised in the lab using the male's sperm.

Q3 Any two from: e.g. IVF treatment can lead to multiple births / the success rate is low / it is emotionally stressful / it is physically stressful.

Q4 E.g. it results in unused embryos, which are potential human lives, being destroyed.

Page 197 — Application Question

Q1 a) $(7768 \div 17\,765) \times 100 = \textbf{43.73\%}$ **(4 s.f.)**

b) $(41.74/100) \times 17\,892 = \textbf{7468}$

c) IVF often involves the transfer of more than one embryo into the uterus, which results in an increased chance of multiple pregnancies, and therefore more multiple pregnancies in those undergoing IVF.

6. Thyroxine and Adrenaline

Page 199 — Fact Recall Questions

Q1 E.g. thyroxine helps to regulate basal metabolic rate and stimulates protein synthesis for growth and development.

Q2 the adrenal glands

Page 199 — Application Question

Q1 a) adrenaline

b) It increases the supply of oxygen and glucose to cells in his brain and muscles, so that his body is ready for 'fight or flight'.

Pages 202-203 — The Endocrine System Exam-style Questions

1.1 B *(1 mark)*

1.2 insulin *(1 mark)*

1.3 People with Type 1 diabetes produce little or no insulin *(1 mark)*. Injecting insulin stops their blood glucose level from rising to a dangerous level *(1 mark)* as insulin causes the body's cells to take up glucose from the blood *(1 mark)*.

1.4 A pancreas transplant could be an effective treatment for Type 1 diabetes because the transplanted pancreas could take over the role of the patient's faulty pancreas and produce the right amount of insulin *(1 mark)*. A pancreas transplant would be ineffective in treating Type 2 diabetes because the patient's pancreas already produces enough insulin *(1 mark)*, but their body's cells don't respond properly to the hormone *(1 mark)*.

1.5 E.g. the patient should eat a carbohydrate-controlled diet / limit their intake of foods rich in simple carbohydrates *(1 mark)*, as simple carbohydrates cause the blood glucose level to rise rapidly *(1 mark)*. The patient should try to do regular exercise *(1 mark)* as this will remove glucose from their blood *(1 mark)*.

2.1 day 14 and day 28 *(1 mark)*

2.2 Advantage: e.g. people who find hormonal and barrier methods unnatural may prefer it. / There are no side effects *(1 mark)*.
Disadvantage: e.g. it's not very effective. / It doesn't protect against sexually transmitted diseases. *(1 mark)*

2.3 It causes egg maturation, and therefore egg release, to stop *(1 mark)*.

2.4 Any three from: contraceptive skin patch / contraceptive implant / contraceptive injection / intrauterine device that releases a hormone/ progesterone *(3 marks)*.

3.1 C *(1 mark)*

3.2 How to grade your answer:
Level 0: There is no relevant information.
[No marks]
Level 1: There is some description of how the level of thyroxine is controlled by negative feed-back, but it is incomplete or points are not clearly linked. *[1 to 2 marks]*
Level 2: There is a detailed description of how the level of thyroxine is controlled by negative feedback, with points that are clearly linked together. *[3 to 4 marks]*
Here are some points your answer may include:
The amount of thyroxine in the blood is kept at the right level by a negative feedback system.
When the level of thyroxine in the blood rises higher than normal, the secretion of thyroid stimulating hormone (TSH) from the pituitary gland is inhibited.
This means the amount of thyroxine released from the thyroid gland is reduced.
So the level in the blood falls back towards normal.
When the level of thyroxine in the blood is lower than normal, the secretion of TSH from the pituitary gland is stimulated again.
This means the amount of thyroxine released from the thyroid gland is increased.
So the level in the blood rises back towards normal.

3.3 1 day = 24 hours
$1860 \div 24 = 77.5$
$77.5 \times 6 = \textbf{465 kcal}$
(2 marks for correct answer, otherwise 1 mark for correct working.)

4.1 luteinising hormone/LH *(1 mark)* and follicle stimulating hormone/FSH *(1 mark)*.

4.2 Because the eggs need to be fertilised in a lab using the father's sperm *(1 mark)*, and then grown in a laboratory incubator *(1 mark)*.

4.3 To increase the chance of pregnancy *(1 mark)*.

4.4 IVF can give an infertile couple a child *(1 mark)*. However, it can result in multiple births, which are risky for the mother and babies *(1 mark)*. Also, the success rate of IVF is low *(1 mark)* and the process can be emotionally / physically stressful *(1 mark)*.

Topic 6 — Inheritance, Variation and Evolution

Topic 6a — DNA and Reproduction

1. DNA

Page 205 — Fact Recall Questions
Q1 In the nucleus.
Q2 (long molecules of coiled up) DNA
Q3 Because they are made up of two strands coiled together in a double helix shape.
Q4 By telling the cell what order to put amino acids in.
Q5 The entire set of genetic material in an organism.

2. Reproduction

Page 207 — Fact Recall Questions
Q1 meiosis
Q2 egg and sperm cells
Q3 one

Page 207 — Application Question
Q1 a) Asexual reproduction. There is only a single parent cell and no fusion of gametes. The offspring are genetically identical/clones.
   b) Sexual reproduction. There are two parents, gametes have fused together and offspring show genetic variation.
   Remember, sexual reproduction doesn't always involve sexual intercourse — it's the fusion of gametes that's important. Both animals and plants can reproduce sexually.
   c) Sexual reproduction. There are two parents and the offspring has characteristics of both parents, suggesting that it has a mixture of genes from both parents.
   d) Asexual reproduction. There is only one parent and no fusion of gametes. The offspring are genetically identical to/clones of the mother snake.

3. Meiosis

Page 209 — Fact Recall Questions
Q1 one
Q2 In the reproductive organs.
Q3 two
Q4 four
Q5 False
Q6 By repeatedly dividing by mitosis.

Page 209 — Application Questions
Q1 a) 39
   b) 38
   c) 32
Q2 Before the first division, the cell duplicates its DNA. So when the first division happens, cells will have one full set of chromosomes again.
   Duplicating the DNA creates X-shaped chromosomes, where each 'arm' of the chromosome has the same DNA.

Pages 211-212 — DNA and Reproduction Exam-style Questions
1.1 Sexual, because it involves the joining of male and female gametes *(1 mark)*.

1.2 They have received genetic material/chromosomes from both the male pig and the female pig *(1 mark)* and it is this genetic material/the chromosomes that control the offspring's characteristics *(1 mark)*.
1.3 So that when two gametes join at fertilisation, the full number of chromosomes is reached (two copies of each) *(1 mark)*.
1.4 mitosis *(1 mark)*
2.1 The human genome is the entire set of genetic material in a human *(1 mark)*.
2.2 Any two from, e.g. it allows scientists to identify genes in the genome that are linked to different types of disease. / Knowing which genes are linked to inherited diseases will help us to understand them better and could help us to develop effective treatments for them. / Scientists can look at genomes to trace the migration of certain populations of people around the world *(2 marks)*.
3.1 D *(1 mark)*
3.2 C *(1 mark)*
3.3 A DNA molecule has two strands which are coiled together *(1 mark)* in the shape of a double helix *(1 mark)*. Each strand is a polymer *(1 mark)*.
3.4 How to grade your answer:
   Level 0: There is no relevant information.
      [No marks]
   Level 1: One or both terms are described clearly but there is no detail on how they are linked together. *[1 to 2 marks]*
   Level 2: Both terms are described fully and the link between them is made clear. *[3 to 4 marks]*
   Here are some points your answer may include:
   Genes are small sections of DNA that code for a particular sequence of amino acids which are put together to make a specific protein.
   Chromosomes are very long structures made up of DNA.
   Genes are found on chromosomes.
3.5 meiosis *(1 mark)*

Topic 6b — Genetics

1. X and Y Chromosomes

Page 216 — Fact Recall Questions
Q1 one
Q2 false
   Half carry X chromosomes, and half carry Y chromosomes.

Page 216 — Application Questions
Q1
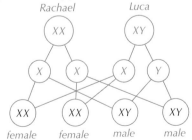
Q2 0.5 or 50% or 1:1 or 1 in 2 or ½.

Q3 Rachael's gametes

2. Alleles and Genetic Diagrams
Page 222 — Fact Recall Questions
Q1 E.g. mouse fur colour / red-green colour blindness in humans
Q2 a) Different versions of the same gene.
b) When an organism has two alleles for a particular gene that are the same, e.g. TT.
c) The allele for the characteristic that's shown even if two different alleles for the same gene are present.
d) The characteristics you have.

Page 222 — Application Questions
Q1 a) heterozygous
b) ss
c) SS
Q2 a) a rough coat
b) i) *gametes' alleles*

ii) 0.25 or 25% or 1:3 or 1 in 4 or ¼.

3. Inherited Disorders
Page 226 — Fact Recall Questions
Q1 cell membrane
Q2 recessive
You need to have two recessive alleles for cystic fibrosis to have the disease.
Q3 E.g. to see if the embryo carries an inherited disorder.

Page 226 — Application Questions
Q1 a) Ff
b) ff
Q2 a) Because there are no carriers of the disease, just sufferers.
b) a purple circle
c) i) dd
ii) Dd
You know from the diagram that Kate has polydactyly, so she must have at least one copy of the dominant allele 'D'. You also know that she doesn't have two copies of the dominant allele, as her father Clark doesn't have polydactyly, so she couldn't have inherited a second 'D' allele from him. Therefore her genotype must be Dd.
d) i) *Kate's alleles*

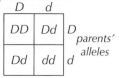

ii) 0.5 or 50% or 1:1 or 1 in 2 or ½

Exam-style Questions
1 C *(1 mark)*
2.1 They have extra fingers or toes *(1 mark)*.
2.2 DD or Dd *(1 mark)*
2.3 A *(1 mark)*
2.4 *parents' alleles*

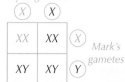

DD and Dd offspring have polydactyly.
3:1 of polydactyly offspring:unaffected offspring *(1 mark for correctly identifying the parents' genotypes, 1 mark for correctly identifying possible genotypes of the offspring, 1 mark for correctly identifying possible phenotypes of the offspring, 1 mark for correct ratio.)*

3.1

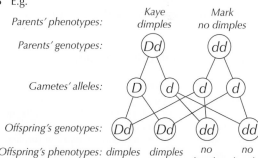

(1 mark for correctly identifying Kaye and Mark's missing gametes, 1 mark for correctly identifying the possible gamete combinations of the offspring.)

3.2 XY *(1 mark)*
Males have the XY chromosome combination, females have the XX chromosome combination.

3.3 E.g.

Parents' phenotypes:	Kaye dimples	Mark no dimples

Parents' genotypes: Dd   dd

Gametes' alleles: D d   d d

Offspring's genotypes: Dd Dd dd dd

Offspring's phenotypes: dimples dimples no dimples no dimples

The baby has a 0.5 / 50% / 1:1 / 1 in 2 / ½ chance of having dimples. *(1 mark for correctly identifying Kaye's genotype, 1 mark for correctly identifying Mark's genotype, 1 mark for correctly identifying possible genotypes of the offspring, 1 mark for correctly identifying possible phenotypes of the offspring, 1 mark for identifying the correct probability of the baby having dimples.)*
You could have drawn a Punnett square to answer this question instead.

4.1 Cystic fibrosis is an inherited disorder *(1 mark)*, which affects the cell membranes *(1 mark)*.
4.2 Homozygous, because he has a recessive disorder *(1 mark)*.

4.3 Ff *(1 mark)*. For a child to have cystic fibrosis, both parents must carry the cystic fibrosis allele *(1 mark)*, as it is a recessive disorder *(1 mark)*.

Tony is a carrier so his alleles must be Ff. As their child has cystic fibrosis (ff) it must have inherited a cystic fibrosis allele from both Tony and Bex, as it's a recessive disorder. Bex doesn't have cystic fibrosis, so she must be a carrier (Ff).

4.4 Any two from: e.g. there may come a point where everyone wants to screen their embryos so they can pick the most 'desirable' one *(1 mark)*. / It implies that people with genetic problems are 'undesirable', which could increase prejudice *(1 mark)*. / Some people think destroying the rejected embryos is unethical as they could have developed into humans *(1 mark)*. / There's a risk of miscarriage with embryo screening *(1 mark)*. / If an inherited disorder is diagnosed, it could lead to a termination/abortion *(1 mark)*. / Screening embryos is expensive *(1 mark)*.

4.5 E.g. *Ivana's alleles*

	f	f
F	Ff	Ff
F	Ff	Ff

Tam's alleles

No, because to have cystic fibrosis you need the genotype ff. None of the offspring are ff. Ivana and Tam's offspring will only have the genotype Ff, so they could only be carriers, not have the disorder.
(1 mark for correctly identifying the Ivana's genotype, 1 mark for correctly identifying Tam's genotype, 1 mark for correctly identifying possible genotypes of the offspring, 1 mark for correctly explaining the answer by identifying possible phenotypes of the offspring.)

Topic 6c — Evolution and Classification

1. Variation

Page 233 — Fact Recall Questions
Q1 False
Q2 a) A change in an organism's DNA.
   b) Because most mutations produce genetic variants that have little or no effect on the protein the gene codes for, or don't affect its function.
   c) Mutations can influence phenotypes or produce new phenotypes in a species (by producing a genetic variant that codes for a different protein).

Page 233 — Application Questions
Q1 a) genes only
   b) both
   c) genes only
Q2 a) both
   b) environment only
Q3 E.g. how often you train / how hard you train / how well you are coached / how good the facilities you train at are / how good your diet is.
   You're not expected to know the answer to this question, just to make sensible suggestions.

Q4 The results from Study 1 suggest that genes must influence IQ because identical twins have the same genes and non-identical twins have different genes. The results from Study 2 suggest that environment also influences IQ. This is because identical twins have exactly the same genes, which means that differences in their IQs must be down to differences in their environment/the way they were brought up.

2. Evolution and Extinction

Page 236 — Fact Recall Questions
Q1 over 3 billion years ago
Q2 They evolved from simple organisms.
Q3 a) (Charles) Darwin
   b) The process by which species evolve.
Q4 When individuals from different populations have changed so much that they can no longer interbreed to produce fertile offspring.
Q5 No living individuals of the species remain.

Page 237 — Application Questions
Q1 E.g. the original rats showed variation — some were resistant to warfarin, others weren't / a genetic variant appeared (due to a mutation) which made some rats resistant to warfarin. The warfarin-resistant rats were better suited to the environment (because they weren't killed by the warfarin), so they were more likely to survive and breed successfully. This meant that the genetic variant for warfarin-resistance was more likely to be passed on to the next generation.
   You could get asked to explain the selection of pretty much any characteristic in the exam — make sure you can apply the key points of Darwin's theory to any context.
Q2 a) By around 3.5 – 2.1 = **1.4 cm**
      (accept any answer between 1.3 and 1.5 cm).
   b) E.g. the reindeer population in 1810 would have shown variation — some would have had shorter fur and some longer fur (due to a mix of genetic variants in the population). The reindeer with shorter fur would have been better suited to the new, warmer environment they found themselves in (as they would have been less likely to overheat), so they would have been more likely to survive and breed successfully. This meant that the genetic variant for short fur was more likely to be passed on to the next generation. This genetic variant became more common in the population, eventually reducing the average fur length.

3. Selective Breeding

Page 239 — Fact Recall Questions
Q1 E.g. high meat production / high milk production / good disease resistance in crops / a good temperament in dogs / big or unusual flowers in plants.
Q2 From your existing stock, select the organisms which have the characteristics you're after. Breed them with each other. Select the best of the offspring, and breed them together. Continue this process over several generations, and the desirable trait gets stronger and stronger. Eventually, all the offspring will have the characteristic.

Q3 E.g. it reduces the gene pool, which known as inbreeding. Inbreeding can cause health problems, such as genetic defects and susceptibility to diseases.

4. Genetic Engineering
Page 242 — Fact Recall Questions
Q1 'Cutting out' and transferring a gene responsible for a desirable characteristic from one organism's genome into another organism, so that it also has the desired characteristic.
Q2 It means that the organism will develop with the characteristic coded for by the gene.
Q3 E.g. producing human insulin.
Q4 a) genetically modified
b) E.g. insects, herbicides

Page 242 — Application Questions
Q1 Enzymes would be used to cut out the *Bt* crystal protein gene from the *B. thuringiensis* DNA. The gene would be inserted into a vector (e.g. a virus or bacterial plasmid). The vector would then be introduced to the target plant, and the *Bt* crystal protein gene would be inserted into its cells.
Q2 E.g. if insects ate the crop, they'd be poisoned by the protein. If less of the crop was eaten by insects, this could improve crop yield.
Q3 E.g. it could affect the number of weeds/flowers/insects that live in and around the crop. / People might develop allergies to the crop. / The gene for the *Bt* protein might get into the natural environment affecting, e.g., weeds.

5. Fossils
Page 245 — Fact Recall Questions
Q1 The remains of an organism from many years ago that are found in a rock.
Q2 That organisms lived ages ago and how today's species have evolved over time.
Q3 Early organisms were soft-bodied and soft tissue tends to decay away completely, without forming fossils. Plus fossils that did form millions of years ago may have been destroyed by geological activity, e.g. the movement of tectonic plates. So the fossil record is incomplete.

Page 245 — Application Question
Q1 A E.g. an organism (or organisms) burrowed into soft material. The material later hardened around the burrows to form casts in the rock.
B E.g. the hard shell of the snail decayed away slowly. It was gradually replaced by minerals as it decayed, forming a rock-like substance shaped like the shell.
C E.g. a leaf became buried in a soft material. The material later hardened around the leaf, which decayed, leaving a cast of itself in the rock.
D E.g. the mammoth died and it's body became trapped in frozen ground. It was too cold for decay microbes to work, so the mammoth's body was preserved.

6. Antibiotic-Resistant Bacteria
Page 247 — Fact Recall Questions
Q1 Because they reproduce rapidly.
Q2 E.g. MRSA
Q3 The rate of development is slow, and it's a very costly process.

Page 247 — Application Questions
Q1 E.g. because it's important for doctors to avoid over-prescribing antibiotics in order to slow down the development of antibiotic resistance. James' infection is only mild.
Q2 E.g. people with a *Streptococcus pneumoniae* infection may have been treated with penicillin. A mutation may have given rise to a genetic variant that caused some of these bacteria to be resistant to the penicillin, meaning that only the non-resistant bacteria would have been killed. The individual resistant bacteria would have survived and reproduced, increasing the population of penicillin-resistant *Streptococcus pneumoniae* bacteria.

7. Classification
Page 250 — Application Question
Q1 a) i) the lion
ii) the snow leopard
b) the jaguar
c) yes
The lion and the snow leopard are two of the most distantly related organisms on this tree, but they still share a common ancestor:

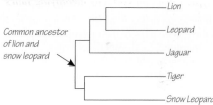

Pages 253-254 — Evolution and Classification Exam-style Questions
1.1 genes *(1 mark)*
1.2 It is caused by differences in their environment *(1 mark)*. / A named environmental factor, e.g. diet *(1 mark)*.
2.1 C *(1 mark)*
2.2 turtles *(1 mark)*
2.3 The original milk snake population showed variation — some had similar colouring to the coral snake, others didn't. / A genetic variant appeared (due to a mutation) which caused some milk snakes to have similar colouring to the coral snake *(1 mark)*. Milk snakes that looked like the coral snake were less likely to be eaten *(1 mark)* and so more likely to reproduce and pass on the genetic variant for coral snake colouring to the next generation *(1 mark)*.

2.4 We now know that beneficial variations are passed on to future generations in the genes that parents contribute to their offspring *(1 mark)*. Fossils of different ages (the fossil record) also show how changes in organisms developed slowly over time *(1 mark)*. We also know how bacteria are able to evolve to become resistant to antibiotics *(1 mark)*.

3.1 The hard shells won't have decayed easily so they will have lasted a long time when buried *(1 mark)*. As the shells did decay, they will have been gradually replaced by minerals, forming a rock-like substance shaped like the original shells *(1 mark)*.

3.2 Soft tissue tends to decay away completely without forming fossils *(1 mark)*.

3.3 E.g. by geological activity / they may have been crushed by the movements of tectonic plates *(1 mark)*.

3.4 Any three from: e.g. the environment changes too quickly. / A new predator kills them all. / A new disease kills them all. / They can't compete with another (new) species for food. / A catastrophic event happens that kills them all. *(3 marks)*

Topic 7 — Ecology

Topic 7a — Organisms and Their Environment

1. Competition
Page 257 — Fact Recall Questions
Q1 The populations of different species living in a habitat.
Q2 The interaction of a community of living organisms with the abiotic parts of their environment.
Q3 Space (territory), food, water and mates.
Q4 A community in which all the species and environmental factors are in balance so that the population sizes are roughly constant.

2. Abiotic and Biotic Factors
Page 260 — Fact Recall Questions
Q1 Any three from: e.g. moisture level / light intensity / temperature / carbon dioxide level / wind intensity / wind direction / oxygen level / soil pH / soil mineral content.
Q2 Any three from: e.g. new predators arriving / competition from other species / new pathogens / availability of food.

Page 260 — Application Question
Q1 a) i) It decreased.
      ii) an abiotic factor
   Remember, it's the oxygen concentration that changed, and oxygen isn't alive — making it an abiotic factor.
   b) The population size of the herons is likely to have decreased because there were fewer fish to eat.
   Here the environmental change was caused by a biotic factor — the availability of food.

3. Adaptations
Page 262 — Fact Recall Questions
Q1 Features of an organism's body structure that allow it to live in the conditions of its environment.
Q2 Things that go on inside an organism's body that can be related to processes like reproduction and metabolism that allow it to live in the conditions of its environment.
Q3 Any two from: e.g. very hot conditions / very salty conditions / high pressure conditions.

4. Food Chains
Page 264 — Fact Recall Questions
Q1 a producer
Q2 tertiary consumers
Q3 Consumers that hunt and kill other animals.

Page 264 — Application Question
Q1 a) zebra
   b) The cheetah population will increase, because an increase in grass means more food for the zebra population, so the zebra population will increase. This means there is more food for the cheetahs, so their population will grow.
   c) As the cheetah population increases, the zebra population will decrease because there are more cheetahs to eat them. This will lead to the cheetah population decreasing as the amount of food available decreases.

5. Using Quadrats and Transects
Page 268 — Fact Recall Questions
Q1 E.g. you would place the quadrat on the ground at a random position in the first sample area and count the number of the organisms within the quadrat. You would then repeat this many times. Next you would repeat this whole process in the second sample area. Finally you would work out the mean number of organisms per quadrat or the population size in each sample area and compare the results.
Q2 A line can be marked out across the area you want to study and all of the organisms that touch the line can be counted. / A line can be marked out across the area you want to study and data can be collected using quadrats placed along the line.

Page 268 — Application Questions
Q1 a) $1 + 5 + 5 + 20 + 43 + 37 = 111$
      $111 \div 6 = \textbf{18.5}$
   Remember the mean is the average you get by adding together all the values in the data and dividing it by the number of values that you have.
   b) End B, as the amount of bulrushes is lower here and you would expect there to be fewer bulrushes further away from the pond as they prefer moist soil or shallow water.

Q2 First calculate how many of the quadrats used by the conservationists would fit in 1 m²: 1 ÷ 0.25 = 4
Then work out how many slugs there would be in 1 m²: 4 × 2.5 = 10
Finally, work out how many slugs there would be in 2000 m²: 10 × 2000 = **20 000 slugs in the area**

6. The Cycling of Materials

Page 270 — Fact Recall Questions
Q1 CO_2 is removed from the atmosphere by green plants and algae during photosynthesis, and the carbon is used to make glucose. The glucose can be turned into carbohydrates, fats and proteins that make up the bodies of the plants and algae.
Q2 Dead leaves are fed on by detritus feeders and microorganisms. These organisms release CO_2 when they respire.

Page 270 — Application Question
Q1 Yes. Water evaporates from plants in transpiration and cools and condenses to form clouds as it gets higher up. Water falls from the clouds as precipitation onto land. It then drains into the sea.

Pages 273-274 — Organisms and Their Environment Exam-style Questions
1.1 55 + 41 + 57 = 153
153 ÷ 3 = **51**
(2 marks for correct answer, otherwise 1 mark for correct working.)
1.2 The number of limpets increases as you move away from the water's edge, and then begins to decrease after the position of quadrat 3 *(1 mark)*. The low number of limpets in quadrats closest to the water's edge could be due to competition for space from other organisms *(1 mark)*. The decrease in the number of limpets after quadrat 3 could be due to there being less water available further from the water's edge, which increases the limpets' chance of drying out *(1 mark)*.
1.3 To increase the validity of their results *(1 mark)*.
2 How to grade your answer:
Level 0: There is no relevant information. *[No marks]*
Level 1: There is a brief description of one or two steps in the carbon cycle, but no names of any processes are given. *[1 to 2 marks]*
Level 2: There is a description of three or four steps in the carbon cycle, but not all of the processes are named. *[3 to 4 marks]*
Level 3: There is a detailed description of five or six steps in the carbon cycle with named processes. *[5 to 6 marks]*
Here are some points your answer may include:
The grass absorbs carbon dioxide from the air in photosynthesis.
The grass uses this carbon to make glucose/carbohydrates/fats/proteins.
This carbon is passed onto the cows when the cows eat the grass, and onto humans when the humans eat the cows, so it moves through the food chain.

Dead organisms/waste materials are broken down/decayed by detritus feeders/microorganisms.
All the organisms/the grass/cows/humans/microorganisms respire and release carbon dioxide into the atmosphere.
Combustion/burning of fossil fuels/wood also releases carbon dioxide into the air.
3.1 A characteristic/feature that helps an organism to survive in the conditions in its natural environment *(1 mark)*.
3.2 It has a thick bushy tail to help it keep warm at night when temperatures drop very low *(1 mark)*. It has a long, pointed muzzle so it can catch prey through the narrow entrance of a burrow *(1 mark)*. It has thick pads on the bottom of its feet to protect them as it's moving over rocky ground *(1 mark)*.
You might not have come across any of these adaptations before, but just use the information you're given about the rocky mountains and think sensibly about how the features would help the wolf survive there.
3.3 It is decreasing *(1 mark)*.
3.4 The outbreak of rabies is responsible for the trend *(1 mark)*. In the years when there were rabies outbreaks the population size fell *(1 mark)*. For example, the numbers fell from 401 to 327 in 2008 / 341 to 265 in 2011 when there was also a rabies outbreak *(1 mark)*.
There's a lot of data to look at in the table so think carefully about what you're looking for. The numbers of prey don't really change much throughout the study so that's unlikely to have caused the change in the number of wolves, so it's sensible to look at the outbreaks of rabies.
3.5 Because in a community, each species depends on other species / species are interdependent (for things such as food, shelter, pollination and seed dispersal) *(1 mark)*. This means that any major change in the ecosystem can have knock-on effects for all the other species in the community too *(1 mark)*.

Topic 7b — Human Impacts on the Environment

1. Biodiversity and Waste
Page 277 — Fact Recall Questions
Q1 It makes sure that ecosystems are stable.
Q2 false
Both the population of the world and the general standard of living are increasing.
Q3 They can be washed from the land into water.
Q4 By using toxic chemicals for farming (e.g. pesticides and herbicides), by burying nuclear waste and by creating landfill sites for other waste.

Page 277 — Application Question
Q1 a) Both the amount of waste recycled and the amount sent to landfill has increased each year. But the amount recycled each year has increased by more than the amount sent to landfill (an extra 50 000 tonnes of waste was recycled in 2010 compared to 2006, but only 20 000 tonnes more was sent to landfill).

b) $(100\,000 \div 250\,000) \times 100 = \mathbf{40\%}$

To find the total amount of waste in 2010, you need to add together the amount recycled (100 000) and the amount sent to landfill (150 000), which equals 250 000. You can then work out the percentage of this figure that was recycled.

c) The population of the world is increasing and so we are producing more waste, some of which ends up in landfill sites. Also, as the standard of living around the world increases we create even more waste. So the amount of space taken up by landfill sites, where waste is dumped, increases.

d) E.g. as the human population and standard of living increase, we use more raw materials (e.g. metal). It's important to recycle products, so that we don't run out of raw materials. / As the human population and standard of living increase, we produce more waste. It's important to recycle products as it reduces the amount of waste sent to landfill and therefore the amount of space taken up by landfill sites.

2. Global Warming

Page 280 — Fact Recall Questions

Q1 False

It's <u>increasing</u> levels of these gases that are contributing to an increase in the average global temperature.

Q2 carbon dioxide and methane

Page 280 — Application Question

Q1 a) Organisms are found in places where they can survive. If the average global temperature increases the distribution of organisms may change. E.g. animals that require cooler temperatures may only exist in a smaller area and animals that require warmer temperatures may become more widely distributed.

b) E.g. global warming could cause a change in birds' migration patterns, so birds that come to the country for only part of the year could be around for a shorter/longer period of time or it might cause birds to arrive and leave at slightly different times of the year. / If some bird species fail to adapt to the changes in their environment caused by global warming, then they might die out. / Birds that live, feed or breed near the coast might have problems if the sea level rises because of global warming.

3. Deforestation and Land Use

Page 283 — Fact Recall Questions

Q1 Any three from: building / quarrying / farming / dumping waste

Q2 The cutting down of forests.

Page 283 — Application Questions

Q1 a) 900 thousand hectares

To find the total amount of forest cleared, you need to read off the value for the full height of the bar. Don't forget to include the units in your answer either.

b) i) 400 thousand hectares

ii) E.g. cattle farming, growing rice crops or growing crops to create biofuels.

Q2 Peat bogs store carbon instead of releasing it into the atmosphere as carbon dioxide. If peat bogs are destroyed (e.g. to use the peat in compost), this carbon dioxide will be released, contributing to global warming. So peat-free compost helps to prevent the destruction of peat bogs, and so could be considered an environmentally-friendly option.

4. Maintaining Ecosystems and Biodiversity

Page 285 — Fact Recall Questions

Q1 They help protect biodiversity by preventing endangered species from becoming extinct.

Q2 They might reintroduce hedgerows and field margins. These protect biodiversity by providing a habitat for a wider variety of organisms around the field than would otherwise survive in the single crop habitat.

Q3 E.g. to reduce the amount of waste that gets dumped in landfill sites, reducing the amount of land taken over for landfill and so leaving ecosystems in place.

Page 287 — Human Impacts on the Environment Exam-style Questions

1.1 The variety of different species of organisms on Earth, or within an ecosystem *(1 mark)*.

1.2 E.g. it would cost money to keep a watch on whether people are following the programme. The local economy could be harmed if people are forced to move away with their family to find work because the jobs that would have been available from shrimp production are not available *(2 marks)*.

1.3 E.g. because people around the world are demanding a higher standard of living *(1 mark)*, and shrimp could be seen as a luxury food *(1 mark)*.

1.4 The removal of the trees will mean that less carbon dioxide will be removed from the atmosphere by the trees in photosynthesis *(1 mark)*. More carbon dioxide will be released into the atmosphere if the trees are burnt to clear the land *(1 mark)* and by the respiration of microorganisms feeding on bits of dead wood *(1 mark)*. This will result in an increased level of carbon dioxide in the atmosphere, contributing to global warming *(1 mark)*.

Glossary

A

Abdomen (humans)
The lower part of the body, ending at the hips.

Abiotic factor
A non-living factor of the environment.

Accurate result
A result that is very close to the true answer.

Active transport
The movement of particles against a concentration gradient (i.e. from an area of lower concentration to an area of higher concentration) using energy transferred during respiration.

Adaptation
A feature or characteristic that helps an organism to survive in the conditions of its natural environment.

Adrenaline
A hormone secreted by the adrenal glands that is released in response to stressful situations in order to prepare the body for 'fight or flight'.

Aerobic respiration
The reactions involved in breaking down glucose using oxygen, to transfer energy. Carbon dioxide and water are produced.

Allele
An alternative version of a gene.

Alveolus
A tiny air sac in the lungs, where gas exchange occurs.

Amino acid
A small molecule that is a building block of proteins.

Amylase
A digestive enzyme that catalyses the breakdown of starch into sugars, in the mouth and small intestine.

Anaerobic respiration
The incomplete breakdown of glucose, which produces lactic acid in humans, and CO_2 and ethanol in plants and yeast. It takes place in the absence of oxygen.

Anomalous result
A result that doesn't seem to fit with the rest of the data.

Antibiotic
A drug used to kill or prevent the growth of bacteria.

Antibiotic resistance
When bacteria aren't killed by an antibiotic.

Antibody
A protein produced by white blood cells in response to the presence of an antigen (e.g. on the surface of a pathogen).

Antigen
A molecule on the surface of a cell. A foreign antigen triggers white blood cells to produce antibodies.

Antitoxin
A protein produced by white blood cells which counteracts the toxins produced by invading bacteria.

Artery
A blood vessel that carries blood away from the heart.

Asexual reproduction
Where organisms reproduce by mitosis to produce genetically identical offspring.

B

Bacterium
A single-celled microorganism without a 'true' nucleus. Some bacteria are able to cause disease.

Bias
Prejudice towards or against something.

Bile
A fluid that is made in the liver, stored in the gall bladder and released into the small intestine. It aids digestion by creating alkaline conditions in the small intestine and by emulsifying fats.

Binomial system
The system used in classification for naming organisms using a two-part Latin name.

Biodiversity
The variety of different species of organisms on Earth, or within an ecosystem.

Biotic factor
A living factor of the environment.

Blood
A tissue which transports substances around the body in the circulatory system.

C

Capillary
A type of blood vessel involved in the exchange of materials at tissues.

Carbohydrase
A type of digestive enzyme that catalyses the breakdown of starch into sugars in the mouth and small intestine.

Cardiovascular disease
Disease of the heart or blood vessels.

Catalyst
A substance that increases the speed of a reaction, without being changed or used up in the reaction.

Cell cycle
The process that all body cells from multicellular organisms use to grow and divide.

Cell membrane
A membrane surrounding a cell, which holds it all together and controls what goes in and out.

Cellulose
A molecule which strengthens cell walls in plants and algae.

Cell wall
A structure surrounding some cell types, which gives strength and support.

Central Nervous System (CNS)
The brain and spinal cord. It's where reflexes and actions are coordinated.

Chlorophyll
A green substance found in chloroplasts which absorbs light for photosynthesis.

Chloroplast
A structure found in plant cells and algae, which contains chlorophyll. Chloroplasts are the site of photosynthesis.

Chromosome
A long molecule of DNA found in the nucleus, which carries genes.

Circulatory system
A system which uses blood to transport materials around the body.

Clinical trial
A set of drug tests on human volunteers.

Clone
An organism that is genetically identical to another organism.

Communicable disease
A disease that can spread between individuals.

Community
The populations of different species living in a habitat.

Contraceptive
A method of preventing pregnancy that can be hormonal or non-hormonal.

Control variable
A variable in an experiment that is kept the same.

Coordination centre
An organ (e.g. the brain, spinal cord or pancreas) that processes information from receptors and organises a response from the effectors.

Coronary artery
A blood vessel which supplies blood to the heart muscle.

Coronary heart disease
A disease in which the coronary arteries are narrowed by the build up of fatty deposits.

Correlation
A relationship between two variables.

Cystic fibrosis
An inherited disorder of the cell membranes caused by a recessive allele.

Cytoplasm
A gel-like substance in a cell where most of the chemical reactions take place.

Deforestation
The cutting down of forests (large areas of trees).

Dependent variable
The variable in an experiment that is measured.

Diaphragm (thorax)
The muscle separating the abdomen from the thorax.

Differentiation
The process by which a cell becomes specialised for its job.

Diffusion
The spreading out of particles from an area of higher concentration to an area of lower concentration.

Distribution
Where organisms are found in a particular area.

DNA (deoxyribonucleic acid)
The molecule in cells that stores genetic information.

Dominant allele
The allele for the characteristic that's shown by an organism if two different alleles are present for that characteristic.

Double-blind trial
A clinical trial where neither the doctors nor the patients know who has received the drug and who has received the placebo until all the results have been gathered.

Ecosystem
The interaction of a community of living organisms with the abiotic parts of their environment.

Effector
Either a muscle or gland which responds to nervous impulses.

Efficacy
Whether something, e.g. a drug, works or not.

Electron microscope
A microscope that uses electrons to form an image.

Embryonic screening
Genetic analysis of either a cell taken from an embryo before it's implanted into the uterus during IVF, or a sample of cells taken from the placenta, in order to check that the embryo doesn't carry any inherited disorders.

Endothermic reaction
A reaction where energy is transferred from the environment.

Enzyme
A protein that acts as a biological catalyst.

Epidemic
A big outbreak of disease.

Epidermal tissue
A type of plant tissue which covers the whole plant.

Eukaryotic cell
A complex cell, such as a plant or animal cell.

Evaporation
The process by which a liquid turns into a gas.

Evolution
The changing of the inherited characteristics of a population over time.

Exchange surface
A specialised surface in an organism used for the exchange of materials, e.g. gases and dissolved substances.

Excretion
The removal of waste products from the body.

Exothermic reaction
A reaction that transfers energy to the environment.

Extinction
When no living individuals of a species remain.

Extremophile
An organism that's adapted to live in seriously extreme conditions.

Eyepiece graticule
Apparatus used with a microscope to work out the real size of the object being viewed.

Fair test
A controlled experiment where the only thing that changes is the independent variable.

Family tree (genetics)
A diagram which shows how a characteristic (or disorder) is inherited in a group of related people.

Fermentation
The process of anaerobic respiration in yeast cells.

Fertilisation
The fusion of male and female gametes during sexual reproduction.

Fertility
The ability to conceive a child.

Follicle stimulating hormone (FSH)
A hormone produced by the pituitary gland involved in the menstrual cycle. It causes eggs to mature in the ovaries and stimulates the ovaries to produce oestrogen.

Fossil
The remains of an organism from many years ago, which is found in rock.

Fossil record
The history of life on Earth preserved as fossils.

Fungus
A microorganism that can cause disease, and that produces spores that can be spread to other organisms.

 G

Gamete
A sex cell, e.g. an egg cell or a sperm cell in animals.

Gene
A short section of DNA, found on a chromosome, which contains the instructions needed to make a protein (and so controls the development of a characteristic).

Genetic engineering
The process of cutting out a useful gene from one organism's genome and inserting it into another organism's cell(s).

Genetic variant
A different form of a gene (produced by a mutation).

Genetically modified (GM) crop
A crop which has had its genes modified through genetic engineering.

Genome
All of the genetic material in an organism.

Genotype
What alleles you have, e.g. Tt.

Gland
The place where hormones are produced and secreted from.

Global warming
The rise in the average global temperature.

Glucagon
A hormone produced and secreted by the pancreas when blood glucose level is too low. It causes glycogen to be converted back into glucose, increasing the blood glucose level.

Glycogen
A molecule that acts as a store of glucose in liver and muscle cells.

Gonorrhoea
A sexually transmitted bacterial disease.

Guard cell
A cell found on either side of a stoma, which controls the stoma's size.

 H

Habitat
The place where an organism lives.

Haemoglobin
A red pigment found in red blood cells which carries oxygen.

Hazard
Something that has the potential to cause harm (e.g. fire, electricity, etc.).

Heterozygous
Where an organism has two alleles for a particular gene that are different.

HIV
A virus that attacks the immune system cells so that eventually it can't cope with other infections or cancers. It causes AIDS.

Homeostasis
The regulation of conditions inside your body (and cells) to maintain a stable internal environment, in response to changes in both internal and external conditions.

Homozygous
Where an organism has two alleles for a particular gene that are the same.

Hormone
A chemical messenger which travels in the blood to activate target cells.

Hypothesis
A possible explanation for a scientific observation.

 I

Immunity
The ability of the white blood cells to respond quickly to a pathogen.

Inbreeding
When closely related animals or plants are bred together.

Independent variable
The variable in an experiment that is changed.

Inherited disorder
A disorder caused by a faulty allele, which can be passed on to an individual's offspring.

Insulin
A hormone produced and secreted by the pancreas when blood glucose level is too high. It causes the body's cells to take up more glucose from the blood, reducing the blood glucose level.

Interdependence
Where, in a community, each species depends on other species for things such as food, shelter, pollination and seed dispersal.

In vitro fertilisation (IVF)
The artificial fertilisation of eggs in the lab.

 L

Lactic acid
The product of anaerobic respiration that builds up in muscle cells.

Large intestine
An organ in the mammalian digestive system where water from undigested food is absorbed, producing faeces.

Limiting factor
A factor which prevents a reaction from going any faster.

Lipase
A type of digestive enzyme that catalyses the breakdown of lipids into fatty acids and glycerol, in the small intestine.

Liver
An organ found in the mammalian digestive system with several important roles in the body, e.g. the production of bile and the conversion of glucose into glycogen.

Lung
A gas exchange organ in mammals.

Luteinising hormone (LH)
A hormone produced by the pituitary gland, which stimulates egg release around the middle of the menstrual cycle.

 M

Malaria
A disease caused by a protist and spread by mosquitoes, which causes repeating episodes of fever.

Mean (average)
A measure of average found by adding up all the data and dividing by the number of values there are.

Measles
A viral disease that causes a red skin rash and fever.

Median (average)
The middle value in a set of data when they're in order of size.

Meiosis
A type of cell division where a cell divides twice to produce four genetically different gametes. It occurs in the reproductive organs.

Menstrual cycle
The monthly sequence of events in which the female body releases an egg and prepares the uterus (womb) in case it receives a fertilised egg.

Meristem tissue
Tissue found at the growing tips of plant shoots and roots that is able to differentiate.

Metabolism
All the chemical reactions that happen in a cell or the body.

Methane
A greenhouse gas.

Mitochondria
Structures in a cell which are the site of most of the reactions for aerobic respiration.

Mitosis
A type of cell division where a cell reproduces itself by splitting to form two identical offspring.

Mode (average)
The most common value in a set of data.

Motor neurone
A nerve cell that carries electrical impulses from the CNS to effectors.

MRSA (methicillin-resistant *Staphylococcus aureus*)
A strain of bacteria that is resistant to the powerful antibiotic methicillin.

Multicellular organism
An organism made up of more than one cell.

Muscle fatigue
Where muscles become tired and can't contract efficiently.

N

Natural selection
The process by which species evolve.

Negative feedback
A mechanism that restores a level back to optimum in a system.

Nervous system
The organ system in animals that allows them to respond to changes in their environment.

Neurone
A nerve cell. Neurones transmit information around the body, including to and from the CNS.

Non-communicable disease
A disease that cannot spread between individuals.

Nucleus (of a cell)
A structure found in animal and plant cells which contains genetic material that controls the activities of the cell.

O

Obesity
A condition defined as being 20% or more over the maximum recommended body mass.

Oestrogen
A hormone produced by the ovaries which is involved in the menstrual cycle. It's found in some oral contraceptives.

Optimum dose (in drug testing)
The dose of a drug that is most effective and has few side effects.

Optimum level (in the body)
A level of something (e.g. water, ions or glucose) that enables the body to work at its best.

Oral contraceptive
A hormone-containing pill taken by mouth in order to reduce fertility and therefore decrease the chance of pregnancy.

Organ
A group of different tissues that work together to perform a certain function.

Organ system
A group of organs working together to perform a particular function.

Osmosis
The movement of water molecules across a partially permeable membrane from a region of higher water concentration to a region of lower water concentration.

Ovary
An organ in the female body which stores and releases eggs. It is also a gland and secretes the hormone oestrogen.

Oxygen debt
The amount of extra oxygen your body needs after exercise to react with the build up of lactic acid and remove it from cells.

Oxyhaemoglobin
A molecule formed when haemoglobin combines with oxygen.

P

Painkiller
A drug that relieves pain.

Palisade mesophyll tissue
Leaf tissue where most photosynthesis happens.

Pancreas
An organ (and gland) in the mammalian digestive system which produces digestive juices. It also produces insulin and glucagon to control blood sugar level.

Partially permeable membrane
A membrane with tiny holes in it, which lets some molecules through it but not others.

Pathogen
A microorganism that causes disease, e.g. a bacterium, virus, protist or fungus.

Peat bog
An area of land that is acidic and waterlogged, so plants don't fully decompose when they die, producing peat.

Penicillin
A type of antibiotic.

Permanent vacuole (plant cells)
A structure in plant cells that contains cell sap.

Phagocytosis
The process by which white blood cells engulf foreign cells and digest them.

Phenotype
The characteristics you have, e.g. blue eyes.

Phloem
A type of plant tissue which transports dissolved sugars around the plant.

Photosynthesis
The process by which plants use energy to convert carbon dioxide and water into glucose and oxygen.

Pituitary gland
A gland located in the brain that is responsible for secreting various hormones.

Placebo (in drug testing)
A substance that's like the drug being tested but doesn't do anything.

Plasma
The liquid component of blood, which transports the contents of the blood around the body.

Platelet
A small fragment of a cell found in the blood, which helps blood to clot at a wound.

Polydactyly
An inherited disorder caused by a dominant allele that results in a person being born with extra fingers or toes.

Precise result
A result that is close to the mean.

Preclinical trial
A set of drug tests on human cells and tissues, and live animals that occurs before clinical trials.

Predator
An animal that hunts and kills other animals.

Prey
An animal that is hunted and killed by another animal.

Primary consumer
An organism in a food chain that feeds on a producer.

Producer
An organism at the start of a food chain that makes its own food using energy from the Sun.

Progesterone
A hormone produced by the ovaries, which is involved in the menstrual cycle. It's found in some oral contraceptives.

Prokaryotic cell
A small, simple cell, e.g. a bacterium.

Protease
A type of digestive enzyme that catalyses the breakdown of proteins into amino acids, in the stomach and small intestine.

Protein
A large biological molecule made up of long chains of amino acids.

Protist
A pathogen that is often transferred to other organisms by a vector, which doesn't get the disease itself.

Punnett square
A type of genetic diagram.

Q

Quadrat
A square frame enclosing a known area which can be used to study the distribution of organisms.

R

Range
The difference between the smallest and largest values in a set of data.

Receptor
A group of cells which are sensitive to a stimulus. E.g. light receptor cells in the eye are sensitive to light.

Recessive allele
An allele whose characteristic only appears in an organism if there are two copies present.

Reflex
A fast, automatic response to a stimulus.

Reflex arc
The passage of information in a reflex.

Relay neurone
A nerve cell that carries electrical impulses from sensory neurones to motor neurones.

Repeatable result
A result that will come out the same if the experiment is repeated by the same person using the same method and equipment.

Reproducible result
A result that will come out the same if someone different does the experiment, or a slightly different method or piece of equipment is used.

Resolution (microscopes)
The ability to distinguish between two parts. A higher resolution gives a sharper image.

Ribcage
A set of bones in the thorax, which protect the lungs.

Ribosome
A structure in a cell, where proteins are made.

Risk
The chance that a hazard will cause harm.

Risk factor
Something that is linked to an increased likelihood that a person will develop a certain disease.

Root hair cell
A cell on the surface of a plant root, which absorbs water and mineral ions.

Rose black spot
A fungus that causes purple or black spots to develop on the leaves of rose plants. The leaves can then turn yellow and drop off.

S

Salivary gland
An organ (and gland) in the mammalian digestive system which produces digestive juices.

Salmonella
A type of bacteria that causes food poisoning.

Sampling
Taking a number of organisms from a population to study.

Secondary consumer
An organism in a food chain that eats a primary consumer.

Selective breeding (artificial selection)
When humans artificially select the plants or animals that are going to breed so that the genes for particular characteristics remain in the population.

Sense organ
An organ which contains receptors that detect stimuli, e.g. the eye.

Sensory neurone
A nerve cell that carries electrical impulses from the receptors in the sense organs to the CNS.

Sex chromosome (humans)
One of the 23rd pair of chromosomes — together they determine whether an individual is male or female.

Sexual reproduction
Where two gametes combine at fertilisation to produce a genetically different new individual.

SI units
A unit of measurement recognised as standard by scientists worldwide.

Single gene cross
Where you cross two parents to look at the inheritance of just one characteristic controlled by a single gene.

Small intestine
An organ in the mammalian digestive system where food is digested and soluble food molecules are absorbed.

Specialised cell
A cell which performs a specific function.

Species
A group of similar organisms that can reproduce to give fertile offspring.

Spongy mesophyll tissue
Tissue in a leaf that contains air spaces.

Stable community
A community where all the species and environmental factors are in balance so that the population sizes are roughly constant.

Stage micrometer
Apparatus used with a microscope to work out the real size of the object being viewed.

Standard of living
A measure of things like what access people have to food, education, health care and luxury goods like TVs, cars and computers.

Starch
An insoluble carbohydrate used as a store of glucose in plants.

Statins
A group of medicinal drugs that are used to decrease the risk of heart and circulatory disease.

Stem cell
An undifferentiated cell which has the ability to become one of many different types of cell or more stem cells.

Stent
A wire mesh tube that's inserted inside an artery to help keep it open.

Stimulus
A change in the environment.

Stoma
A tiny hole in the surface of a leaf.

Stomach
An organ in the mammalian digestive system where food is digested.

Sulfur dioxide
A gas released by burning fossil fuels, which can cause acid rain if it mixes with rain clouds in the atmosphere.

Synapse
The connection between two neurones.

T

Target cell
A particular cell in a particular place, which is affected by a hormone.

Tertiary consumer
An organism in a food chain that eats a secondary consumer.

Testosterone
The main male reproductive hormone, produced by the testes.

Therapeutic cloning
A type of cloning where the embryo is made to have the same genetic information as the patient.

Thorax (humans)
The upper part of the body, excluding the arms and head. Contains the lungs.

Thyroxine
A hormone secreted by the thyroid gland that regulates metabolism and stimulates protein synthesis for growth and development.

Tissue
A group of similar cells that work together to carry out a particular function. It can include more than one type of cell.

Tobacco mosaic virus
A virus that affects many species of plants, e.g. tomatoes, and causes a mosaic pattern on the leaves.

Toxicity
How harmful something is, e.g. a drug.

Toxin
A poison. Toxins are often produced by bacteria.

Transect
A line which can be used to study the distribution of organisms across an area.

Translocation
The movement of dissolved sugars around a plant.

Transpiration stream
The movement of water from a plant's roots, through the xylem and out of the leaves.

Tumour
A growth of abnormal cells.

Type 1 diabetes
A condition where the pancreas produces little or no insulin, which means blood glucose can rise to a dangerous level.

Type 2 diabetes
A condition in which the body is unable to control blood sugar level.

Urea
A waste product produced from the breakdown of amino acids in the liver.

Uterus
The main female reproductive organ and where the embryo develops during pregnancy. (Another word for the womb.)

V

Vaccination
The injection of dead or inactive microorganisms to provide immunity against a particular pathogen.

Valid result
A result that is repeatable, reproducible and answers the original question.

Valve (in the circulatory system)
A structure within the heart or a vein which prevents blood from flowing in the wrong direction.

Variable
A factor in an investigation that can change or be changed (e.g. temperature or concentration).

Variation
The differences that exist between individuals.

Vector (in genetic engineering)
Something used to transfer DNA into a cell, e.g. a virus or a bacterial plasmid.

Vein
A blood vessel that carries blood to the heart.

Virus
A disease-causing agent about 1/100th of the size of a bacterial cell. Can only replicate within host body cells.

White blood cell
A cell which forms part of the blood and part of the immune system, helping to defend the body against disease.

Xylem
A type of plant tissue which transports water and mineral ions around the plant.

Acknowledgements

Data Acknowledgements

Data used to construct the table on the use of stents on page 108 reprinted from the Journal of the American College of Cardiology, Vol 49/19. H Vernon Anderson et al. Drug-Eluting Stents for Acute Myocardial Infarction, pgs 1931-1933. © 2007, with permission from Elsevier.

Data used to construct the measles graph on page 143 from http://www.who.int/immunization/monitoring_surveillance/burden/vpd/surveillance_type/active/big_measles_global_coverage.jpg accessed March 2016.

Data used to produce the IVF table and question on page 197 from the Human Fertilisation and Embryology Authority (HFEA).

Data on pregnancy rates used in question on page 197 from the Human Fertilisation and Embryology Authority (HFEA).

Data used to construct the big cat evolutionary tree on page 250 reprinted from Molecular Phylogenetics and Evolution, Vol 56. Brian W. Davis, Gang Li, William J. Murphy. Supermatrix and species tree methods resolve phylogenetic relationships within the big cats, Panthera (Carnivora: Felidae). Pages 64-76. © 2010, with permission from Elsevier.

Photograph Acknowledgements

Cover Photo **darnell_vfx**/Adobe Stock, p 3 Science Photo Library, p 5 iStock.com/**LourdesPhotography**, p 6 **Tony Craddock**/Science Photo Library, p 8 iStock.com/**muslian** (Fig. 1), p 8 **Tony McConnell**/Science Photo Library (Fig. 2), p 9 **Tek Image**/Science Photo Library, p 12 iStock.com/**tunart**, p 21 **Adam Hart-Davis**/Science Photo Library, p 23 **Alfred Pasieka**/Science Photo Library, p 24 **Dr. Martha Powell, Visuals Unlimited**/Science Photo Library, p 25 **Biophoto Associates**/Science Photo Library (Fig. 1), p 25 **National Cancer Institute**/Science Photo Library (Fig. 2), p 27 **Kevin & Betty Collins, Visuals Unlimited**/Science Photo Library, p 31 **Steve Gschmeissner**/Science Photo Library (Fig. 2), p 31 **Steve Gschmeissner**/Science Photo Library (Fig. 4), p 31 **Dr Keith Wheeler**/Science Photo Library (Fig. 5), p 33 **Sovereign, ISM**/Science Photo Library (Fig. 2), p 33 **Power And Syred**/Science Photo Library (Fig. 3), p 34 **Manfred Kage**/Science Photo Library, p 36 **Steve Gschmeissner**/Science Photo Library (all images on page), p 37 **Herve Conge, ISM**/Science Photo Library, p 39 **Pascal Goetgheluck**/Science Photo Library, p 40 iStock.com/**Epitavi**, p 44 **Dr T E Thompson**/Science Photo Library, p 45 **Andrew Lambert Photography**/Science Photo Library, p 55 iStock.com/**EcoPic** (Fig. 1 top), p 55 iStock.com/**GlobalP** (Fig. 1 bottom), p 57 **E. R. Degginger**/Science Photo Library (left), p 57 **Tom & Pat Leeson**/Science Photo Library (right), p 58 **Biophoto Associates**/Science Photo Library, p 59 **Eye Of Science**/Science Photo Library, p 61 iStock.com/**petrescudaniel**, p 66 **Steve Gschmeissner**/Science Photo Library, p 67 **Dr Keith Wheeler**/Science Photo Library, p 70 **Zephyr**/Science Photo Library, p 76 iStock.com/**Suljo**, p 77 **Steve Gschmeissner**/Science Photo Library, p 78 **CNRI**/Science Photo Library, p 80 **Steve Gschmeissner**/Science Photo Library, p 81 **Power And Syred**/Science Photo Library (Fig. 3), p 81 **Biophoto Associates**/Science Photo Library (Fig. 4), p 81 **Susumu Nishinaga**/Science Photo Library (Fig. 5), p 81 **Antonia Reeve**/Science Photo Library (Fig. 6), p 83 **Eye Of Science**/Science Photo Library, p 85 **Dr. Richard Kessel & Dr. Gene Shih/Visuals Unlimited, Inc.**/Science Photo Library (Fig. 2), p 85 **Biophoto Associates**/Science Photo Library (Fig. 4), p 88 **Dr Jeremy Burgess**/Science Photo Library (top), p 88 **Dr Jeremy Burgess**/Science Photo Library (bottom), p 89 **Ted Kinsman**/Science Photo Library, p 94 **Power And Syred**/Science Photo Library (Fig. 3), p 94 **Eye Of Science**/Science Photo Library (Fig. 4), p 97 **Dr P. Marazzi**/Science Photo Library, p 98 **Hank Morgan**/Science Photo Library, p 99 **CNRI**/Science Photo Library, p 103 **James Stevenson**/Science Photo Library, p 104 **CNRI**/Science Photo Library, p 107 iStock.com/**Willsie**, p 110 **Clive Freeman, The Royal Institution**/Science Photo Library, p 118 **Martyn F. Chillmaid**/Science Photo Library, p 119 **Andrew Lambert Photography**/Science Photo Library (Fig. 4), p 119 **Andrew Lambert Photography**/Science Photo Library (Fig. 6), p 123 **Martyn F. Chillmaid**/Science Photo Library, p 124 **Juergen Berger**/Science Photo Library (Fig. 2 top), p 124 **AMI Images**/Science Photo Library (Fig. 2 bottom), p 125 **Dr Keith Wheeler**/Science Photo Library (Fig. 3), p 125 **Steve Gschmeissner**/Science Photo Library (Fig. 4 top), p 125 Science Photo Library (Fig. 4 bottom), p 126 **Norm Thomas**/Science Photo Library, p 127 **Ian Gowland**/Science Photo Library, p 129 **CDC**/Science Photo Library, p 130 **Juergen Berger**/Science Photo Library (Fig. 1), p 130 **Biology Media**/Science Photo Library (Fig. 2), p 133 **Saturn Stills**/Science Photo Library, p 135 **Scott Camazine**/Science Photo Library, p 137 **James King-Holmes**/Science Photo Library, p 138 **St. Bartholomew's Hospital**/Science Photo Library, p 144 **Biophoto Associates**/Science Photo Library, p 146 **Biophoto Associates**/Science Photo Library (Fig. 1), p 146 **Angel Fitor**/Science Photo Library (example box left), p 146 **Victor De Schwanberg**/Science Photo Library (example box right), p 147 **The Picture Store**/Science Photo Library, p 149 Science Photo Library, p 153 **E. R. Degginger**/Science Photo Library, p 156 **Angel Fitor**/Science Photo Library (Fig. 1), p 156 iStock.com/**36clicks** (Fig. 3), p 160 **Samuel Ashfield**/Science Photo Library, p 162 **Sputnik**/Science Photo Library, p 164 **BSIP, Laurent/B. Hop Ame**/Science Photo Library (Fig. 2), p 164 iStock.com/**milla1974** (Fig. 3), p 172 **Sovereign, ISM**/Science Photo Library, p 174 **Thomas Deerinck, NCMIR**/Science Photo Library, p 175 **PH. Gerbier**/Science Photo Library, p 178 iStock.com/**Spanishalex**, p 181 **Scott Camazine**/Science Photo Library, p 185 **Coneyl Jay**/Science Photo Library, p 190 **Professors P. M. Motta & J. Van Blerkom**/Science Photo Library, p 193 **Cordelia Molloy**/Science Photo Library, p 194 **Gustoimages**/Science Photo Library, p 195 **Zephyr**/Science Photo

Library, p 196 **Zephyr**/Science Photo Library, p 205 **Lawrence Berkeley National Laboratory**/Science Photo Library, p 206 **Eye Of Science**/Science Photo Library, p 207 **Wim Van Egmond**/Science Photo Library, p 208 **Adrian T Sumner**/Science Photo Library, p 214 Science Photo Library, p 215 iStock.com/**kutipie**, p 217 iStock.com/**MGJdeWit** (Fig. 1 left), p 217 iStock.com/**ivosar** (Fig 1. right), p 218 **Wally Eberhart, Visuals Unlimited**/Science Photo Library, p 223 **Sovereign, ISM**/Science Photo Library, p 225 **Pascal Goetgheluck**/Science Photo Library, p 230 **Kate Jacobs**/Science Photo Library (Fig. 1), p 230 **Coneyl Jay**/Science Photo Library (example box), p 236 **Science Source**/Science Photo Library, p 242 **Alfred Pasieka**/Science Photo Library (Fig. 2, top), p 242 **Bill Barksdale/AGStockUSA**/Science Photo Library (Fig. 2 bottom), p 243 **Sinclair Stammers**/Science Photo Library (Fig. 1), p 243 **Natural History Museum, London**/Science Photo Library (Fig. 2), p 244 **Dirk Wiersma**/Science Photo Library (Fig. 3), p 244 **John Reader**/Science Photo Library (Fig. 4), p 244 **Alfred Pasieka**/Science Photo Library (Fig. 5), p 244 **Silkeborg Museum, Denmark/Munoz-Yague**/Science Photo Library (Fig. 6), p 245 **Josie Iselin, Visuals Unlimited**/Science Photo Library (top left), p 245 **Herve Conge, ISM**/Science Photo Library (top right), p 245 **Herve Conge, ISM**/Science Photo Library (bottom left), p 245 **Philippe Plailly**/Science Photo Library (bottom right), p 253 **Gary Parker**/Science Photo Library, p 254 **Ken M. Highfill**/Science Photo Library, p 257 iStock.com/**bogdanhoria** (Fig. 1 top), p 257 iStock.com/**Aleksander** (Fig. 1 bottom), p 259 **John Devries**/Science Photo Library, p 261 iStock.com/**JohnPitcher**, p 266 **Martyn F. Chillmaid**/Science Photo Library, p 267 **Martyn F. Chillmaid**/Science Photo Library, p 270 **Dr Jeremy Burgess**/Science Photo Library, p 276 **Michael Marten**/Science Photo Library, p 277 **Robert Brook**/Science Photo Library, p 279 **NASA**/Science Photo Library (Fig. 3), p 279 **Dr. John Brackenbury**/Science Photo Library (Fig. 4), p 282 **Mark A. Schneider**/Science Photo Library, p 283 **Ailsa M Allaby**/Science Photo Library, p 284 **Peter Skinner**/Science Photo Library, p 285 **Matteis/Look At Sciences**/Science Photo Library, p 287 iStock.com/**bobhackettphotos**, p 288 **GIPhotoStock**/Science Photo Library, p 289 **Andrew Lambert Photography**/Science Photo Library, p 290 **Martyn F. Chillmaid**/Science Photo Library, p 291 Science Photo Library, p 292 iStock.com/**Thawatchai Tumwapee**, p 293 **Christopher McGarry**, p 295 **Martyn F. Chillmaid**/Science Photo Library, p 297 **David Maliphant**, p 311 **Photostock-Israel**/Science Photo Library.

Every effort has been made to locate copyright holders and obtain permission to reproduce sources. For those sources where it has been difficult to trace the originator of the work, we would be grateful for information. If any copyright holder would like us to make an amendment to the acknowledgements, please notify us and we will gladly update the book at the next reprint. Thank you.

Index

A

abiotic factors 255, 258-260
abstinence 194
accurate results 12
active sites 109
active transport 52, 53
adaptations 261, 262
adrenal glands 181, 199
adrenaline 199
aerobic respiration 159
algebra symbols 301
alleles 217
alveoli 58, 59, 71
amino acids 146
amylase 115, 116
anaerobic respiration 161, 162
  in plants 162
  in yeast 162
animal cells 23
anomalous results 13
antibiotic resistance
    134, 135, 246, 247
antibiotics 134
antibodies 130, 131
antitoxins 130
aorta 73
Archaea (three-domain system)
   249
arteries 77
artificial
  blood 99
  hearts 98, 99
  pacemakers 76
asexual reproduction 207
aspirin 135
atria 73-75

B

bacteria 124, 128
Bacteria (three-domain system)
   249
bacterial cells 24
bacterial diseases 128
bar charts 16
Benedict's test 118
bile 116

binomial system 249
biodiversity 275, 280, 281, 284
  maintenance of 284, 285
biomass 263
biotic factors 255, 258, 259
blood 80, 81
blood flow (rate of) 78
blood glucose (control of)
   184-187
blood vessels 77, 78
breathing rate 72, 164
breeding programmes 284
bronchi 70
Bunsen burners (using) 290

C

calculation tips 310, 311
calibration 13
cancer 103
capillaries 77
carbohydrases 115
carbon cycle 270
carbon dioxide 278
carcinogens 101
cardiovascular disease 97
categoric data 16
causation 21, 22
cell
  cycle 35, 37
  membranes 23
  organisation 66-68
  structure 23
  walls 24
cellulose 146
central nervous system (CNS) 172
chlorophyll 24, 144, 148
chloroplasts 24, 144
chromosomes 33, 34, 204, 213
cilia 130
circulatory system 73, 74
classification systems 248
climate change 278
clinical trials 137
clones 207
command words 308
communicable diseases 95, 124
communities 255

competition 255, 256
computational models 3
conclusions 21
condoms 194
consumers 263
continuous data 16
contraceptives 193
control experiments 10
control groups 10
control variables 10
coordination centres 170
coronary arteries 74
coronary heart disease 97
correlation 21
cystic fibrosis 223
cytoplasm 23

D

Darwin, Charles 234, 235
decay 270
deforestation 281, 282
dependent variables 10
descriptive models 3
diaphragm (thorax) 70
diaphragms (contraceptives) 194
differentiation 30, 66
diffusion 45-47
digestive system 67, 116
digitalis 135
discrete data 16
distribution of organisms
   265, 279
  investigating 265-267
DNA 33, 204, 205
dominant alleles 217
double-blind trials 138
double circulatory system 73
double helix 204
drugs 134, 135
  testing 137, 138

E

ecosystems 255
effectors 172
eggs (gametes) 213
electric heaters 290

electron microscopes 25
embryonic screening 225
embryonic stem cells 38, 39
endocrine system 181
endothermic reactions 144, 165
enzymes 109-111, 114-116
    investigating enzymatic
        reactions 112, 113
epidermal tissues (plant) 84
equations 301
errors (in experiments) 13
estimating
    in calculations 299
    size of cell structures 29
ethics 6, 295
Eukaryota (three-domain system)
    249
eukaryotes 23
eukaryotic cells 23
evaluations 22
evaporation 269
evolution 234
evolutionary trees 249
exam technique 306
exchange
    in fish 60, 61
    in humans 58, 59
    in plants 60
exchange surfaces 54-56
exercise 163, 164
exothermic reactions 165
extinction 236
extremophiles 262
eyepiece graticules 292

F

family trees 224
fermentation 162
fertilisation 206
fertility drugs 195
field margins 284
Fleming, Alexander 135
follicle stimulating hormone (FSH)
    190
food chains 263
food tests 118, 119
    for lipids 120
    for proteins 119
    for starch 119
    for sugars 118
food webs 257
fossil record 236, 245

fossils 243, 244
fungal diseases 127
fungi 125

G

gametes 206
gas exchange 58
    in fish 60, 61
    in humans 58
    in plants 60
gas syringes 289
genes 34, 204, 217
genetic diagrams
    214-216, 218-224
genetic engineering 240, 241
genetic variants 231, 232
genetically modified (GM) crops
    241
genomes 205
genotype 217
gills 60
glands 67, 181, 182
global warming 278-281
glucagon 185
glucose 184, 185
    uses of 146, 147
glycogen 185
gonorrhoea 128
gradients 303
graphs 16-18, 302-304
greenhouses 156, 157
guard cells 60, 88

H

habitats 255
haemoglobin 80
hazards 7, 8
health 95
heart 73, 74
heart rate 164
heating substances 290, 291
hedgerows 284
heterozygous organisms 217
histograms 16
HIV 126
homeostasis 170
homozygous organisms 217
hormones 181, 182
human population growth 275
hypotheses 2, 9

I

immune system 130
implants (contraceptive) 194
in vitro fertilisation (IVF)
    195, 196
inbreeding 239
independent variables 10
indicators (of pH) 289
inherited disorders 223
injections (contraceptive) 194
insulin 184-187
intercepts 302
interdependence 255
intrauterine devices 194
inverse proportion 155, 301
inverse square law 155
isolation (of infected individuals)
    129

L

lactic acid 161
land use 281
leaf structure 83
levels of response questions 309
light microscopes 25, 26
limiting factors 148
linear graphs 302
Linnaeus, Carl 248
lipases 115
lungs 70, 71
luteinising hormone (LH)
    190, 191

M

magnification (of microscopes)
    25
    calculating 27, 28
malaria 127
mathematical models 3
mean 14
measles 126
measuring
    gas volumes 289
    liquid volumes 288
    mass 288
    pH 289
    temperature 288
    time 289
median 14

meiosis 208
menstrual cycle 189
meristem tissues 83
metabolism 165
methane 278
microorganisms 269
microscopes 25-27, 292
  observing onion cells 25-27
mitochondria 23
mitosis 35, 36
mode 14
models 3
mosquitoes 127
motor neurones 173
MRSA 246
mucus 130
muscle cells 31
muscle fatigue 163
mutations 231, 232

N

natural selection 235
negative feedback 170, 171, 198
nerve cells 31
nervous system
   172, 173, 182, 183
non-communicable diseases
   95, 101
nucleus 23, 33

O

oestrogen 189-191
  in contraceptives 193
oral contraceptives 193
organ systems 67
organs 67
osmosis 48, 49
  investigating 49, 50
ovaries 182
ovulation 189
oxygen debt 161, 163

P

pacemakers 75, 76
painkillers 134
palisade mesophyll tissues 83, 84
pancreas 67, 181, 184
partially permeable membranes
  48

pathogens 124, 125
peat bogs 282, 283
peer-review 2
penicillin 134, 135
percentage change 298
percentage cover 267, 268
percentages 298
percentiles 300
permanent vacuoles 24
pH meters 289
phagocytosis 130
phenotype 217
phloem cells 32, 85
phloem tissues 83, 84
photosynthesis 144, 145, 270
  investigating the rate of
    153, 154
  rate of 148-151
pipettes 289
pituitary gland 181
placebos 137
plant cells 24
plasma 81
plasmids 24
platelets 81
pollution 276, 277
polydactyly 223
population size (estimating) 266
populations 255
potometers 87, 291
precipitation 269
precise results 12
preclinical trials 137
predator-prey cycles 263, 264
predators 263
predictions 2, 9
prey 263
primary consumers 263
probability 215
producers 263
progesterone 190, 191
  in contraceptives 193
prokaryotic cells 23
proteases 115, 116
protist diseases 127
protists 124, 127
puberty 189
pulmonary artery 73
pulmonary vein 73
pulse 164
Punnett square diagrams
   214, 215, 218-221

Q

quadrats 265
question types (in the exam)
   308-310

R

random errors 13
random sampling 293, 294
range 14
ratios 297
reaction time 177
  investigating 177, 178
rearranging equations 301
receptors 172
recessive alleles 217
recycling 284
red blood cells 80
reflex arcs 175
reflexes 175
relay neurones 173
repeatable results 9, 12
representational models 3
reproducible results 9
reproduction 206, 207
Required Practical Activities
   25-27, 49, 50, 112, 113,
   118-120, 153, 154, 177,
   178, 265-267, 308, 309
resolution (of microscopes) 25
respiration 146, 159-162, 270
  aerobic 159
  anaerobic 161, 162
ribosomes 23
risk factors 101, 102
  for cancer 103, 104
risks 7, 8
root hair cells 31, 52
rose black spot 127

S

safety (in labs) 295
salivary glands 67
Salmonella 128
sample size 11
sampling 293, 294
scaling prefixes 19
secondary consumers 263
selective breeding 238, 239
sensory neurones 173

sex hormones 189
sex inheritance 214-216
sexual reproduction 206
significant figures 15
SI units 19
skin patches (contraceptives) 194
spatial models 3
specialised cells 30-32
speciation 236
sperm cells 30, 31, 206
spermicides 194
spongy mesophyll tissues 83
stable communities 257, 269
stage micrometers 292
standard form 296, 297
standard of living 276
starch 147
statins 98
stem cells 30, 38-40
    in plants 40
stents 97, 98
sterilisation (contraceptive) 194
stimuli 170, 172
stomata 60, 86, 88, 89
surface area to volume ratios
        54, 55
surgical methods
        (of contraception) 194
synapses 174
systematic errors 13

T

tables 14
target organs 181
tertiary consumers 263
testes 182
testosterone 189
theories 2, 3
therapeutic cloning 39
three-domain system
        (of classification) 248, 249
thyroid gland 181, 198
thyroxine 198
tissues 66
tobacco mosaic virus (TMV) 126
trachea 70
transects 266, 267
translocation 85
transpiration 86-88, 269
transpiration stream 85, 86
trial runs 11

tumours 103
Type 1 diabetes 185-187
Type 2 diabetes 186

U

uncertainty 15
units 19
    converting between 28
urea 165

V

vaccinations 132, 133
valid results 9
valves (of the heart) 74
    replacement 99
variation 230, 231
vectors
    in genetic engineering 240
    of disease 124, 127, 129
veins 78
vena cava 73, 74
ventricles 73, 75
villi 59
viral diseases 126
viruses 124, 126

W

waste 276
water baths 291
water cycle 269
white blood cells 81, 130, 131
Woese, Carl 248

X

X chromosomes 213
x-intercept 302
xylem cells 32, 85
xylem tissues 83, 84

Y

Y chromosomes 213
yeast cells 162
y-intercept 302
$y = mx + c$ 304